SANITARY LANDFILL
TECHNOLOGY

Samuel Weiss

NOYES DATA CORPORATION

Park Ridge, New Jersey   London, England

1974

Published in the United States of America by
Noyes Data Corporation
Noyes Building, Park Ridge, New Jersey 07656

Foreword

This Pollution Technology Review surveys information available up to the end of 1973, and is based primarily on studies conducted by industrial or engineering firms, under the auspices of the Environmental Protection Agency.

Sanitary landfill practice is an engineering method of disposing of solid wastes on land, whether they are of municipal or industrial origin. There is no resemblance to the old-fashioned garbage and rubbish dump. There are no fires, no obnoxious fumes or smoke, no flies and no rodents or other scavengers. As stated in the Introduction, a sanitary landfill is not only an acceptable and economic method of solid waste disposal, it provides also an excellent way to improve the commercial value of otherwise unsuitable or marginal land areas within a few years.

In the United States, we are fortunate in receiving direct help from the numerous surveys, together with active research and development programs that are being supported by the Federal Government to help industry and municipalities to control their wastes and rubbish.

In this book are condensed vital data that are scattered and difficult to pull together. Important processes are interpreted and explained by actual case histories. This condensed information will enable you to establish a sound background for action towards combating pollution by solid waste management through sanitary landfills.

Advanced composition and production methods developed by Noyes Data are employed to bring our new durably bound books to you in a minimum of time. Special techniques are used to close the gap between "manuscript" and "completed book." Industrial technology is progressing so rapidly that time-honored, conventional typesetting, binding and shipping methods are no longer suitable. We have bypassed the delays in the conventional book publishing cycle and provide the user with an effective and convenient means of reviewing up-to-date information in depth.

The Table of Contents is organized in such a way as to serve as a subject index and provides easy access to the information contained in this book.

Contents and Subject Index

Introduction

Sanitary landfilling is an acceptable and recommended method for ultimately disposing of solid wastes. The method has sometimes been confused with waste disposal on open, burning dumps, but this is a misconception. The sanitary landfill is an engineering project that requires sound and detailed planning and specifications, careful construction, and efficient operation. Basically, solid wastes are disposed of by spreading them in thin layers, compacting them to the smallest practical volume, and covering them with earth each day in a manner that minimizes environmental pollution.

The nation is emerging from a prolonged period in which it neglected solid waste management, and it is becoming increasingly aware that our present solid waste storage, collection, and disposal practices are inadequate. Much of this awareness has been brought about by active campaigns directed against air and water pollution and has resulted in a third campaign — the abatement of land pollution.

The magnitude of the problem can be appreciated when we consider that the nation produced 250 million tons of residential, commercial, and institutional solid wastes in 1969. Only 190 million tons were collected. Much of the remainder found its way to scattered heaps across the countryside, was left to accumulate in backyards and vacant lots, or was strewn along our roadways. To compound the problem, an estimated 110 million tons of industrial wastes and nearly 4 billion tons of mineral and agricultural wastes were generated.

Because of our affluence and increasing population, these quantities are expected to increase. In 1920, solid waste collected in our urban areas amounted to only 2.75 lbs. per capita. In 1970, the figure stood at over 5 lbs., and it is estimated that it will reach 8 lbs. by 1980.

More than 90% of our nation's solid waste is directly disposed of on land, the

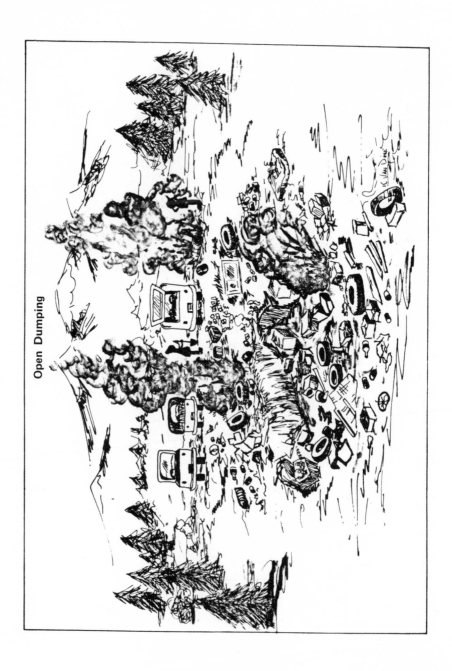

Open Dumping

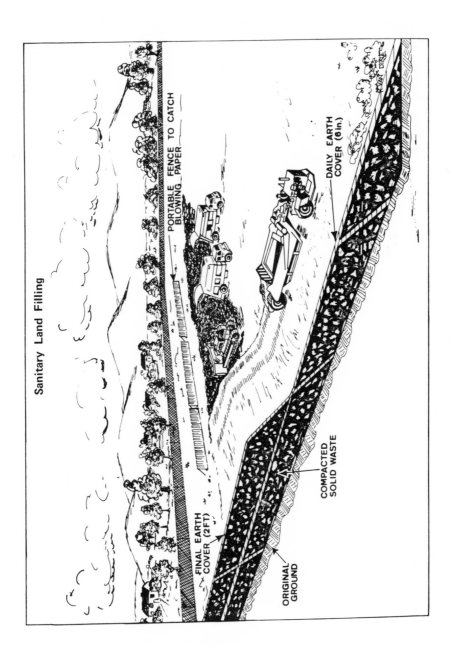

Sanitary Land Filling

PORTABLE FENCE TO CATCH BLOWING PAPER

DAILY EARTH COVER (6 in.)

FINAL EARTH COVER (2FT)

COMPACTED SOLID WASTE

ORIGINAL GROUND

vast majority of it in an unsatisfactory manner. Open and burning dumps, which are all too common, contribute to water and air pollution and provide food, harborage, and breeding grounds for insects, birds, rodents, and other carriers of disease.

Flies, particularly, are recognized agents for the transmission of various enteric diseases such as dysentery, diarrhea, etc. Rats find open dumps ideal habitats in which to breed, feed, and thrive. They are of public health importance primarily for their role as host to the flea that transmits murine typhus fever. Furthermore, open dumps for garbage and rubbish are obnoxious because of the smoke and odor associated with them, as well as the unsightly appearance of the dumping area. Nearby streams may also be polluted by dumps.

In addition, these dumps very often lessen the value of nearby land and residences. An acceptable alternative to the present poor practices of land disposal is the sanitary landfill. This alternative involves the planning and applying of sound engineering principles and construction techniques. By definition, no burning of solid waste occurs at a sanitary landfill. A sanitary landfill is not only an acceptable and economic method of solid waste disposal, it is also an excellent way to make otherwise unsuitable or marginal land valuable.

The drawings on the two previous pages taken from a 1972 U.S. Department of Interior Geological Survey contrast the appearance of an open dump with that of a sanitary landfill. In the former, open dumping and burning, with wastes indiscriminately spread over a large area blight the land and foul the air and water. The sanitary landfill, on the other hand, minimizes environmental pollution.

PART I

DESIGN AND OPERATION

Basic Parameters

CHARACTERISTICS OF SOLID WASTE DECOMPOSITION

Solid wastes deposited in a landfill degrade chemically and biologically to produce solid, liquid, and gaseous products. Ferrous and other metals are oxidized; organic and inorganic wastes are utilized by microorganisms through aerobic and anaerobic synthesis. Liquid waste products of microbial degradation, such as organic acids, increase chemical activity within the fill. Food wastes degrade quite readily, while other materials, such as plastics, rubber, glass and some demolition wastes, are highly resistant to decomposition.

Some factors that affect degradation are the heterogeneous character of the wastes, their physical, chemical, and biological properties, the availability of oxygen and moisture within the fill, temperature, microbial populations, and type of synthesis. Since the solid wastes usually form a very heterogeneous mass of nonuniform size and variable composition and other factors are complex, variable, and difficult to control, it is not possible to accurately predict contaminant quantities and production rates.

Biological activity within a landfill generally follows a set pattern. Solid waste initially decomposes aerobically, but as the oxygen supply is exhausted, facultative and anaerobic microorganisms predominate and produce methane gas, which is odorless and colorless. Temperatures rise to the high mesophilic-low thermophilic range (60° to 150°F.) because of microbial activity.

Characteristic products of aerobic decomposition of waste are carbon dioxide, water, and nitrate. Typical products of anaerobic decomposition of waste are methane, carbon dioxide, water, organic acids, nitrogen, ammonia, and sulfides of iron, manganese, and hydrogen.

6

GAS EVOLVED

Characteristics

Gas is produced naturally when solid wastes decompose. The quantity generated in a landfill and its composition depend on the types of solid waste that are decomposing. A waste with a large fraction of easily degradable organic material will produce more gas than one that consists largely of ash and construction debris. The rate of gas production is governed solely by the level at which microbial decomposition is occurring in the solid waste. When decomposition ceases, gas production also ends. In a field study conducted over a 907-day period, approximately 40 cu. ft. of gas were produced per cu. yd. of solid waste.

Methane and carbon dioxide are the major consituents of landfill decomposition gas, but other gases are also present and some may impart a repugnant odor. Hydrogen sulfide, for example, may be generated at a landfill, especially if it contains a large amount of sulfate, such as gypsum board (calcium sulfate) or if brackish water infiltrates the solid waste.

Landfill gas is important to consider when evaluating the effect a landfill may have on the environment, because methane can explode and because mineralization of ground water can occur if carbon dioxide dissolves and forms carbonic acid. Methane is explosive only when present in air at concentrations between 5 and 15%. Since there is no oxygen present in a landfill when methane concentrations in it reach this critical level, there is no danger of the fill exploding. If however, methane vents into the atmosphere (its specific gravity is less than that of air) it may accumulate in buildings or other enclosed spaces on or close to a sanitary landfill.

The potential movement of gas is, therefore, an essential element to consider when selecting a site. It is particularly important if enclosed structures are built on or adjacent to the sanitary landfill or if it is to be located near existing industrial, commercial, and residential areas.

Gas permeability of the soils surrounding the landfill can influence the movement of decomposition gas. A dry soil will not significantly impair its flow, but a saturated soil, such as clay, can be an excellent barrier. A well-drained soil acts as a vent to gas flow. If cover material acts as a barrier, then the landfill gases will migrate laterally until they can vent to the atmosphere. More research is needed to reliably predict rate and distance of gas movement.

Landfill gas movement can be controlled if sound engineering principles are applied. Of the several methods that have been devised and tested, permeable vents and impermeable barriers are the two basic types.

Energy Recovery

According to *Air Pollution Notes* published by Rutgers University, January 1974, an experimental gas recovery program aimed at deriving energy benefits from gas produced by decomposition of landfill wastes will be conducted at the Palos Verdes landfill by NRG Technology, Inc., Newport Beach, Calif., under contract awarded by the Los Angeles County Sanitation District #2. NRG Technology will install an experimental station to recover gases from the fill and upgrade them to pipeline quality by removing contaminants. Developmental activities will be assumed by the company at no cost to the county.

If production of gas proves commercially feasible, NRG plans to sell the gas to Southern California Gas Co. Anticipated initial production of the landfill gas would supply an annual consumption for about 2,500 homes, the company estimates. County sanitation districts will share in any revenues from sale of the natural gas.

The experiment, if successful, could be of broad national significance in the development of additional sources of energy since there are some 1,000 landfills in the U.S. that meet the requirements of gas recovery projects. The L.A. program anticipates a minimum production of 1,000 cubic feet of gas per minute. NRG said that there is no means of scientifically determining the size of gas reserved in the landfill, since actual recovery of gas from a large landfill has never before been attempted. More than 13 million tons of refuse are now in the Palos Verdes landfill. Upon completion in about 5 years, this site will house more than 20 million tons of potential energy-producing waste.

The Los Angeles Departments of Water and Power and Public Works announced in January 1974 that electricity generated from sanitary landfill gases would be used to light approximately 350 Los Angeles homes for three months during a demonstration of a new fuel source for power generation.

Methane gas produced during organic decaying processes at the city's Sheldon-Arleta landfill will fuel a small generating unit which will then supply 200 kw. of power to DWP customers in the central San Fernando Valley service area. The small demonstration unit is expected to save the burning of 250 barrels of oil each month during the three month test period.

Methane and other gases are drawn from the 125 ft. deep refuse pit through one deep well and several shallow, perimeter wells and fed to a specially modified 300 horsepower internal combustion engine which drives an electric generator. The 200 kw. energy output is then distributed on the DWP's 34,000 v. subtransmission system.

Although the methane concentration of gas produced at the Sheldon-Arleta landfill is only about 40 to 50%, it would be sufficient to fuel the demonstration engine and larger units which would be installed if the test program is successful.

The DWP estimates that the Sheldon-Arleta landfill could be developed to produce up to 5,000 kw. of power. Total cost for the demonstration facility is expected to be about $30,000.

This project is a joint venture between the DWP and the City Bureau of Sanitation and is believed to be the first attempt to utilize methane gas to produce electricity commercially at a landfill site.

If successful, the installation of generating units at other landfill sites throughout the city and county could produce 50,000 kw. of power, enough to serve 85,000 to 90,000 residential customers, according to DWP projections.

Full utilization of methane-fueled generating units could reduce the need for up to 650,000 barrels of fuel oil a year. This type of generation has become economically competitive with other fossil-fueled power generation as a result of recently spiraling increases in fuel oil prices.

The high percentage of carbon dioxide contained in landfill gases must be removed to achieve pipeline quality. Carbon dioxide and other contaminants will be removed by a proprietary energy adsorption process, using natural molecular sieve material mined in Bowie, Arizona.

If this program is successful in California it is possible that some of the landfills in New Jersey might be applicable to the extraction of commercial grades of methane. This would provide the use of a resource which has previously been wasted and which, in a number of cases has caused problems of vegetation death as well as fire and explosive hazards.

LEACHATE CHARACTERISTICS

Groundwater or infiltrating surface water moving through solid waste can produce leachate, a solution containing dissolved and finely suspended solid matter and microbial waste products. Leachate may leave the fill at the ground surface as a spring or percolate through the soil and rock that underlie and surround the waste.

Composition of leachate is important in determining its potential effects on the quality of nearby surface water and groundwater. Contaminants carried in leachate are dependent on solid waste composition and on the simultaneously occurring physical, chemical, and biological activities within the fill. The quantity of contaminants in leachate from a completed fill where no more waste is being disposed of can be expected to decrease with time.

The limited data available indicate a removal of large quantities of contaminants by leaching during active stages of decomposition, and a slackening off of removal as the fill stabilizes.

If the fill is considered as a mass of material containing a finite amount of leachable material, then depending on the removal rate, leaching should eventually cease.

The types and quantities of contaminants that enter the receiving water and the ability of that water to assimilate these contaminants will determine the degree of leachate control needed. In some cases it may be established that introduction of leachate will not upset the ecology or usefulness of the receiving water.

Careful examination of dilution and oxygen demand criteria of the stream can be useful tools in showing the ability of a stream to assimilate leachate. In all cases, water quality criteria and the laws and ordinances of federal, state, and local agencies pertaining to water pollution must be followed.

Some investigators believe that even in a sanitary landfill, leachate production is inevitable and that some leachate will eventually enter surface water or groundwater. This has not been proven but neither has the opposite view.

The present philosophy held by the Office of Solid Waste Management Programs, most state solid waste control agencies, and many experts in the field is that through sound engineering and design, leachate production and movement may be prevented or minimized to the extent that it will not create a water pollution problem. The most obvious means of controlling leachate production and movement is to prevent water from entering the fill to the greatest extent practicable.

Leachate percolating through soils underlying and surrounding the solid waste is subject to purification (attenuation) of the contaminants by ion exchange, filtration, adsorption, complexing, precipitation, and biodegradation. It moves either as an unsaturated flow if the voids in soil are only partially filled with water or as a saturated flow if they are completely filled. The type of flow affects the mechanism of attentuation, as do soil particle size and shape and soil composition.

Attenuation of contaminants flowing in the unsaturated zone is generally greater than in the saturated zone because there is more potential for aerobic degradation, adsorption, complexing, and ion exchange or organics, inorganics, and microbes. Aerobic degradation of organic matter is more rapid and complete than anaerobic degradation. Because the supply of oxygen is extremely limited in saturated flow, anaerobic degradation prevails. Adsorption and ion exchange are highly dependent on the surface area of the liquid and solid interface. The surface area to flow volume ratio is greater in an unsaturated flow than in a saturated flow.

Leachate travel in the saturated zone is primarily controlled by soil permeability and hydraulic gradient, but a limited amount of capillary diffusion and dispersion do occur. The leachate is diluted very little in groundwater unless a natural geologic mixing basin exists. Leachate movement will closely follow the streamlines of groundwater flow.

Information on leachate travel in the unsaturated zone is lacking. Most of the studies made of residential and industrial wastewaters traveling through the unsaturated zone indicate that the organic and microbial removal level achieved is very good. However, the rate and frequency at which the waste liquid is applied and the type of soil have great influence on attenuation efficiency. Nitrification can also occur in the unsaturated soil zone and produce nitrate and nitrite from ammonia-nitrogen. A water that was bacteriologically safe, according to USPHS Drinking Water Standards for the coliform group, was obtained by percolating settled domestic wastewater through at least 4 ft. of a fine, sandy loam soil. This last study is especially important since pathogens have been detected in solid waste and leachate.

Natural purification processes have only a limited ability to remove contaminants, because the number of adsorption sites and exchangeable ions available is finite. In addition, the processes are time dependent — residence time is shortened by high flow rates. Flow rates through soils near landfills may be reduced naturally by filtering and settling of suspended contaminants. Porosity and permeability of the soil are then reduced. Thus, additional protection against contaminant travel may be possible as time passes. To a large extent, hydrology will determine whether the formation of leachate will produce a water pollution problem.

When solid wastes are placed in a sanitary landfill, they may vary tremendously with regard to moisture content. Wood, concrete, and other construction rubble may have very little, whereas many food wastes may be extremely wet. Paper, a major constituent of solid waste, is usually quite low in moisture. Metals and glass are also generally present in solid waste but are essentially free of moisture.

In general, the moisture content of mixed solid waste generated by a community ranges from 20 to 30% by weight. (Wide fluctuations can occur depending on climatic conditions during storage and collection.) In this general range, the moisture alone should not produce leachate provided the solid waste is fairly well mixed and has been well compacted. The water that results from decomposition of the relatively small amounts of intermixed food wastes and other moist, readily degradable organic can be absorbed by the comparatively large amounts of paper and other dry components present.

Leachate is not produced until all of the sanitary landfill or a sizable portion of it becomes saturated by water entering it from outside. For this reason, it is extremely important that a study of the site hydrology be made. Precipitation, surface runoff characteristics, evapo-transpiration, and the location and movement of groundwater with relation to the solid waste are the major factors that should be considered.

Surface water that infiltrates the cover soil and enters the underlying solid waste can increase the rate of waste decomposition and eventually cause leachate to leave the solid waste and create water pollution problems. Unless rapid decomposition is planned and the sanitary landfill is so designed that leachate is collected and treated, as much surface water as is practicable should be kept from entering the fill.

The permeability of a soil is the measure of the ease or difficulty with which water can pass through it. This is greatly affected by the texture, gradation, and structure of the soil and the degree to which it has been compacted. Coarse grained soils (gravels and sands) are usually much more permeable than fine grained soils (silts and clays). However, small amounts of silts and clays (fines) in a coarse grained soil may greatly decrease permeability while cracks in fine grained soils may do the opposite.

The quantity of water that can infiltrate the soil cover of a sanitary landfill depends not only on these physical characteristics but also on the residence time of the surface water. It can be minimized by: (1) diverting upland drainage; (2) grading and sloping the daily and final cover to allow for runoff; (3) decreasing the permeability of the cover material.

Groundwater is water that is contained within the zone of saturation of soil or rock — that is, all the pores in the containing earth materials are saturated. This zone is just beneath the land surface in many parts of the country and is on the surface at many springs, lakes, and marshes. In some areas, notably most of the arid west, the zone of saturation is deep in the ground.

The water table is the surface where water stands in wells at atmospheric pressure. In highly permeable formations, such as gravel, the water table is essentially the top of the zone of saturation. In many fine grained formations, however, capillary action causes water to rise above this zone, and the inexperienced observer might think this capillary fringe is part of the zone.

The zone of saturation commonly is not continuous with depth nor does it necessarily have lateral continuity. In exploring for underground water, a saturated zone may be found that yields water at a shallow depth, but if the exploration hole is continued, dry material is encountered at a greater depth and then another zone of saturation is found. Isolated high zones or lenses of saturated material are referred to as perched water. Perched water is common to glacial soil (till plain) areas where interstratified lenses or patches of porous sand and gravel are underlaid by relatively impervious glacial clay.

Because the conditions affecting groundwater occurrence are so complex, it is essential that the sanitary landfill site investigation include an evaluation by a qualified groundwater hydrologist. This is needed not only to locate the zone of saturation but also to predict the direction and rate of flow of groundwater and the quality of the aquifer.

Leachate from a landfill can contaminate groundwater. In order to determine if leachate will produce a subsurface pollution problem it is essential that the quality of the groundwater be established and that the aquifer's flow rate and direction be determined. Water within the zone of saturation is not static. It moves vertically and laterally at varying rates, depending on the permeability of the soil or rock formation in which it is located and the external hydraulic forces acting upon it.

CLIMATIC EFFECTS

Wind, rain, and temperature directly affect sanitary landfill design and operation. Windy sites need to have litter fences at the operating area and personnel to clean up the area at the end of the day. Such sites can also be very dusty when the soil dries, and this may irritate people living or working nearby. Trees planted on the perimeter of a sanitary landfill help keep dust and litter within the site. Water sprinkling or the use of other dust palliatives are often necessary along haul roads constructed of soil, crushed stone, or gravel.

Rain infiltrates the sanitary landfill and influences solid waste decomposition. It can also cause operational problems; many wet soils are difficult to spread and compact, and traffic over such soils is impeded.

Freezing temperatures may also cause problems. If the frost line is more than 6 in. below the ground surface, cover material may be difficult to obtain. A crawler dozer equipped with a ripper may be required, or it may be necessary to stockpile cover soil and protect it from freezing. A well-drained soil is more easily worked in freezing weather than one that is poorly drained.

Elements of Design

The designing of a sanitary landfill calls for developing a detailed description and plans that outline the steps to be taken to provide for the safe, efficient disposal of the quantities and types of solid wastes that are expected to be received. The designer outlines volume requirements, site improvements (clearing of the land, construction of roadways and buildings, fencing, utilities), and all the equipment necessary for day-to-day operations of the specific landfilling method involved. He also provides for controlling water pollution and the movement of decomposition gas. The sanitary landfill designer should also recommend a specific use of the site after landfilling is completed. Finally, he should determine capital costs and projected operating expenditures for the estimated life of the project.

SANITARY LANDFILLING METHODS

General Observations

The designer of a sanitary landfill should prescribe the method of construction and the procedures to be followed in disposing of the solid waste, because there is no "best method" for all sites. The method selected depends on the physical conditions involved and the amount and types of solid waste to be handled.

The two basic landfilling methods are trench and area; other approaches are only modifications. In general, the trench method is used when the groundwater is low and the soil is more than 6 ft. deep. It is best employed on flat or gently rolling land. The area method can be followed on most topographies and is often used if large quantities of solid waste must be disposed of. At many sites, a combination of the two methods is used.

14

The building block common to both methods is the cell. All the solid waste received is spread and compacted in layers within a confined area. At the end of each working day, or more frequently, it is covered completely with a thin, continuous layer of soil, which is then also compacted. The compacted waste and soil cover constitute a cell. A series of adjoining cells, all of the same height, makes up a lift (Figure 2.1). The completed fill consists of one or more lifts.

FIGURE 2.1: CROSS-SECTION OF CELL CONSTRUCTION

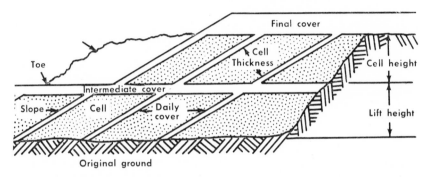

Source: Sanitary Landfill Design and Operation, EPA, 1972

The dimensions of the cell are determined by the volume of the compacted waste, and this, in turn, depends on the density of the in-place solid waste. The field density of most compacted solid waste within the cell should be at least 800 lbs./yd.^{3}. (It should be considerably higher if large amounts of demolition rubble, glass, and well-compacted inorganic materials are present.) The 800-lbs. figure may be difficult to achieve if brushes from bushes and trees, plastic turnings, synthetic fibers, or rubber powder and trimmings predominate. Because these materials normally tend to rebound when the compacting load is released, they should be spread in layers up to 2 ft. thick, then covered with 6 in. of soil. Over this, mixed solid waste should be spread and compacted. The overlying weight keeps the fluffy or elastic materials reasonably compressed.

An orderly operation should be achieved by maintaining a narrow working face (that portion of the uncompleted cell on which additional waste is spread and compacted). It should be wide enough to prevent a backlog of trucks waiting to dump, but not be so wide that it becomes impractical to manage properly, never over 150 ft.

No hard-and-fast rule can be laid down regarding the proper height of a cell. Some designers think it should be 8 ft. or less, presumably because this height will not cause severe settlement problems. On the other hand, if a multiple lift operation is involved and all the cells are built to the same height, whether 8 or 16 ft. total settlement should not differ significantly. If land and cover material are readily available, 8-ft. height restriction might be appropriate, but heights up to 30 ft. are common in large operations. Rather than deciding on an arbitrary figure, the designer should attempt to keep cover material volume at a minimum while adequately disposing of as much waste as possible.

Cover material volume requirements are dependent on the surface area of waste to be covered and the thickness of soil needed to perform particular functions. As might be expected, cell configuration can greatly affect the volume of cover material needed. The surface area to be covered should, therefore, be kept minimal.

In general, the cell should be about square, and its sides should be sloped as steeply as practical operation will permit. Side slopes of 20° to 30° will not only keep the surface area, and hence the cover material volume, at a minimum but will also aid in shredding and obtaining good compaction of solid waste, particularly if it is spread in layers not greater than 2 ft. thick and worked from the bottom of the slope to the top.

Trench Method

Waste is spread and compacted in an excavated trench. Cover material, which is taken from the spoil of the excavation, is spread and compacted over the waste to form the basic cell structure (Figure 2.2).

FIGURE 2.2: TRENCH METHOD

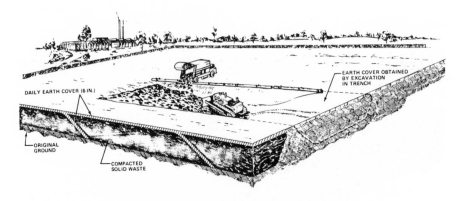

In the trench method of sanitary landfilling, the collection truck deposits its load into a trench where a buildozer spreads and compacts it. At the end of the day, the trench is extended, and the excavated soil is used as daily cover material.

Source: Sanitary Landfill Design and Operation, EPA, 1972

In this method, cover material is readily available as a result of the excavation. Spoil material not needed for daily cover may be stockpiled and later used as a cover for an area fill operation on top of the completed trench fill.

Cohesive soils, such as glacial till or clayey silt, are desirable for use in a trench operation because the walls between the trenches can be thin and nearly vertical. The trenches can, therefore, be spaced very closely. Weather and the length of time the trench is to remain open also affect soil stability and must be considered when the slope of the trench walls is being designed. If the trenches are aligned perpendicularly to the prevailing wind, this can greatly reduce the amount of blowing litter. The bottom of the trench should be slightly sloped for drainage, and provision should be made for surface water to run off at the low end of the trench. Excavated soil can be used to form a temporary berm on the sides of the trench to divert surface water.

The trench can be as deep as soil and groundwater conditions safely allow, and it should be at least twice as wide as any compacting equipment that will work in it. The equipment at the site may excavate the trench continuously at a rate geared to landfilling requirements. At small sites, excavation may be done on a contract basis.

Area Method

In this method, the waste is spread and compacted on the natural surface of the ground, and cover material is spread and compacted over it (Figure 2.3). The area method is used on flat or gently sloping land and also in quarries, strip mines, ravines, valleys, or other land depressions.

FIGURE 2.3: AREA METHOD

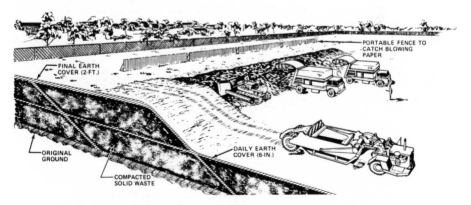

In the area method, a bulldozer spreads and compacts the waste on the ground, and a scraper is used to haul the cover material at the end of the day's operations.

Source: Sanitary Landfill Design and Operation, EPA, 1972

Combination Methods

A sanitary landfill does not need to be operated by using only the area or trench method. Combinations of the two are possible, and flexibility is, therefore, one of sanitary landfilling's greatest assets. The methods used can be varied according to the constraints of a particular site.

One common variation is the progressive slope or ramp method, in which the solid waste is spread and compacted on a slope. Cover material is obtained directly in front of the working face and compacted on the waste (Figure 2.4).

FIGURE 2.4: COMBINATION METHOD

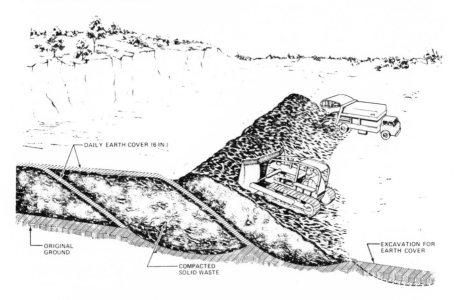

In the progressive slope or ramp method of sanitary landfilling, solid waste is spread and compacted on a slope. Cover material is obtained directly in front of the working face and compacted on the waste.

Source: Sanitary Landfill Design and Operation, EPA, 1972

In this way, a small excavation is made for a portion of the next day's waste. This technique allows for more efficient use of the disposal site when a single lift is constructed than the area method does, because cover does not have to be imported, and a portion of the waste is deposited below the original surface.

Both methods might have to be used at the same site if an extremely large amount of solid waste must be disposed of. For example, at a site with a thick soil zone over much of it but with only a shallow soil over the remainder, the designer would use the trench method in the thick soil zone and use the extra spoil material obtained to carry out the area method over the rest of the site. When a site has been developed by either method, additional lifts can be constructed using the area method by having cover material hauled in.

The final surface of the completed landfill should be so designed that ponding of precipitation does not occur. Settlement must, therefore, be considered. Grading of the final surface should induce drainage but not be so extreme that the cover material is eroded. Side slopes of the completed surface should be 3 to 1 or flatter to minimize maintenance.

Finally, the designer should consider completing the sanitary landfill in phases so that portions of it can be used as parks and playgrounds, while other parts are still accepting solid wastes.

VOLUME REQUIREMENTS

If the rate at which solid wastes are collected and the capacity of the proposed site are known, its useful life can be estimated. The ratio of solid waste to cover material volume usually ranges between 4:1 and 3:1; it is, however, influenced by the thickness of the cover used and cell configuration. If cover material is not excavated from the fill site, this ratio may be compared with the volume of compacted soil waste and the capacity of a site determined.

FIGURE 2.5: SOLID WASTE GENERATED BY LARGE COMMUNITIES

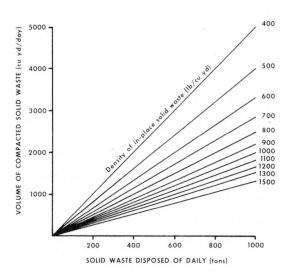

Source: Sanitary Landfill Design and Operation, EPA, 1972

For example, a town having a 10,000 population and a per capita collection rate of 5 lbs. per day must dispose of, in a year, 11 acre-feet of solid waste if it is compacted to 1,000 lbs./yd.^{3}. If it were compacted to only 600 lbs./yd.^{3}, the volume disposed of in a year would occupy 19 acre-feet. The volume of soil required for the 1,000-lbs. density at a solid waste-to-cover ratio of 4:1 would be 2.75 acre-feet; the 600-lbs. density waste would need 4.75 acre-feet. A density of 800 lbs./yd.^{3} is easily achievable if the compacting of a representative municipal waste is involved. A density of 1,000 lbs./yd.^{3} can usually be obtained if the waste is spread and compacted.

The number of tons to be disposed of at a proposed sanitary landfill can be estimated from data recorded when solid wastes are delivered to disposal sites. The daily volume of compacted solid waste can then be easily determined for a large community (Figure 2.5) or for a small community (Figure 2.6). The volume of soil required to cover each day's waste is then estimated by using the appropriate solid waste-to-cover ratio.

FIGURE 2.6: SOLID WASTE GENERATED BY SMALL COMMUNITIES

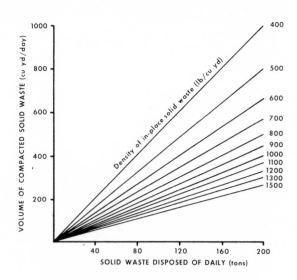

Source: Sanitary Landfill Design and Operation, EPA, 1972

SITE IMPROVEMENTS

Clearing Land

The plan for a sanitary landfill should prescribe how the site will be improved to provide an orderly and sanitary operation. This may simply involve the clearing of shrubs, trees and other obstacles that could hinder vehicle travel and landfilling operations or it could involve the construction of buildings, roads, and utilities.

Trees and brush that hinder landfill equipment or collection vehicles must be removed. Trees that cannot be pushed over should be cut as close as possible to the ground so that the stumps do not hinder compaction or obstruct vehicles. Brush and tall grass in working areas can be rolled over or grubbed. A large site should be cleared in increments to avoid erosion and scarring of the land. If possible, natural windbreaks and green belts of trees or brush should be left in strategic areas to improve appearance and operation.

Access

Permanent roads should be provided from the public road system to the site. A large site may have to have permanent roads that lead from its entrance to the vicinity of the working area. They should be designed to support the anticipated volume of truck traffic. In general, the roadway should consist of two lanes (total minimum width, 24 ft.), for two-way traffic. Grades should not exceed equipment limitations. For loaded vehicles, most uphill grades should be less than 7% and downhill grades less than 10%. Road alignments and pavement designs have been adequately discussed elsewhere. The initial cost of permanent roads is higher than that of temporary roads, but the savings in equipment repair and maintenance could justify the building of permanent, on-site roads.

Temporary roads are normally used to deliver wastes to the working face from the permanent road system, because the location of the working face is constantly changing. Temporary roads may be constructed by compacting the natural soil present and by controlling drainage or by topping them with a layer of a tractive material, such as gravel, crushed stone, cinders, broken concrete, mortar, or bricks. Lime, cement, or asphalt binders may make such roads more serviceable.

If fewer than 25 round trips per day to the landfill are expected a graded and compacted soil will usually suffice. More than 50 round trips per day generally justifies the use of calcium chloride as a dust inhibitor or such binder materials as soil cement or asphalt. A base course plus a binder is desirable if more than 100 to 150 round trips per day are anticipated.

Buildings

A building is needed for office space and employee facilities at all but the smallest landfill; it can also serve as a scale house. Since a landfill operates in wet and cold weather, some protection from the elements should be provided. Operational records may also be kept at a large site. Sanitary facilities should be provided for both landfill and collection personnel. A building should also be provided for equipment storage and maintenance.

Buildings on sites that will be used for less than 10 years should be temporary types and, preferably, be movable. The design and location of all structures should consider gas movement and differential settlement caused by the decomposing solid waste.

Utilities

All sanitary landfill sites should have electrical, water, and sanitary services. Remote sites may have to extend existing services or use acceptable substitutes. Portable chemical toilets can be used to avoid the high cost of extending sewer lines, potable water may be trucked in, and an electric generator may be used instead of having power lines run into the site.

Water should be available for drinking, fire fighting, dust control, and employee sanitation. A sewer line may be called for, especially at large sites and at those where leachate is collected and treated with domestic wastewater. Telephone or radio communications are also desirable.

Scale

Recording the weights of solid waste delivered to a site can help regulate and control the sanitary landfill operation as well as the solid waste collection system that serves it.

The scale type and size used will depend on the scope of the operation. Portable scales may suffice for a small site, while an elaborate system employing load cells, electronic relays, and printed output may be needed at a large sanitary landfill. Highly automated electronic scales and recorders cost more than a portable, simple, beam scale, but their use may often be justified, because they are faster and more accurate. The platform or scale deck may be constructed of wood, steel, or concrete. The first type is the least expensive, but also the least durable.

The scale should be able to weigh the largest vehicle that will use the landfill on a routine basis; 30 tons is usually adequate. Generally, the platform should be long enough to weigh all axles simultaneously. Separate axle-loading scales (portable versions) are the cheapest, but they are less accurate and slower operating. The scale platform should be 10 by 34 ft. to weigh most collection vehicles. A 50-ft. platform will accommodate most trucks with trailers.

The accuracy and internal mechanism of the scale and the recording device should meet the commercial requirements imposed by the State and any other jurisdiction involved, particularly if user fees are based on weight.

Both mechanical and electronic scales should be tested quarterly under load. The inspection should include: (1) checking for a change in indicated weight as a heavy load is moved from the front to the back of the scale; (2) observing the action of the dial during weighing for an irregularity or "catch" in its motion; (3) using test weights.

Fencing

Peripheral and litter fences are commonly needed at sanitary landfills. The first type is used to control or limit access, keep out children, dogs, and other large animals, screen the landfill, and delineate the property line. If vandalism and trespassing are to be discouraged, a 6-ft. high fence topped with three strands of barbed wire projecting a 45° angle is desirable. A wooden fence or a hedge may be used to screen the operation from view.

Litter fences are used to control blowing paper in the immediate vicinity of the working face. As a general rule, trench operations require less litter fencing because the solid waste tends to be confined within the walls of the trench. At a very windy trench site, a 4-ft. snow fence will usually suffice. Blowing paper is more of a problem in an area operation; 6 to 10-ft. litter fences are often needed. Some litter fences have been specially designed and fabricated. Since the location of the working face shifts frequently, litter fences should be movable.

GROUNDWATER CONTROL

Surface water courses should be diverted from the sanitary landfill. Pipes may be used in gullies, ravines, and canyons that are being filled to transmit upland drainage through the site and open channels employed to divert runoff from surrounding areas (Figure 2.7).

FIGURE 2.7: PLAN AND SECTION VIEWS OF THE USE OF A DIVERSION DITCH TO TRANSMIT UPLAND DRAINAGE AROUND A SANITARY LANDFILL

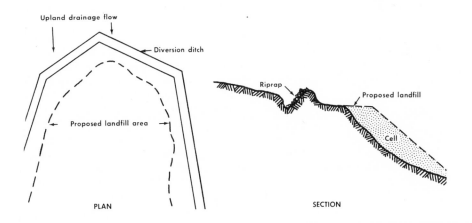

Source: Sanitary Landfill Design and Operation, EPA, 1972

A landfill located in a flood plain should be protected by impervious dikes and liners. The top of the dike should be wide enough for maintenance work to be carried out and may be designed for use by collection and landfill vehicles.

The top cover material of a landfill should be graded to allow runoff of rainfall. The grade of the cover will depend on the material's ability to resist erosion and the planned use of the completed site. Portable or permanent drainage channels may be constructed to intercept and remove runoff water.

It is a basic premise that groundwater and the deposited solid waste not be allowed to interact. It is unwise to assume that a leachate will be diluted in groundwater because very little mixing occurs in an aquifer since the groundwater flow there is usually laminar.

When issuing permits or certificates, many states require that groundwater and deposited solid wastes be 2 to 30 ft. apart. Generally, a 5-ft. separation will remove enough readily decomposed organics and coliform bacteria to make the liquid bacteriologically safe. On the other hand, mineral pollutants can travel long distances through soil or rock formations. In addition to other considerations, the sanitary landfill designer must evaluate the: (1) current and projected use of the water resources of the area; (2) effect of leachate on groundwater quality; (3) direction of groundwater movement; (4) interrelationship of this aquifer with other aquifers and surface waters.

An impermeable liner may be employed to control the movement of fluids. One of the most commonly used is a well-compacted natural clay soil, usually constructed as a membrane 1 to 3 ft. thick. It must, however, be kept moist. If sufficient clay soil is not available locally, natural clay additives, such as montmorillonite, may be disked into it to form an effective liner. The use of additives requires evaluation to determine optimum types and amounts.

Since synthetic liners have been used to construct wastewater-holding-and-treatment ponds, they may have an application in solid waste disposal operations. They are usually made of butyl rubber, polyethylene, or polyvinyl chloride and are installed in multiple layers. (If the movement of both gas and leachate is to be controlled, polyvinyl chloride should work better than polyethylene because it is less permeable by gas.) The membranes must be put down carefully to avoid punctures, and layers of soil (usually sand) must be placed on both sides of them. Asphalt liners, which have been used to reduce seepage from canals and ditches, may also have an application in a solid waste disposal operation.

The use of an impermeable barrier requires that some method be provided for removal of the contained fluid. If a natural ravine or canyon is involved, the removal point should be the downstream end of the filled area. The fluid in a bowl-shaped liner could be pumped by a well or series of wells or it could exit through gravity outlets in the bottom of the liner. In the latter case, the pipes should be sloped $1/8$ to $1/4$ in. per ft.

It is often possible to permanently or temporarily lower the groundwater in free-draining, gravelly, and sandy soils. Drains, canals, and ditches are frequently used to intercept the groundwater and channel it to surface water or recharge area at a lower elevation. Doing this generally requires that the designer have a thorough knowledge of the soil permeabilities and the groundwater flow system in the area. It is inadvisable to use temporary methods, such as wells, to lower the water table because it will rise after pumping ceases, and the waste will be inundated. It is well to recognize that highly permeable soils that can be readily drained by ditching or pumping will offer equally little resistance to the movement of leachate from the decomposing solid waste.

Even though groundwater can be kept from coming into direct contact with the solid waste, in most climates infiltrated surface water will probably enter the solid waste eventually, cause leaching, and then percolate through the underlying porous soil to enter the lowered groundwater. It is advisable, therefore, to view sites in highly permeable material with extreme caution. To help establish if a landfill is creating a groundwater and surface water pollution problem, a series of observation wells and sampling stations can be used to periodically monitor the water quality. Data on the upstream or uncontaminated water and downstream water quality are necessary to evaluate the pollution potential.

GAS CONTROL

An important part of sanitary landfill design is controlling the movement of decomposition gases, mainly carbon dioxide and methane. Traces of hydrogen sulfide and other odorous gases may also be involved.

Methane (CH_4) is a colorless, odorless gas that is highly explosive in concentrations of 5 to 15% when in the presence of oxygen. In a few instances, methane gas has moved from a landfill and accumulated in explosive concentrations in sewer lines and nearby buildings. Gas from landfills has also killed nearby vegetation, presumably by excluding oxygen from the root zone. Carbon dioxide (CO_2) is also a colorless, odorless gas, but it does not support combustion. It is approximately 1.5 times as heavy as air and is soluble in water. The CO_2 reacts to a limited extent to form carbonic acid (H_2CO_3), which can dissolve mineral matter, particularly carbonates, in refuse, soil, and rock. If this occurs, the mineral content or hardness of the water increases, as has been noted at wells located near landfills and dumps.

In general, no problems arise when landfill gas can disperse into the atmosphere. If the fill has a relatively impermeable cover, however, the methane will try to vent into the atmosphere by moving laterally through a more permeable material.

Lateral gas movement can be prevented by using a material that is, under all circumstances, more permeable than the surrounding soil; gravel vents or gravel-filled trenches have been employed (Figure 2.8). Preferably, the trenches should be somewhat deeper than the fill to make sure they intercept all lateral gas flow.

FIGURE 2.8: GRAVEL VENTS OR GRAVEL-FILLED TRENCHES TO CONTROL LATERAL GAS MOVEMENT IN A SANITARY LANDFILL

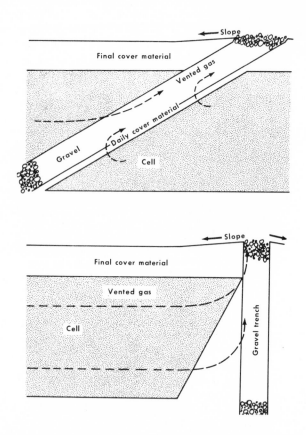

Source: Sanitary Landfill Design and Operation, EPA, 1972

The filter material should be graded to avoid infiltration and clogging by adjacent soil carried in by water. If possible, the trench should be built so that it drains naturally; field tile is often placed in the bottom of the trench. The surface of gravel trenches should be kept free of soil and vegetation, because they retain moisture and hinder venting.

In another method, vent pipes are inserted through a relatively impermeable top cover (Figure 2.9). Collecting laterals placed in shallow gravel trenches within or on top of the waste can be connected to the vertical riser. The sizes and spacings required have not been established, but they depend on the rate of gas production, total weight of solid waste, and the gas permeability of both the cover and the surrounding soil. In some cases, vertical risers have been used to burn off the gas. Pipe vents should not be located near buildings, but if this is unavoid-able, they should discharge above the roof line.

FIGURE 2.9: LATERAL AND VERTICAL VENT SYSTEMS

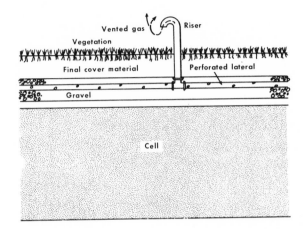

Gases are sometimes vented out of a sanitary landfill via pipes that are inserted through a relatively impermeable top cover and are connected to collecting laterals placed in shallow gravel trenches within or on top of the waste.

Source: Sanitary Landfill Design and Operation, EPA, 1972

Construction

GENERAL OBSERVATIONS

A study of the soils and geologic conditions of any area in which a sanitary landfill may be located is essential to understanding how its construction might affect the environment. The study should outline the limitations that soils and geologic conditions impose on safe, efficient design and operation.

A comprehensive study identifies and describes the soils present, their variation, and their distribution. It describes the physical and chemical properties of bedrock, particularly as it may relate to the movement of water and gas (Figure 3.1). Permeability and workability are essential elements of the soil evaluation.

Rock materials are generally classified as sedimentary, igneous, or metamorphic. Sedimentary rocks are formed from the products of erosion of older rocks and from the deposits of organic matter and chemical precipitates. Igneous rocks derive from the molten mass in the depths of the earth. Metamorphic rocks are derived from both igneous and sedimentary rocks that have been altered chemically or physically by intense heat or pressure

Sands, gravels, and clays are sedimentary in origin. The sedimentary rocks, sometimes called aqueous rocks, are often very permeable and therefore represent a great potential for the flow of groundwater. If leachate develops and enters the rock strata, contaminant travel will usually be greatest in sedimentary formations. Other rocks commonly classed as sedimentary are limestone, sandstone, and conglomerates. Fracturing and jointing of sedimentary formations are common and they increase permeability. In fact, the most productive waterbearing strata for wells are formations of porous sandstone, highly fractured limestone, and sand and gravel deposits. Siltstones and shales, which are also of sedimentary origin, usually have a very low permeability unless they have been subjected to jointing and form a series of connected open fractures.

FIGURE 3.1: LEACHATE AND INFILTRATION MOVEMENTS ARE AFFECTED BY THE CHARACTERISTICS OF THE SOIL AND BEDROCK

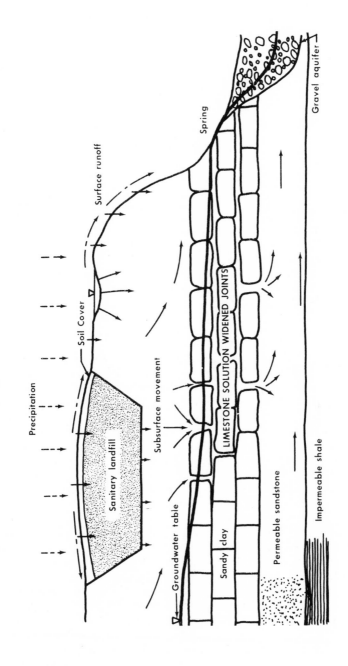

Source: Sanitary Landfill Design and Operation, EPA, 1972

Igneous and metamorphic rocks, such as shist, gneiss, quartzite, obsidian, marble, and granite, generally have a very low permeability. If these rocks are fractured and jointed, however, they can serve as aquifers of limited productivity. Leachate movement through them should not, therefore, be categorically discounted.

SOIL COVER

The striking visual difference between a dump and a sanitary landfill is the use of soil cover at the latter. Its compacted solid waste is fully enclosed within a compacted earth layer at the end of each operating day, or more often if necessary.

The cover material is intended to perform many functions at a sanitary landfill as shown in the table on the following page. The cover material controls the ingress and egress of flies, discourages the entrance of rodents seeking food, and prevents scavenging birds from feeding on the waste. Tests have demonstrated that 6 in. of compacted sandy loam will prevent fly emergence. Daily or more frequent application of soil cover greatly reduces the attraction of birds to the waste and also discourages rodents from burrowing to get food. The cover material is essential for maintaining a proper appearance of the sanitary landfill.

Many soils, when suitably compacted, have a low permeability, will not shrink, and can be used to control moisture that might otherwise enter the solid waste and produce leachate.

Suitability of General Soil Types as Cover Material

Function	Clean gravel	Clayey-silty gravel	Clean sand	Clayey-silty sand	Silt	Clay
Prevent rodents from burrowing or tunneling	G	F-G	G	P	P	P
Keep flies from emerging	P	F	P	G	G	E†
Minimize moisture entering fill	P	F-G	P	G-E	G-E	E†
Minimize landfill gas venting through cover	P	F-G	P	G-E	G-E	E†
Provide pleasing appearance and control blowing paper	E	E	E	E	E	E
Grow vegetation	P	G	P-F	E	G-E	F-G
Be permeable for venting decomposition gas‡	E	P	G	P	P	P

* E, excellent; G, good; F, fair; P, poor.
† Except when cracks extend through the entire cover.
‡ Only if well drained.

Control of gas movement is also an essential function of the cover material. Depending on anticipated use of the completed landfill and the surrounding land, landfill gases can be either blocked by or vented through the cover material. A permeable soil that does not retain much water can serve as a good gas vent. Clean sand, well-graded gravel, or crushed stone are excellent when kept dry. If gases are to be prevented from venting through the cover material, a gas-impermeable soil with high moisture-holding capacity compacted at optimum conditions should be used.

Enclosing the solid waste within a compacted earth shell offers some protection against the spread of fire. Almost all soils are noncombustible, thus the earth side walls and floor help to confine a fire within the cell. Top cover over a burning cell offers less protection because it becomes undermined and caves in, thus exposing the overhead cell to the fire. The use of a compactible soil of low permeability is an excellent fire-control measure, because it minimizes the flow of oxygen into the fill.

To maintain a clean and sightly operation, blowing litter must be controlled. Almost any workable soil satisfies this requirement, but fine sands and silts without sufficient binder and moisture content may create a dust problem.

The soil cover often serves as a road bed for collection vehicles moving to and from the operating area of the fill. When it is, it should be trafficable under all weather conditions. In wet weather, most clay soils are soft and slippery.

In general, soil used to cover the final lift should be capable of growing vegetation. It should, therefore, contain adequate nutrients and have a large moisture-storage capacity. A minimum compacted thickness of 2 ft. is recommended.

Comparison of the soil characteristics needed to fulfill all of these functions indicates that some anomalies exist. To serve as a road base, the soil should be well-drained so that loaded collection vehicles do not bog down. On the other hand, it should have a low permeability if water is to be kept out of the fill, fire is to be kept from spreading, and gas is not to be vented through the final cover. These differences can be solved by placing a suitable road base on top of the normally low permeability-type cover material.

There are many soils capable of fullfilling the functions of cover material. Minor differences in soil grain size or clay mineralogy can make significant differences in the behavior of soils that fall within a given soil group or division. In addition, different methods of placing and compacting the same soil can result in a significantly different behavior. Moisture content during placement, for example, is a critical factor, it influences the soil's density, strength, and porosity.

The soils present at proposed sites should be samples by augering, coring, or excavating, and then be classified. The volume of suitable soil available for use as cover material can then be estimated and the depth of excavation for waste disposal can be determined.

Clay soils are very fine in texture even though they commonly contain small to moderate amounts of silt and sand. They vary greatly in their physical properties, which depend not only on the small particle size but on the type of clay minerals and soil water content. When dry, a clay soil can be almost as hard and tough as rock and can support heavy loads. When wet, it often becomes very soft, is sticky or slippery, and is very difficult to handle. A clay soil swells when it becomes wet, and its permeability is very low.

Many clay soils can absorb large amounts of water but, after drying, usually shrink and crack. These characteristics make many clays less desirable than other soils for use as a cover material. The large cracks that usually develop allow water to enter the fill and permit decomposition gases to escape. Rats and insects can also enter or leave the fill through these apertures.

Clay soil can, however, be used for special purposes at a landfill. If it is desirable to construct an impermeable lining or cover to control leachate and gas movement, many clays can be densely compacted at optimum moisture. Once they are in place, it is almost always necessary to keep them moist so they do not crack.

The suitability of coarse grained material (gravel and sand) for cover material depends mostly on grain size distribution (gradation), the shape of grains, and the amount of clay and silt fines present. If gravel, for example, is poorly graded and relatively free of fines, it is not suitable as cover material for moisture, gas, or fly control. It cannot be compacted enough, and the gravel layer will be porous and highly permeable; this would allow water to enter the fill easily. Flies would have little difficulty emerging through the loose particles. On the other hand, a gravel layer no more than 6 in. deep would probably discourage rats and other rodents from burrowing into the fill and would provide good litter control.

If gravel is fairly well-graded and contains 10 to 15% sand and 5% or more fines it can make an excellent cover. When compacted, the coarse particles maintain grain-to-grain contact, because they are held in place by the binding action of the sand and fines and cohesion of the clays. The presence of fines greatly decreases a soil's permeability. A well-graded, sandy, clayey gravel does not develop shrinkage cracks. It can control flies and rodents, provide odor control, can be worked in any weather, and supply excellent traction for collection trucks and other vehicles.

Many soils classified as sand (grain size generally in the range of 4.0 to 0.05 mm.) contain small amounts of silt and clay and often some gravel-size material as well. A well-graded sand that contains less than 3% fines usually has good compaction characteristics. A small increase in fines, particularly silt, usually improves density and allows even better compaction. A poorly graded sand is difficult to compact unless it contains abundant fines. The permeability of clean sand soils is always high, even when compacted, and they are not, therefore, suitable for controlling the infiltration of water. They are also ineffective in constraining flies and gases. A well-drained sandy soil can be easily worked even if temperatures fall below freezing, while a soil with a large moisture-storage capacity will freeze

Practically the only soils that can be ruled out for use as cover material are peat and highly organic soils. Peat is an earthy soil (usually brown to black) and is composed largely of partially decomposed plant matter. It usually contains a high amount of voids, and its water content may range from 100 to 400% of the weight of dried solids. Peat is virtually impossible to compact, whether wet or dry. Peat deposits are scattered throughout the country but are most abundant in the states bordering the Great Lakes. Highly organic soils include sands, silts, and clays that contain at least 20% organic matter. They are usually very dark, have an earthy odor when freshly turned, and often contain fragments of decomposing vegetable matter. They are very difficult to compact, are normally very sticky, and can vary extremely in their moisture content.

TERRAIN

A sanitary landfill can be constructed on virtually any terrain, but some land forms require that extensive site improvements be made and expensive operational techniques be followed. Flat or gently rolling land not subject to flooding is best, but this type is also highly desirable for farming and industrial parks, and this drives up the purchase price.

Depressions, such as canyons and ravines, are more efficient than flat areas from a land use standpoint since they can hold more solid waste per acre. Cover material may, however, have to be hauled in from surrounding areas. Depressions usually result when surface waters run off and erode the soil and rock. By their nature, they require special measures to keep surface waters from inundating the fill. Permeable formations that intersect the side walls or floor of the fill may also have to be lined with an impervious layer of clay or other material to control the movement of fluids.

There are also numerous man-made topographic features scattered over the country, strip mines, worked-out stone and clay quarries, open pit mines, and sand and gravel pits. In most cases, these abandoned depressions are useless, dangerous eyesores. Many of them could be safely and economically reclaimed by utilizing them as sanitary landfills. Clay pits, for example, are located in most impermeable formations, which are natural barriers to gas and water movement. Abandoned strip mines also are naturally suited for use as sanitary landfills. Most coal formations are underlaid by clays, shales, and siltstones that have a very low permeability. When permeable formations, such as sandstones, are encountered near an excavation, impermeable soil layers can be constructed from the nearby abundant spoil. Abandoned limestone, sandstone, siltstone, granite, and traprock quarries and open pit mines generally require more extensive improvements because they are in permeable or often open-fractured formations. The pollution potential of sand and gravel pits is great, and worked-out pits consequently require extensive investigation and probably expensive improvements to control gas movement and water pollution.

Marsh and tidal lands may also be filled, but they are less desirable from an ecological point of view. They have little value as real estate, but possess considerable ecological value as nesting and feeding grounds for wildlife. Filling of such areas requires, however, the permanent lowering of the groundwater or the raising of the ground surface to keep organic and soluble solid waste from being deposited in standing water. Roads for collection vehicles are also needed, and cover material generally has to be hauled in.

Operation

HOURS

The hours a sanitary landfill operates depend mainly on when the wastes are delivered, and generally this is done during normal working hours. In large cities, however, waste collection systems sometimes operate 24 hours a day. In this case, a site should not be located in a residential area. The usual landfill is open 5 to 6 days a week and 8 to 10 hours a day.

WEIGHING

The efficiency of filling and compacting operations can be adequately judged if the amount of solid waste delivered, the quantity of cover material used, and the volume occupied by the landfilled solid waste and cover are known. (Weighing is the most reliable means of measurement.) These values are also used to determine the density of the fill and to estimate the amount of settlement that will probably occur. Weight and volume data can also be used in designing new landfills and predicting the remaining capacity of currently operating landfills.

The number of vehicles that can be weighed in a unit of time will vary. An experienced weigh-master is able to record manually, for short periods of time, the net weight and types of material delivered at a rate of 60 trucks per hour, but it is extremely taxing to maintain this pace for long periods. A highly automated weighing procedure can easily accommodate over 60 trucks per hour, record more data, require less supervision, and be more accurate. Landfills disposing of 1,000 tons or more per day will usually require two or more automatic scales. Truck scales require little maintenance if inspected and maintained as recommended by their manufacturers.

TRAFFIC FLOW

Traffic flow on the site can affect the efficiency of daily operations. Traffic should be allowed to bypass the scale only if it is inoperative. Haphazard routing between the scale and the disposal area can lead to indiscriminate dumping and cause accidents. Pylons, barricades, guardrails, and traffic signs can be used to direct traffic. Large sites may need posted maps to direct drivers. If separate working areas are established for different types of wastes, signs should be used to direct drivers to the appropriate disposal areas.

Wastes are delivered to a landfill in vehicles that range from automobiles to large transfer trailers. Operationally, they comprise groups that are unloaded manually or mechanically. The two categories are established because of the difference in time it takes to unload them at the working face. If large numbers of manually unloaded vehicles must be handled, special procedures may be necessary.

Mechanically discharging vehicles include dump trucks, packer-type collection trucks, tank trucks, and open or closed body trucks equipped with a movable bulkhead that requires the use of a crawler dozer or loader. These vehicles are capable of rapidly discharging their loads and should be routed directly to the working face without delay.

Manually discharging vehicles take more time to unload and should not be permitted to slow the unloading of vehicles that can discharge mechanically. Many of the drivers will not be familiar with the landfill operation and will require close supervision. If a large number of manually discharging vehicles is involved, a separate unloading area may be necessary to avoid delaying other vehicles.

Scavenging should not be permitted, and no vehicle should be left unattended. Waste should be deposited at the toe of the working face, because it can be compacted better there since it is worked up the slope rather than down. If it is necessary to discharge solid wastes at the top of the slope, as in a narrow trench operation, telephone poles or similar objects should be emplaced to warn drivers that they are near its edge. The unloading area should be as level as practical for dump trucks and other vehicles having high centers of gravity in the raised position.

WASTE HANDLING

Wastes come from residences, commercial establishments, institutions, municipal operations, industries, and farms. Some may require special methods of handling and burial. The landfill designer should know all the types that will likely be involved and make provision for their disposal. Materials that cannot be safely buried should be excluded.

Residential, Commercial and Industrial Plant Wastes

These wastes (exclusive of process wastes discussed later) are usually highly compactible. They contain a heterogeneous mixture of such materials as paper, cans, bottles, cardboard and wooden boxes, plastics, lumber, metals, yard clippings, food waste, rocks, and soil. When exposed, boxes, plastic and glass containers, tin cans, and brush can be compressed and crushed under relatively low pressure. In a landfill, however, these items are incorporated within the mass of solid waste, which acts as a cushion and often bridges, thus protecting the relatively low-strength materials from being crushed under the load of the compaction equipment.

Cushioning and bridging can be reduced and greater volume reduction achieved if the waste is spread in layers less than 2 ft. deep and is then compacted by tracked, rubber-tired, or steel-wheeled vehicles that pass over it 2 to 5 times. Solid waste that contains a high percentage of brush and yard clippings requires the expenditure of more compactive effort. If entire loads of these items are received, they should be spread and compacted near the bottom of the cell so that less resilient wastes can be compacted on top.

The equipment operator should try to develop the working face on a slope between $20°$ and $30°$ (Figure 4.1). Waste is spread against the slope, and the machine moves up and down it, thus tearing and compacting the waste and eliminating voids. The equipment operator should make passes until he no longer can detect that the surface of the waste layer is being depressed more than it is rebounding.

Bulky Wastes

Bulky wastes include car bodies, demolition and construction debris, large appliances, tree stumps, and timbers. Significant volume reduction of construction rubble and stumps by compaction cannot be achieved, but car bodies, furniture, and appliances can be significantly reduced in volume. A small crawler dozer (110 HP and 20,000 lbs. or less) has greater difficulty in compacting washing machines and auto bodies than would heavy machines, but some volume reduction can be achieved. Such items should be crushed on solid ground and then pushed onto the working face, near the bottom of the cell or into a separate disposal area. Once in place, most bulky items do not degrade (at least not at a rate comparable to surrounding refuse).

Consequently, if bulky items are incorporated into degradable wastes, uneven settlement will result. Special areas for bulky items should be identified on the final plan of the completed site. Even though bulky wastes do not usually contain putrescibles, they should be completely covered at the end of each operating day to eliminate harborage for rats and other pets. Selected loads of demolition and construction debris, broken concrete, asphalt, bricks, and plaster, can be stockpiled and used to build on-site roads.

FIGURE 4.1: DEPOSITION OF WASTES

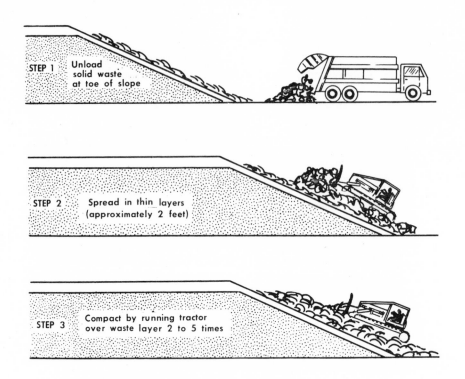

STEP 1   Unload
         solid waste
         at toe of slope

STEP 2   Spread in thin layers
         (approximately 2 feet)

STEP 3   Compact by running tractor
         over waste layer 2 to 5 times

Cushioning and bridging can be reduced and greater volume reduction
achieved if the waste is spread in layers less than 2 ft. deep and is then
compacted by a tracked, rubber-tired, or steel-wheeled vehicle that
passes over it 2 to 5 times. The equipment operator should try to develop the working face on a slope between 20° and 30°.

Source: Sanitary Landfill Design and Operation, EPA, 1972

Industrial Process Wastes

Because of the wide variety of industrial process wastes and their different chemical, physical, and biological characteristics, it is difficult to generalize about handling them. The best source of information concerning their characteristics is
the industries that produce them. It is extremely important to evaluate the influence of these wastes on the environment. If an industrial waste is determined
to be unsuitable for disposal at the landfill, it should be excluded and the respective industries notified. Another important factor is the health and safety of
landfill personnel.

Industrial wastes delivered to a landfill may be in the form of a liquid, semi-liquid, films, sheets, granules, shavings, turnings, powders, and defectively manu-factured products of all shapes and sizes. Whether or not these are disposed of in the sanitary landfill depends on the environmental conditions of the site and whether or not they are chemically and biologically stable. They should not be allowed to pollute surface water or groundwater.

Liquids and semiliquids, if deemed safe to place in a landfill, should be admixed with relatively dry, absorbent solid waste or they may be disposed of in a pit well above the groundwater table. The pit should be fenced and the gate locked to prevent unauthorized access; its location should be recorded in the final plan of the completed site.

Films and other light, fluffy, easily airborne materials can be a nuisance at the working face, and they should be covered immediately when deposited there. Spraying them with water may be helpful, but the detrimental effects of adding water should be considered.

Large sheets of metal, plastic, or wood can also be nuisances at the working face. The equipment operator should align the sheets parallel to one another. Random placement leads to large voids, poor compaction, and substantial settle-ment of the completed landfill.

Granules, shavings, turnings, and powders can be health hazards to operating personnel, nuisances if they become airborne, and very abrasive or corrosive to the landfill equipment; they should be covered immediately. The workers may have to wear face masks, goggles, or protective clothing to avoid respiratory, eye, or skin ailments.

Defectively manufactured products are delivered to the landfill to keep them off the market. These wastes should be incorporated into the sanitary landfill immediately so that drivers, helpers, and others at the working face are not tempted to engage in scavenging. Their doing so would violate the manufac-turer's trust and, even more importantly, would expose them to injury.

COVER

The operations plan should specify what soils are to be used as cover material, where they are to be obtained, and how they are to be placed over the com-pacted solid waste. The first two specifications are determined by the land-fill designer after he has evaluated the soil investigation and the functional re-quirements of the cover material. Cover materials used at a sanitary landfill are classed as daily, intermediate, and final; the classification depends on the thickness of soil used.

Daily Cover: The important control functions of daily cover are vector, litter, fire, and moisture. Generally, a minimum compacted thickness of 6 in. of soil will perform these functions. The cover is applied to the compacted waste at least at the end of each operating day. If possible, it should be spread and compacted on the top and sideslopes as construction of the cell progresses, thus leaving only the working face exposed. At the end of the operating day, the working face is also covered. No waste should be exposed, and the cover should be graded to prevent erosion and to keep water from ponding.

Intermediate Cover: Functions of intermediate cover are the same as daily cover but include gas control and possibly service as a road base. It is applied in the same manner as daily cover, but the minimum compacted depth recommended is one foot. Periodic grading and compacting may be necessary to repair erosion damage and to prevent ponding of water. Cracks and depressions may develop because of moisture loss and settlement of the fill, and periodic maintenance is required.

Final Cover: Final cover serves basically the same functions as intermediate cover, but it must also support vegetative growth. At a minimum 2 ft. of soil should be used, compacted into 6-in. thick layers. Such factors as soil type and anticipated use of the completed landfill may require more than 2 ft.

Grading is extremely important, and grades should be specified in the landfill design. The general topographic layout of the completed landfill surface is attained by carefully locating solid waste cells, but the final cover is graded and compacted to achieve the desired configuration. Water should not be allowed to pond on the landfill surface and grades should not exceed 2 to 4% to prevent the erosion of cover material. Sideslopes should be less than 1 vertical to 3 horizontal. Preferably, topsoil from the site should be stockpiled and reserved for placement on top of the final cover. Since the topsoil will be seeded, it should not be highly compacted.

MODEL SANITARY LANDFILL OPERATION AGREEMENT

The following agreement is taken from EPA Publication PB 213,472, (1971) jointly prepared by The National Solid Wastes Management Association and the Federal solid waste management program.

This agreement made and entered into this_____ day of 19___, by and between_____ _____(a City, Village, County, etc.) organized under the laws of the State of_____ _____, hereinafter referred to as the City (Village, etc) and_____ (a Corporation or a Partnership, Proprietorship, etc.) organized under the laws of the State of_____ _____ and having its principal place of business at_____, hereinafter referred to as the Contractor.

WITNESSETH:

Whereas, the Contractor is qualified to operate a sanitary landfill for the disposal of solid waste in accordance with the attached ordinances, specifications, and Instructions to Bidders; and

Whereas, the City desires the Contractor to operate the site(s) designated to be used for a sanitary landfill operation;

Now Therefore, in consideration of the mutual covenants and agreements contained herein, and of the consideration to be paid by the City to the Contractor, as hereinafter set forth, the City and the Contractor hereby agree as follows:

1. *Disposal Site.* All solid wastes shall be disposed of at the location(s) specified herein, same being the property under the control of the City (or Contractor), and more specifically described as follows:

(Insert Legal Description)

2. *Materials to be Disposed of.* The Contractor shall accept, upon payment of fees as scheduled, all solid waste created within the jurisdiction of the City or for which the City has accepted responsibility. Toxic, volatile, and other hazardous materials must be clearly identified to allow for special handling during the disposal operation. (Note: A definition of the solid wastes to be disposed of under the provisions of the contract should be included here. In addition, clarification of who shall be allowed to deliver solid waste to the site must be provided.)

3. *Operation of Site(s).* The Contractor shall have the exclusive right and responsibility to operate the disposal site(s) in accordance with the provisions of this Agreement and the attached ordinances and specifications for the term of this Agreement and any extension thereof.

4. *Compliance with Laws.* The Contractor shall operate the disposal site(s) in compliance with all applicable laws, ordinances, specifications and regulations, including the applicable solid waste disposal act of the State of_____, the rules and regulations of the State Board of Health and the City and/or County Board of Health, and the ordinances of the City and/or County; copies of each are attached hereto and are hereby made a part of this Agreement. Copies of all such laws, ordinances and regulations shall be furnished to the Contractor by the City and shall include new legislation as well as amendments.

(In the event that there are no statutes or ordinances regulating the disposal of wastes, then the City may utilize the concepts contained in the first section of this publication to develop its own ordinances and standards.)

5. *Labor and Equipment.* The Contractor shall furnish all labor, tools, and equipment necessary to operate the site(s) and shall be responsible for all required maintenance thereof. Supervision by an experienced and qualified person shall be provided at all times when the sanitary landfill is open for use or operation.

6. *Service Facilities.* The Contractor shall construct and maintain at his expense any facilities, improvements, and buildings within the site necessary for the operation of the site.

(To be included if the site is City property: The use of such land within the site shall be made available to the Contractor free of charge for the period of this Agreement or any extension thereof. At the expiration of this Agreement all permanent structures and improvements thereon shall become the property of the City or shall be removed by the Contractor, at the option of the City. [If permanent structures and improvements become the property of the City, there should be some provision for compensation to the Contractor, such as book value or fair market value. If the Contractor is required to remove such structures and improvements, he should be paid for doing so.])

7. *Offsite Improvements.* The City agrees to provide, at its expense, all required offsite improvements including any required to be made to public streets or roads, drainage facilities, etc.; it shall also provide to the site all required utilities, including adequate power and water supplies. (If any of this work is to be performed by the Contractor, it should be included in a separate contract with detailed engineering plans.)

8. *Charges for Utilities.* The Contractor agrees to pay normal and standard charges for all water, electrical power, natural gas, and phone service utilized at the site. (If any of these services are to be provided free of charge by the City, this section should be modified accordingly.)

9. *Salvage.* Neither scavenging nor salvage operations shall be permitted at the operating face of the sanitary landfill. Salvage operations, if any, shall be conducted at a location separate from the operating face of the landfill by persons licensed by the City so as not to interfere with the Contractor's operation.

10. *Title to Waste.* Title to waste shall vest, as it is deposited, in the owner of the fee simple estate.

11. *Completion of the Site.* Upon completion of disposal operations, the site shall be contoured and finished in accordance with the Approved Final Plan, which is attached hereto and is hereby made a part of this Agreement. Any changes of the Approved Final Plan must be agreed to by both the City and the Contractor. The liability of the Contractor under this Agreement shall cease upon acceptance of the site by the City.

12. *Compensation.* Compensation shall be paid pursuant to the attached schedule. (A schedule should be attached and provide for payment by weight, volume, or load. A minimum charge should be set out. Hazardous materials should be handled on a mandatory basis with fees paid by type and quantity. Experience should soon establish fees for such materials.)

(If materials are to be accepted from users other than those paid for and designated by the City, a similar schedule of prices which the Contractor can charge these users should be established. There should be clear provisions regarding the distribution of such fees to the Contractor and/or the City.)

13. *Changes in Regulations.* In the event that compliance with subsequent statutes, ordinances and/or rules and regulations changes operating costs, the parties hereto agree to renegotiate this Agreement so that the compensation shown herein shall reflect such changes.

14. *Change in Sanitary Landfill Site.* In the event that the parties hereto mutually agree to transfer said sanitary landfill operations to another site or additional sites, this Agreement shall be renegotiated to reflect any changes required; they shall include but not be limited to increased compensation due to higher operating costs.

15. *Change in Cost of Doing Business.* The fees and/or compensation payable to the Contractor for the second and subsequent years of the term hereof shall be adjusted to reflect changes in the cost of doing business, as measured by fluctuations in the Consumer Price Index (CPI) published by the U.S. Department of Labor, Bureau of Labor Statistics, for the_____ _____area. At the start of the second year and every six (6) months thereafter, the fees and/or compensation to the Contractor shall be altered in a percentage amount equal to the net percentage change in the said CPI as follows:

Compensation made for the first six months of the second year shall reflect the change, if any, that has occurred in the said CPI during the first year of this Agreement.

Beginning with the seventh month of the second year of this Agreement and every six months thereafter, the net change in compensation shall be the change in the CPI over the preceding six-month period.

16. *Term.* The initial term of this Agreement shall be for the_____-year period beginning _____, 19___, and ending_____, 19___. The initial_____-year term of this Agreement shall be extended for successive additional_____-year terms, unless one party notifies the other that it intends to terminate this Agreement. This intent must be conveyed in writing not less than ninety (90) days prior to the expiration of the initial_____-year term or of any_____-year extension thereof.

17. *Performance Bond.* The Contractor shall furnish a Performance Bond for the faithful performance of this Agreement. Said bond shall be executed by a surety company licensed to do business in this State and to be in a penal sum equal to 50 percent of the minimum compensation to be paid to the Contractor by the City for the first year of this Agreement. For each year thereafter it shall be in the penal sum of 50 percent of the total compensation paid by the City to the Contractor for the last preceding year. Said Performance Bond shall be furnished annually by the Contractor within ten (10) days of the execution of this Agreement or any extension thereof. It shall indemnify the City against any loss resulting from any failure of performance by the Contractor, not exceeding, however, the penal sum of the bond.

18. *Payment Bond.* The Contractor shall within ten (10) days of the execution of this agreement, deliver or cause to be delivered to the City a bond in the amount of $_____ executed by a surety company licensed to do business in this State. It shall guarantee payment of wages to all employees of the Contractor at the site or sites and the cost of all supplies, materials, and insurance premiums required to fulfill this Agreement.

19. *Indemnity.* The Contractor hereby binds himself to indemnify and hold harmless the City from all claims, demands and/or actions, legal and/or equitable, arising from the Contractor's operation of all disposal sites herein above described.

(Liability insurance policies approved by the City as to type and coverage may be required as a part of the indemnity provisions of this Agreement. If such policies as automobile liability, general liability, or owner's protective liability are required, the type and amount of coverage should be clearly spelled out in this section. Minimum motor vehicle liability limits set by State financial responsibility laws are seldom adequate.)

Proof of all insurance shall be furnished by the Contractor to the City by certificates of insurance. They shall have a minimum cancellation time of thirty (30) days, said time to commence after delivery of said notice to the City at the address shown above.

20. *Workmen's Compensation.* The Contractor shall carry in a company authorized to transact business in the State of_____, a policy of insurance fulfilling all requirements of the Workmen's Compensation Act of said State, including all legal requirements for occupational diseases. (Would not apply in monopoly States.)

21. *Standard of Performance.* The City may move to act if the Contractor fails to dispose of the solid waste herein provided for a period in excess of five (5) consecutive working days or fails to operate the site in accordance with the attached ordinances and specifications for a similar period. (He shall not be held liable if such failure is due to war, insurrection, riot, Act of God, or any other cause or causes beyond his control.) The City may, at its option, after sending written notice to the Contractor as provided hereinafter take over and operate any or all of the equipment he uses in carrying out this Agreement, and it may provide for such operation until such matter is resolved and the Contractor is again able to operate. Any and all operating expenses incurred by the City in so doing may be deducted by it from compensation paid to the Contractor hereunder.

During such period, the liability of the City to the Contractor for loss or damage to such equipment so used shall be that of a bailee for hire; ordinary wear and tear is specifically exempt from such liability. The liability of the Contractor to third persons shall cease and all claims or demands arising out of the operation and/or control of the site or sites shall be directed solely to the City.

Provided however; if the Contractor is unable for any cause to resume performance at the end of thirty (30) working days, all liability of the City under this contract shall cease and the City shall be free to negotiate with other contractors regarding the operation of said site or sites. If Agreement with another contractor is reached, this shall not release the Contractor herein of his liability to the City for breach of this Agreement.

22. *Arbitration..* Any controversy or claim arising out of or related to this Agreement, or breach thereof, shall be settled by arbitration in accordance with the Rules of The American Arbitration Association, and the judgment rendered may be entered in any court having jurisdiction thereof. Such controversy or claim shall be submitted to one arbitrator selected from the National Panel of The American Arbitration Association.

23. *Landfill Inspection.* To ensure that the detailed ordinances, specifications, regulations, and laws for the operation of a sanitary landfill are complied with, a representative of the City shall inspect the landfill site and operation at least once a month during the term of this Agreement. The City may make inspections of the sanitary landfill site accompanied by designated personnel during business hours.

24. *Contractor's Personnel.*

a. The Contractor shall assign a qualified person or persons to be in charge of his operations in the City and shall inform it of said person or persons' identity with a description of his experience, etc.

b. The Contractor's employees may be required to wear clean uniforms that bear the company's name.

c. The City has the right to request the dismissal of any employee of the Contractor who violates any provision hereof, or who is wanton, negligent, or discourteous in the performance of his duties.

d. The Contractor should provide suitable operating and safety training for all his personnel. The site should be staffed at all times with at least one employee who is trained in first aid and has a first aid kit.

e. Wages of all employees of the Contractor shall equal or exceed the minimum scales prevailing for similar work in the locality of the project. The wages for each classification of employee shall be provided to the City as an attachment to the bid document.

f. No person shall be denied employment by the Contractor by reason of race, creed, or religion.

g. Employees of the Contractor shall have the right to organize and affiliate with recognized labor unions and shall have the right to collective bargaining.

25. *Assignment.* No assignment of this Agreement or any right occurring under it shall be made in whole or part by the Contractor without the express written consent of the City; in the event of any assignment, the assignee shall assume the liability of the Contractor.

26. *Books and Records.* The Contractor shall keep daily records of wastes received, and the City shall have the right to inspect the same insofar as they pertain to the operation of the sanitary landfill site(s). The records shall show: the type, weight, and volume of solid waste received; the portion of the landfill used, as determined by cross section and survey; any deviations made from the plan of operation; equipment maintenance; and cost records. The Contractor shall submit a proposed record and accounting system for approval. All information

so obtained shall be confidential and shall not be released by the City unless expressly authorized in writing by the Contractor.(A recommended set of cost accounting records is in "An Accounting System for Solid Waste Collection" developed by the Federal solid waste management program.)

27. *Bankruptcy.* This Contract shall terminate in the case of bankruptcy, voluntary or involuntary, or insolvency of the Contractor. In the case of bankruptcy, such termination shall take effect on the day and at the time the bankruptcy is filed.

28. *Number of Copies.* This Agreement may be executed in any number of counterparts, all of which shall have the full force and effect of an original for all purposes.

29. *Law to Govern.* This Agreement shall be governed by the laws of the State of_____ _____, both as to interpretation and performance.

30. *Modification.* This Agreement constitutes the entire Agreement and understanding between the parties hereto, and it shall not· be considered modified, altered, changed, or amended in any respect unless in writing and signed by the parties hereto.

31. *Right to Require Performance.* The failure of the City at any time to require performance by the Contractor of any provisions hereof shall in no way affect the right of the City thereafter to enforce same. Nor shall waiver by the City of any breach of any provisions hereof be taken or held to be á waiver of any succeeding breach of such provisions or as a waiver of any provision itself.

32. *Point of Contact.* All dealings, contacts, etc. between the Contractor and the City shall be directed by the Contractor to

(Some duly designated official of the City must be identified to serve as the contact point for the Contractor. A similar clause could designate a contact point with the Contractor.)

33. *Illegal Provisions.* If any provision of this Agreement shall be declared illegal, void, or unenforceable, the other provisions shall not be affected and shall remain in full force and effect.

34. *Notice.* A letter addressed and sent by certified United States mail to either party at its business address shown hereinabove shall be sufficient notice whenever required for any purpose in this Agreement.

35. *Effective Date.* This contract shall become effective and the City or its designated agents and citizens shall begin delivery of the solid waste to the Contractor_____days after the date of execution hereof.

City: _____ _____ _____

Contractor: _____ _____ _____

IN WITNESS WHEREOF, the City and Contractor have executed this Agreement as of the day and year first above written.

Approved as to Form _____
City Attorney

City of _____
A municipal corporation of the State of_____

By _____
By _____
By _____

(Name of Contractor)

By _____
By _____

(Sealed, witnessed, and/or notarized as required by the laws of applicable State.)

FEE SCHEDULE

(Alternate methods of charge)

1. $ _____ per ton of solid waste
2. $ _____ per yard of compacted solid waste
3. $ _____ per yard of uncompacted solid waste
4. $ _____ minimum fee per load
5. $ _____ per ton of solid waste consisting solely of
    material such as bricks, concrete, dirt, etc.

6. The City shall pay to the contractor a minimum fee of $_____ for each year or yearly extension of this agreement.

Toxic, volatile, or other hazardous materials requiring special handling shall be clearly marked by the City and, upon payment of mutually agreed upon fees, shall be disposed of by the Contractor pursuant to the terms of Item 2 of the contract.

The Contractor shall submit billings to the City at the close of business at the end of each month for all other waste placed in the sanitary landfill and the City shall pay the Contractor on or before the tenth day of the following month; payments shall be mailed to the Contractor at the address shown above.

RECOMMENDED STANDARDS

The following recommended standards were developed by the Caterpillar Tractor Co.

Design

Item 1. Topographic Maps: The design of the sanitary landfill shall include one or more topographic maps at a scale of not over 200 feet to the inch with 5-foot contour intervals. These maps shall show: the proposed fill area; any borrow area; access roads; grades for proper drainage of each lift required and a typical cross-section of a lift; special drainage devices if necessary; fencing; equipment shelter; existing and proposed utilities; employee facilities; and all other pertinent information to clearly indicate the orderly development, operations, and completion of the sanitary landfill.

Reason — Clear plans and procedures are essential to the efficient and successful operation of any sanitary landfill. Topographic maps will show to all those involved (planners, legislative bodies, health officials, supervisors, equipment operators, etc.) the existing situation and the sequence of operations planned. Topographic maps are necessary for the same reasons that they are necessary in road construction or other earth-moving projects.

Satisfactory Compliance — This item shall be deemed to have been satisfied when:

(1) Topographic maps of the proposed fill area have been submitted. These maps shall contain pertinent information for the orderly development, conduct, and completion of the sanitary landfill.

Item 2. Geology: The geological characteristics of the proposed site shall be determined by on-site testing or from earlier reliable survey data.

Reason — Exploratory geological investigations are one of the most important studies required in selecting a site for a sanitary landfill. From such investigations, it can be determined if cover material of suitable quality is available or whether it will have to be obtained elsewhere. Such investigations also will permit evaluation of geological factors that influence ease of excavation, water pollution, and lateral gas movement.

Satisfactory Compliance — This item shall be deemed to have been satisfied when:

(1)   A report on sufficient exploratory investigations, including a series of borings, taken to the depth cover material will be removed and sufficient in number to give a valid indication of the underlying conditions, has been submitted, or

(2)   Where only a few acres are involved and the geological formations are known to be consistent, satisfactory evidence of existing conditions has been submitted in lieu of borings.

Item 3. Characteristics of Cover Material: The soil used as cover material shall be of such character that it can be compacted to provide a tight seal, does not crack excessively when dry, and is relatively free of putrescible materials and large objects. Soil surveys, published by the Soil Conservation Service of the U.S. Department of Agriculture, are particularly helpful in locating sanitary landfill sites with the most suitable soil conditions.

Reason — When cover material is spread over the refuse and compacted to form a tight seal or cover, it performs several vital functions. This barrier prevents flies from laying eggs on the refuse or rodents from invading the fill. It seals in odors, prevents rain water from entering the fill, and minimizes the blowing and scattering of refuse. It reduces the fire hazard, and helps to produce a dense, stable fill. In addition, fly eggs and larvae which complete their development in the refuse are prevented from emerging as adult flies.

The type of soil used for cover material is important since it dictates the equipment requirements for excavating, hauling, and compacting. When sandy loam soil is used, a tight cover can be provided and maintained with the least expense. Other types of soil can be used, but frequently require additional work for excavation, compaction, or maintenance of cover.

Satisfactory Compliance — This item shall be deemed to have been satisfied when:

(1)   The cover material is "sandy loam" as defined by the Guide for Textural Classification, page 209, *Soil Survey Manual*, U.S.D.A. Handbook No. 18 available from the United States Department of Agriculture.

(2)   The cover material available is not "sandy loam" but is of such character that it compacts well, does not crack excessively when dry, and is relatively free of putrescible materials and large objects.

Item 4. Water Pollution: Sanitary landfill operations shall be limited to areas where water pollution is not likely to occur.

Reason — In general, landfills should not be located on a site where ground or surface water will intercept the deposited refuse. Refuse often contains infectious material and other harmful substances that can cause serious health hazards or nuisances if permitted to enter ground or surface water. Provisions (i.e., diversion of surface water, diking and dewatering or draining and filling) can often be made to minimize or prevent pollution from sanitary landfill operations. In areas sufficiently remote, dilution and biological processes in bodies of water may reduce the hazard to public health to the extent that landfill operations may be permitted where water intercepts the deposited refuse.

Satisfactory Compliance — This item shall be deemed to have been satisfied when:

(1)   Plans indicating suitable provisions to minimize or prevent water pollution have been submitted.

(2)   A report on sufficient exploratory investigations of the site has been submitted indicating that problems of water pollution are not likely to occur if the plan of operation is followed.

Item 5. Equipment: Adequate numbers, types, and sizes of equipment shall be specified for operating the landfill in accordance with good engineering practice and with these standards.

Reason — The maintenance of sanitary landfills requires that equipment be provided that is capable of satisfactorily performing the various operations of excavation, compaction, and transportation made necessary by the site, the operational plan, and these standards. Undersized, inadequate, or unreliable equipment may result in breakdowns, higher operational costs, improper landfill operation, and the development of health hazards or nuisances.

Satisfactory Compliance — This item shall be deemed to have been satisfied when:

(1)   The equipment specified will meet the performance requirements made necessary by the quantities of refuse expected, the landfill site, the operational plan, and these standards.

Item 6. Plans and Specifications: All sanitary landfills shall be designed in accordance with these standards by a registered engineer. Detailed plans, specifications, and necessary reports shall be submitted by the engineer to the State

Department of Health for review and approval.

Reason — To be sanitary, economical, and successful, a sanitary landfill must be considered as an engineering endeavor. There are many factors to be considered when planning and operating a sanitary landfill, some of which have significant health implications. Landfills operated without proper planning nearly always are inefficient and result in unsanitary conditions.

Satisfactory Compliance — This item shall be deemed to have been satisfied when:

(1)   The plans and specifications include the following background data: Present and estimated future contributory population, refuse quantities in weight and volume per capita per day, and ratio of maximum to average day.

(2)   A registered professional engineer signs the plans and specifications and states that the sanitary landfill has been designed in accordance with these standards.

(3)   The plans, specifications, and necessary reports, including consideration of the items in these standards, have been approved by the State Department of Health.

Preparation of the Site

Item 7. Access: Access roads shall be designed and constructed so that traffic will flow smoothly and will not be interrupted by ordinary inclement weather. Access to the site by unauthorized persons shall be limited by suitable fencing.

Reason — In order to avoid needless expense, it is of the utmost importance that collection vehicles are not delayed at the disposal site and that all refuse is unloaded only at the fill area. Since the refuse hauling operation is unproductive time for the refuse collectors, any unnecessary delays are costly and can result in unfinished collection routes. Fencing limits access so that indiscriminate unloading of refuse and accident hazards are minimized.

Satisfactory Compliance — This item shall be deemed to have been satisfied when:

(1)   An all-weather access road, negotiable by loaded collection vehicles, has been provided to the entrance of the landfill site.

(2)   Suitable fencing, with a gate that can be locked at the entrance of the landfill site, has been provided.

(3)   (a) Provisions have been made for all-weather access from the entrance gate of the site to an unloading area, or

(b) All-weather access has been provided to an alternate sanitary landfill.

Item 8. Equipment Shelter: Suitable shelter for landfill equipment shall be provided.

Reason — Protection of equipment from the weather reduces deterioration and maintenance. Shelter is also necessary for equipment servicing; for routine maintenance; and for storage of tools, service equipment, spare parts, and other supplies.

Satisfactory Compliance — This item shall be deemed to have been satisfied when:

(1)   A permanent or temporary shelter of suitable size has been provided to accommodate the equipment and other necessary service supplies.

Item 9. Employee Facilities: Suitable shelter and sanitary facilities shall be provided for personnel.

Reason — Shelter is necessary for protection of the landfill employees from inclement weather. Toilet and handwashing facilities are necessary for good personal hygiene of the landfill employees and of collection personnel.

Satisfactory Compliance — This item shall be deemed to have been satisfied when:

(1)   Permanent or temporary shelter has been constructed of adequate size, provided with safe drinking water, sanitary handwashing and toilet facilities, electricity, suitable heating facilities, and proper screening.

Item 10. Weighing Facilities: Provision shall be made for weighing all refuse delivered to the sanitary landfill.

Reason — A method of measuring incoming refuse is necessary to provide reliable quantity data, to determine trends, and to estimate future disposal needs. Experience has shown that refuse quantities must be based on weight rather than volume if the data are to be reasonably accurate for comparative purposes. Weighing provides an equitable basis for establishing fees for refuse disposal. Weighing also provides the basis for cost analyses of landfill operations. In addition, weighing provides a means for the constant surveillance of collection crews and encourages the delivery of adequate payloads by each truck.

Satisfactory Compliance — This item shall be deemed to have been satisfied when:

(1)   Suitable fixed or portable scales have been installed at the sanitary landfill to determine net weights delivered, or

(2)   Other arrangements have been made to weigh and report the net weights of refuse delivered by each truck.

Item 11. Communications: Telephone or radio communications shall be provided at the sanitary landfill site.

Reason — Communications are necessary at the generally remote sanitary landfill sites in cases of emergency. Better administration of both the collection and disposal operation is facilitated by good communications.

Satisfactory Compliance — This item shall be deemed to have been satisfied when:

(1)   A reliable telephone or radio system has been installed at the sanitary landfill site.

Item 12. Fire Protection: Suitable measures shall be taken to control fires.

Reason — Fires endanger life and property. Smoke and odors create nuisances to surrounding property owners and also interfere with landfilling operations.

Satisfactory Compliance — This item shall be deemed to have been satisfied when:

(1)   (a) An adequate supply of water under pressure is available at the site, or
      (b) A stockpile of earth is maintained reasonably close to the working face of the fill, or
      (c) A nearby organized fire department will provide immediate service whenever called.

(2)   Suitable fire extinguishers, maintained in working order, are kept on the equipment and in all buildings.

Operations

Item 12. Limited Access: Access to a sanitary landfill shall be limited to those times when an attendant is on duty and only to those authorized to use the site for the disposal of refuse.

Reason — If public use of a sanitary landfill is allowed when no attendant is on duty, scavenging and indiscriminate dumping commonly occur. It then becomes necessary to divert men and equipment to policing the area to restore sanitary conditions. When only authorized persons are permitted access to the site during operating hours, traffic and other accident hazards are minimized.

Satisfactory Compliance — This item shall be deemed to have been satisfied when:

(1)   The gate is open only when an attendant or equipment operator is on duty and is locked at all other times.

(2)   Hours of operation and other limitations on access are displayed prominently at the entrance gate.

(3)   (a)   An attendant is on duty during operating hours to prevent unauthorized persons from entering the area, or

(b)   On small landfills, the equipment operator is responsible for preventing unauthorized persons from entering the area.

Item 14. Unloading of Refuse: Unloading of refuse shall be continuously supervised.

Reason — Systematic placement of refuse, restricted to a small unloading area and coordinated with spreading and compacting operations, reduces work, minimizes scattering of refuse, and expedites unloading of collection vehicles.

Satisfactory Compliance — This item shall be deemed to have been satisfied when:

(1)   Appropriate signs are posted to indicate clearly where vehicles are to unload.

(2)   (a)   An attendant is on duty during operating hours to direct unloading of refuse, or

(b)   On small landfills the equipment operator directs unloading of refuse.

(3)   Unloading of refuse is confined to as small an area as possible.

Item 15. Blowing Paper: Blowing paper shall be controlled by providing a portable fence near the working area. The entire area shall be policed regularly.

Reason — The purpose of the sanitary landfill is to dispose of the refuse in a sanitary and nuisance-free manner. If papers and other light materials are allowed to be scattered by wind and the area is not policed, fire hazards and nuisances are created.

Satisfactory Compliance — This item shall be deemed to have been satisfied when:

(1)   A portable fence is placed near the unloading and spreading area to catch windblown paper and other light materials.

(2)   The portable fence and the surrounding area are policed daily and all scattered material collected and placed in the fill.

Item 16. Spreading and Compacting of Refuse: Refuse shall be spread and compacted in shallow layers not exceeding a depth of 2 feet of compacted material.

Reason — A successful sanitary landfill operation depends upon the adequate compaction of the refuse. Settlement will be excessive and uneven when the refuse is not well compacted. Such settlement permits the ingress and egress of insects and rodents and severely limits the usefulness of the finished area.

Compaction is best initiated by spreading the refuse evenly in shallow layers rather than placing the material in a single deep lift. Further compaction is provided by the repeated travel of landfill equipment over the layers and, if necessary, by the use of special compacting equipment. Additional compaction also can be achieved by routing collection trucks so that they travel repeatedly over the finished portion of the fill. These procedures result in the greatest compaction and the least ultimate settlement, providing the most useful finished fill and best utilizing the capacity of the site.

Satisfactory Compliance — This item shall be deemed to have been satisfied when:

(1)   Additions of refuse are spread evenly by repeated passages of landfill equipment.

(2)   Each layer is compacted thoroughly to a depth not greater than approximately 2 feet.

(3)   The refuse fill is continued to the total depth of lift (Item 17) by repeating (1) and (2) above.

Item 17. Depth of Lifts in Fill: Individual lifts in sanitary landfills shall be no greater than 8 feet in depth.

Reason — The total depth of a landfill is governed by the characteristics of the site, the desired elevation of the completed fill, and good engineering practice. Construction of a fill in well-compacted lifts of not more than 8 feet each in depth minimizes settlement, surface cracking, and release of odors. Fills using lifts shallower than 8 feet do not generally make maximum use of available land, but provide for earlier reuse of the site.

Satisfactory Compliance — This item shall be deemed to have been satisfied when:

(1)   All lifts are 8 feet or less in depth.

(2)   No health hazards or nuisances result from the use of more than one lift.

Item 18. Daily Cover: A compacted layer of at least 6 inches of suitable cover material shall be placed on all exposed refuse by the end of each working day.

Reason — Daily covering of the refuse is necessary to prevent fly and rodent attraction, blowing of papers, productions of odors, fire hazards, and an unsightly appearance. Fly emergence generally is prevented by 6 inches of compacted soil. Daily covering divides the fill into "cells" that limit the spread of fires within the fill.

Satisfactory Compliance — This item shall be deemed to have been satisfied when:

(1)   The quality of the daily cover material meets the requirements specified in Item 3.

(2)   At least 6 inches of well-compacted cover material (measured perpendicularly to the surface of the compacted refuse) is placed daily to cover completely all refuse deposited that day in the fill.

Item 19. Intermediate Cover: In all but the final lift of a landfill, a layer of suitable cover material compacted to a minimum depth of one foot shall be placed daily on all surfaces of the fill except those where operations will continue on the following working day.

Reason — More than one foot of soil cover might be wasteful in a landfill in which there is a clear intention to provide at least one additional lift within one year. Under such circumstances, a one-foot layer of properly compacted and maintained cover will prevent health hazards or nuisances until the next lift is placed.

Satisfactory Compliance — This item shall be deemed to have been satisfied when:

(1)   The quality of the intermediate cover material meets the requirements specified in Item 3.

(2)   At least one foot of well-compacted cover material (measured perpendicularly to the surface of the compacted refuse) is placed daily on all surfaces of each lift on which another lift will be constructed within one year, except where 6 inches of daily cover are provided as specified in Item 18.

(3)   The entire surface of the intermediate cover is inspected weekly and all cracked, eroded, and uneven areas repaired.

Item 20. Final Cover: A layer of suitable cover material compacted to a minimum thickness of 2 feet shall be placed over the entire surface of each portion of the final lift not later than one week following the placement of refuse within that portion.

Reason — A minimum final cover of 2 feet of compacted earth will prevent emergence of insects from the compacted refuse, minimize escape of odors and gases, and prevent rodent burrowing. This cover also provides an adequate bearing surface for vehicles, and sufficient thickness for cover integrity in the event of settling or erosion.

Satisfactory Compliance — This item shall be deemed to have been satisfied when:

(1)   The quality of the final cover material meets the requirements specified in Item 3.

(2)   At least 2 feet of well-compacted cover material (measured perpendicularly to the surface of the compacted refuse) is placed within a week of the completion of each portion of the final lift.

(3)   Until completion of the landfill, the entire surface of the final cover is inspected monthly and all cracked, eroded, and uneven areas repaired.

Item 21. Equipment Maintenance: Provisions shall be made for the routine operational maintenance of equipment at the landfill site and for the prompt repair or replacement of landfill equipment.

Reason — Equipment breakdowns of a day or more result in the accumulation of refuse as in an open dump with all the attendant health hazards or nuisances. Systematic, routine maintenance of equipment reduces repair costs, increases life expectance, and helps to prevent breakdowns that interrupt landfill operations. In event of breakdown, prompt repair of equipment or immediate procurement of standby equipment insures continuity of operations. Special advance arrangements for making major repairs and for providing standby equipment will materially reduce down time. Prompt repair of equipment and availability of standby equipment insure continuity of operations.

Satisfactory Compliance — This item shall be deemed to have been satisfied when:

(1)   Adequate routine maintenance of sanitary landfill equipment is carried out.

(2)   Inoperative equipment is repaired or replaced within 24 hours.

Item 22. Sewage Solids or Liquids and Other Hazardous Materials: Sewage solids or liquids (septic tank or cesspool pumpings and sewage sludge and grit) and other hazardous materials shall be disposed of in a sanitary landfill only if special provisions are made for such disposal.

Reason — Sewage solids or liquids are infectious and create health hazards if not properly handled. Other materials, including oil sludges, waste chemicals, magnesium shavings, and empty insecticide containers, may also present special hazards. Unless properly handled, these wastes can be dangerous to landfill employees. When the design of the sanitary landfill includes special provisions for disposal of hazardous materials, they can be disposed of safely and need not be excluded.

Satisfactory Compliance — This item shall be deemed to have been satisfied when:

(1)   Suitable procedures are established and followed for disposal of hazardous materials.

Item 23. Large Items: Special provisions shall be made for the disposal of large, heavy, or bulky items at small landfills or at landfills operated with light equipment.

Reasons — Some special method may be necessary for the disposal of such large items as car bodies, refrigerators, water heaters, large tires; some demolition wastes; and large tree stumps, trunks, and branches. Some of these items are noncombustible, and it may not be advisable or permissible to burn some of the combustible materials. At landfills with heavy equipment, such items generally can be handled routinely with other refuse; however, special provisions are necessary to incorporate large or bulky items into the fill at small landfills or at landfills operated with light equipment.

Satisfactory Compliance — This item shall be deemed to have been satisfied when:

(1) A separate unloading area on the fill or an alternate site, operated in a sanitary manner, is utilized for the disposal of large items that cannot be handled with the other refuse. Burning of combustible materials is permissible if carried out as prescribed in Item 24.

Item 24. Burning: No garbage or refuse containing garbage shall be burned at the sanitary landfill. Burning of select materials shall be severely restricted, and shall be conducted only with the permission of the appropriate authorities.

Reason — Garbage cannot be burned without nuisance except in high-temperature incinerators. Any other method of combustion creates odors, air pollution, and fire and safety hazards. Such burning adversely affects public acceptance of the operation and proper location of future sanitary landfill sites. Controlled burning of certain combustible materials not readily incorporated in the fill, such as lumber, brush, and tree stumps, may provide a satisfactory means of disposal of these materials at some isolated sites.

Satisfactory Compliance —This item shall be deemed to have been satisfied when:

(1) No garbage or refuse containing garbage is burned at the landfill site.

(2) Burning of other materials is conducted only at a separate unloading area and with permission of and in accordance with regulations established by the local department of health, air pollution authority, and fire department. The regulations established should specify the hours and meteorologic conditions when burning may be permitted; prescribe safety precautions; stipulate the quantity, type, and condition of materials to be burned; and set forth any other necessary limitations.

Item 25. Salvage: When salvaging is permitted, it shall be so organized that it will not interfere with prompt sanitary disposal of refuse or create unsightliness or health hazards. Scavenging shall not be permitted.

Reason — Nothing should be tolerated that interferes with prompt sanitary disposal of refuse. Improperly conducted, salvaging delays landfilling operations and creates unsanitary conditions. The accumulation of salvage at the disposal site often results in vector problems and unsightliness, which are detrimental to public acceptance of the operation. Scavenging is an unhealthy, aesthetically-objectionable practice that interferes with the orderly and efficient operation of a landfill.

Satisfactory Compliance — This item shall be deemed to have been satisfied when:

(1)   Salvage operations are conducted according to a definite plan and in a sanitary, orderly, and dependable manner with minimum interference to landfill operations.

(2)   All salvaged materials are removed from the site or incorporated into the fill and covered by the end of each working day.

(3)   No scavenging is conducted at the landfill.

Item 26. Vector Control: Conditions unfavorable for the production of insects and rodents shall be maintained by carrying out routine landfill operations promptly in a systematic manner. Supplemental vector control measures shall be instituted whenever necessary.

Reason — While operation of a sanitary landfill according to these standards will reduce insect and rodent problems to a minimum, any lapse in proper operating procedures may result in attraction and rapid production of insects and rodents. Supplemental vector control measures may occasionally be necessary to prevent health hazards or nuisances.

Satisfactory Compliance — This item shall be deemed to have been satisfied when:

(1)   There is proper maintenance of daily, intermediate, and final cover; adequate drainage; and compliance with other landfill standards.

(2)   Supplemental vector control measures are performed, when necessary, within 24 hours.

Item 27. Dust Control: Suitable control measures shall be taken wherever dust is a problem.

Reason — Excessive dust slows operations, creates accident hazards and aesthetic problems, and may cause eye irritation or other injury to landfill personnel.

Satisfactory Compliance — This item shall be deemed to have been satisfied when:

(1) Suitable measures are taken to control dust wherever necessary on the site or on the access road.

Item 28. Drainage of Surface Water: The entire site, including the fill surface, shall be graded and provided with drainage facilities to minimize runoff onto and into the fill, to prevent erosion or washing of the fill, to drain off rain water falling on the fill, and to prevent the collection of standing water.

Reason — Runoff from above the fill and rain falling on the fill may, unless diverted, leach into the fill and pollute ground or surface water with the leachate. The cover may be removed by erosion of the fill. Standing water may permit mosquito breeding and may interfere with the operation of the landfill.

Satisfactory Compliance — This item shall be deemed to have been satisfied when:

(1) Diversion channels of adequate size and grade, based on runoff estimates from the area above the fill, are provided.

(2) The surface of the fill is smooth and graded to a minimum slope of 1 on 100.

(3) Maximum slope of the sides or toe of the completed fill is not greater than 1 on 2, the slope is adequately protected against erosion, and the bottom of the slope is protected against raveling and is so constructed as to provide either surface or subsurface drainage to prevent ponding.

(4) Weekly inspections are made for standing water on the site and on the access road, and all accumulations are eliminated promptly.

Item 29. Completion of Landfill: An inspection of the entire site shall be made by a representative of the State or local department of health before the earth-moving equipment is removed from the site. Any necessary corrective work shall be performed before the landfill project is accepted as completed. Arrangements shall be made for the repair of all cracked, eroded, and uneven areas in the final cover during the year following completion of the fill.

Reason — As constructed, the fill may not comply with the original plans and specifications. Any corrections necessary to prevent health hazards or nuisances can best be made before the earth-moving equipment is removed from the site.

Since the most rapid settlement occurs during the first year after each section of the fill is completed, routine maintenance of the final cover is necessary to repair all cracked, eroded, and uneven areas that are found. As long as operations continue in other areas of the site, this maintenance can be provided easily.

However, after filling operations are finished and the equipment has been removed from the site, some arrangements are necessary to provide this maintenance.

Satisfactory Compliance — This item shall be deemed to have been satisfied when:

(1)   A representative of the State or local department of health inspects and accepts the landfill project as completed before the earth-moving equipment is removed from the site.

(2)   Arrangements are made so that the entire surface of the final cover is inspected monthly for one year and all cracked, eroded, and uneven areas repaired.

(3)   A plat of the completed landfill and other operational records are filed.

Item 30. Supervision of Operation: A landfill operation shall be under the direction of a qualified individual.

Reason — The operation of a landfill so that no health, nuisance, or aesthetic problems result is best accomplished when the work is directed by a responsible person who is both able to understand and to implement the plans and specifications.

Satisfactory Compliance — This item shall be deemed to have been satisfied when:

(1)   The landfill operation is directed by an individual deemed qualified as a Sanitary Landfill Supervisor by the State Department of Health.

Item 31. Animal Feeding: Domestic animals shall be excluded from the site.

Reason — Garbage is an important factor in the transmission of trichinosis in man, as well as trichinosis, hog cholera, and vesicular exanthema in hogs. Such transmission can be prevented by not allowing hogs to feed on uncooked garbage. When domestic animals are allowed on the site they interfere with the operation of equipment and scatter the refuse.

Satisfactory Compliance — This item shall be deemed to have been satisfied when:

(1)   Domestic animals are excluded from the site.

Item 32. Accident Prevention and Safety: Employees shall be instructed in the principles of first aid and safety and in the specific operational procedures necessary to prevent accidents, including limitation of access. An adequate stock of first-aid supplies shall be maintained at the site.

Reason — The use of heavy earth-moving equipment, the maneuvering of collection trucks and other vehicles, and the explosive or flammable items that may be in the refuse create accident-prevention problems at landfills. The remote location of some landfills makes it particularly important that personnel be oriented to accident hazards, trained in first aid, and provided with first-aid supplies. For reasons of safety, access should be limited to those authorized to use the site for the disposal of refuse.

Satisfactory Compliance — This item shall be deemed to have been satisfied when:

(1) At least one person trained in first aid is on duty during operating hours.

(2) An educational program is maintained on safety and first aid.

(3) Adequate first-aid supplies are available at the site at all times.

(4) Access to the site is limited as specified in Item 13.

Item 33. Inspection and Evaluation: Routine inspections and evaluations of landfill operations shall be made by a representative of the State or local Department of Health. A notice of any deficiencies, together with any recommendations for their correction, shall be provided to the owner or agent responsible for the use of the land; and the appropriate individual, firm, or governmental agency responsible for the landfill operation.

Reason — Regular monthly inspections and evaluations of operating conditions serve to maintain sanitary conditions by bringing any deficiencies to the attention of the Sanitary Landfill Supervisor and the owner of the property. After an operation has been found to be satisfactory for 2 consecutive months, subsequent inspections and evaluations usually need to be made only twice a year.

Satisfactory Compliance — This item shall be deemed to have been satisfied when:

(1) A representative of the State or local Department of Health routinely inspects and evaluates the landfill operation:
   (a) each month until the operation has been found to be satisfactory for 2 consecutive months, and
   (b) at least once each 6 months hereafter.

(2) The landfill operation is evaluated according to these standards.

(3) A notice of any deficiencies, together with any recommendations for their correction, is provided to the owner or agent responsible for the use of the land; and the appropriate individual firm, or governmental agency responsible for the landfill operation.

Equipment

Types of Equipment

The various types of equipment described below are illustrated in Figure 5.1.

FIGURE 5.1: TYPES OF LANDFILL EQUIPMENT

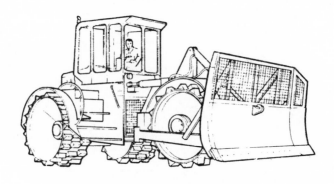

Steel-Wheel Compactor

(continued)

FIGURE 5.1: (continued)

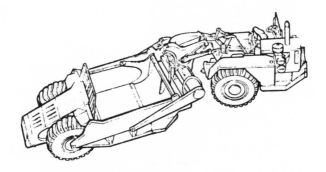

Scraper

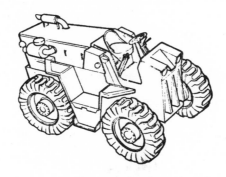

Rubber-Tired Tractor

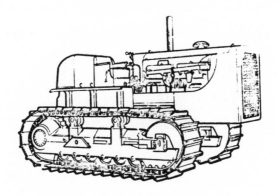

Crawler Tractor

(continued)

FIGURE 5.1: (continued)

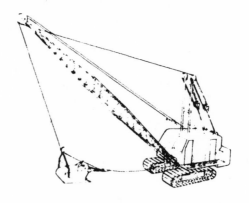

Dragline

Front-End Accessories

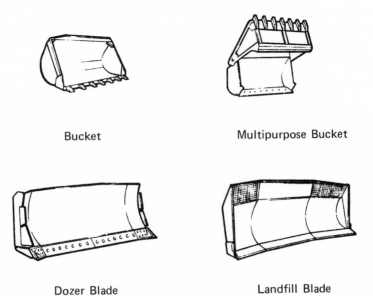

Bucket   Multipurpose Bucket

Dozer Blade   Landfill Blade

Source: PB 204,403 (1970)

Crawler Machines

Crawler machines are of two types: dozer and loader. Other common names for them are: bulldozer, crawler, crawler dozer, track loader, front end loader, and bullclam; many trade names are also used. They all have good flotation and traction capabilities, because their self-laying tracks provide large ground contact areas. The crawler is excellent for excavating work and moving over unstable surfaces, but it can operate approximately only 8 mph, forward or reverse.

The crawler dozer is excellent for grading and can be used economically for dozing waste or earth over distances of up to 300 feet. It is usually fitted with a straight dozer blade for earthwork, but at a sanitary landfill it should be equipped with a U-shaped blade that has been fitted with a top extension (trash or landfill blade) to push more solid waste.

Unlike the crawler dozer, the crawler loader can lift materials off the ground, but its bucket is not as wide, and it is not able, therefore, to spread as much solid waste. The crawler loader is an excellent excavator and can carry soil as much as 300 feet. There are two types of buckets usually used for sanitary landfilling: the general purpose and the multiple purpose. The general-purpose bucket is a scoop of one-piece construction. The multiple-purpose bucket, which is also known as a bullclam or 4 in 1, is of two-piece construction, is hinged at the top, and is hydraulically operated.

It can thus clamp onto such objects as tree trunks or telephone poles and lift and place them in the fill, or it can crush junked autos or washing machines. It is also useful in spreading cover material. The general-purpose and multiple-purpose buckets come in many sizes. Matching a bucket to a machine should be done with the advice of the machine manufacturer. A landfill blade similar to that used on dozers can also be fitted to loaders.

Rubber-Tired Machines

Both dozers and loaders are available with rubber-tired wheels. They are generally faster than crawler machines (maximum forward or reverse speed of about 29 mph) but do not excavate as well. The plausible claim has been made that because the weight of rubber-tired machines is transferred to the ground over a much smaller contact area, they provide better compaction, but significant differences of in-place density have not been proven.

Because their loads are concentrated more, rubber-tired machines have less flotation and traction than crawler machines. Their higher speed, however, allows them to complete more cycles or passes in the same amount of time than a crawler machine. Rubber-tired machines perform satisfactorily on landfill sites if they are equipped with steel guarded tires, called rock tires or landfill tires. Rubber-tired machines can be economically operated at distances of up to 600 feet.

The rubber-tired dozer is not commonly used at a sanitary landfill. Because of the rough and spongy surface formed by compacted solid waste and the concentrated wheel loads, the rubber-tired dozer does not grade as well as a crawler dozer. The flotation of the crawler dozer makes it much more suitable for grading operations. The rubber-tired dozer should be equipped with a land-fill or trash blade similar to that recommended for a track dozer.

The rubber-tired loader is usually equipped with a general-purpose or multiple-purpose bucket. A particular asset of this machine is the high speed and mobility of its operation. When it is only needed part time at a sanitary land-fill, it can be driven over public roads to perform other jobs. Because of its high operating speed, the rubber-tired loader is especially suited for putting cover material into haul trucks or carrying it economically over distances of up to 600 feet.

Landfill Compactors

Several equipment manufacturers are marketing landfill compactors equipped with large trash blades. In general, these machines are modifications of road compactors and log skidders. Rubber-tired dozers and loaders have also been modified. The power train and structure of landfill compactors are similar to those of rubber-tired machines, and their major asset is their steel wheels. The wheels are either rubber tires sheathed in steel or hollow steel cores; both types are studded with load concentrators.

Steel-wheeled machines probably impart greater crushing and compactive effort than do rubber-tired or crawler machines. A study comparing a 47,000-lb. steel-wheeled compactor, the same unit equipped with rubber tires, and a 62,000-lb. crawler dozer indicated that under the same set of conditions, the in-place dry density of solid waste compacted by the steel-wheeled compactor was 13% greater than that effected by the crawler dozer and the rubber-tired compactor.

The landfill compactor is an excellent machine for spreading and compacting on flat or level surfaces and operates fairly well on moderate slopes, but it lacks traction when operating on steep slopes or when excavating. Its maximum achievable speed while spreading and compacting on a level surface is about 23 mph, forward and reverse. This makes it faster than a crawler but slower than a rubber-tired machine.

Since landfill compactors operate at high speeds and produce good in-place densities, they are best applied when they are used only for spreading and compacting solid waste and cover material. When the cover material is a clay, it and some of the solid waste lodge between the load concentrators and must be continually removed by cleaner bars. The surface of a soil layer compacted with a landfill compactor is usually covered by pits or indentations formed by the load concentrators. Numerous passes are needed to minimize the roughness of the surface.

Scrapers

Scrapers are available as self-propelled and towed models having a wide range of capacities. This type of earthmoving machine can haul cover material economically over relatively long distances (more than 1,000 feet for the self-propelled versions and 300 to 1,000 feet for towed models). Their prime function is to excavate, haul, and spread cover material. Since they are heavy when loaded, routing them over the fill area will help compact the solid waste. Hauling capacities range from 2 to 40 cubic yards.

Dragline

Large excavations can be made economically with a dragline. Its outstanding characteristic is its ability to dig up moderately hard soils and cast or throw them away from the excavation. Because of this feature, it can also be used to spread cover material over compacted solid waste. It is particularly useful in wetland operations. The dragline is most commonly found at large landfills where the trench method is used or where cover material is obtained from a borrow pit. As a rule of thumb, the boom length should be two times the trench width. Buckets used at landfills usually range from 1 to 3 cubic yards.

Special-Purpose Equipment

Several pieces of earthmoving and road construction equipment are put to limited use on landfills that dispose of less than 1,000 tons a day. Their purchase may not, therefore, be warranted. When they are needed, they can be borrowed, leased, rented, or the work can be performed under contract.

The road grader can be used to maintain dirt and gravel roads on the site, to grade the intermediate and final cover, and to maintain drainage channels surrounding the fill.

Water is useful in controlling blowing litter at the working face and control of dust from on-site roads. Water wagons range from converted tank trucks to highly specialized, heavy vehicles that are generally used in road construction operations. They can also be used at the landfill to fight fires.

The road sweeper is a real asset at sites where mud is tracked onto the public road system. Its periodic use will encourage local residents to accept the landfill because roadways remain safe.

Accessories

The equipment used at landfills can be provided with accessories that protect the machine and operator and increase the effectiveness and versatility of the machine.

Engine screens and radiator guards keep paper and wire from clogging radiator

pores and causing the engine to overheat. A reversible fan can also help alleviate this problem, because the direction of air flow or vane pitch can be changed
in less than 5 minutes. Under-chassis guards can be installed to shield the engine, and hydraulic lines and other essential items of the machine should also
be protected if they are susceptible to damage.

The operator's comfort, safety, and efficiency can be increased by providing
roll bars, a canopy or cab, cab or helmet air conditioning, and backup warning
systems. A canopy is especially desirable for machines that operate in a trench
into which waste is dumped from above. Cabs are particularly useful when the
working area is very dusty or the operator must work in very cold weather.
Because rubber-tired machines and landfill compactors operate at relatively
high speeds, an audible backup warning system should be provided to alert
other equipment operators and personnel in the immediate area. This system
is also desirable on crawler machines, especially when two or more are operating in the same area.

Equipment versatility and effectiveness can be increased by use of a number
of accessories. A hydraulically operated ripper is needed when extensive excavation must be carried out in hard soils. It should be mounted on a tracked
machine to take advantage of its greater traction. (Backrippers, hinged teeth
attatched to buckets or blades that dig into the soil when the machine is
reversing, are not as effective as hydraulically operated rippers.) To give rubber-
tired machines and landfill compactors more traction, their wheels can be
ballasted with a calcium chloride solution or water, and steel or concrete
counterweights can be used on loaders and landfill compactors.

Different power trains can be used on many large machines. The power shift
and torque converter options are preferable to the dry clutch, direct-drive
models because greater speed of operation and less strain on the engine and
operator are possible with them.

Densifiers

As human population grows, suitable sanitary landfill areas become more difficult to locate and more expensive. One obvious alternative is to make maximum
use of available areas by reducing the bulk of the solid wastes. In most sanitary landfills, crawler or rubber-tired bulldozers have been used to work the fills.
Depending on the character of the refuse, these machines can effect a compaction ratio of about 3 to 1.

A machine designed specifically for sanitary landfill work has become available.
This is a 25-ton compactor-dozer employing lugged or gear-tooth-like wheels.
The claim has been made that it quickly reduces packing crates and other large
debris. It was reported that twice as much refuse can be placed in a given area
without increasing the depth of fill as was formerly possible when a crawler
tractor was used for compaction.

Another landfill-compaction device is a ballasted-drum type with lugs; it is pulled behind a dozer. It also vibrates to improve compaction. A gasoline engine carried on the frame of the compactor supplies the energy of vibration.

Vacuum-type leaf collectors seem to be increasingly common. The high velocities at which the leaves enter the collection box result in a significant amount of compaction. An article in *Public Works* described a 30-horsepower "Giant Vac" leaf loader that uses a 14-cubic-yard plywood collection box fitted to a 13-foot-long dump-body chassis.

Compacting of solid wastes at the point of collection has been practiced in the United States since 1950 when packer-type refuse trucks were introduced. These trucks normally carry 10- to 30-cubic-yard bodies on a standard heavy-duty truck chassis. An exception to the practice of using a standard heavy-duty truck chassis is the Wesco Jet, a packer truck designed specifically for refuse collection. Depending on the character of the refuse, packer-type trucks can reduce the material to as little as one-third of its original loose volume.

COMPARISON OF CHARACTERISTICS

The ability of various machines to perform the many functions that must be carried out at a sanitary landfill should be analyzed with respect to the needs and conditions of each site.

Performance Characteristics of Landfill Equipment*†

Equipment	Solid Waste		Cover Material			
	Spreading	Compacting	Excavating	Spreading	Compacting	Hauling
Crawler dozer	E	G	E	E	G	NA
Crawler loader	G	G	E	G	G	NA
Rubber-tired dozer	E	G	F	G	G	NA
Rubber-tired loader	G	G	F	G	G	NA
Landfill compactor	E	E	P	G	E	NA
Scraper	NA	NA	G	E	NA	E
Dragline	NA	NA	E	F	NA	NA

* Basis of evaluation: Easily workable soil and cover material haul distance greater than 1,000 ft.
† Rating Key: E, excellent; G, good; F, fair; P, poor; NA, not applicable.

EQUIPMENT COSTS

The equipment selected for a sanitary landfill must not only be able to perform well under conditions present at the site, it must also do so at the least total cost. Equipment costs, both capital and operating, represent a significant portion of the expenses incurred in operating a sanitary landfill.

Capital Costs

Except for land, the cost of equipment may be the greatest portion of initial expenditures. The sanitary landfill equipment market is very competitive, but rough approximations of costs have been developed (1972). A crawler machine weighing 29,000 lbs. without accessories costs about $29,000. With engine sidescreens, radiator guards, reversible fan, roll bar, and a multiple-purpose bucket, the same machine costs approximately $32,000. A new dragline can cost between $75,000 and $110,000 depending on the length of its boom and cables, and the size of its bucket. In general, most landfill equipment used for excavating, spreading, and compacting has a useful life of five years or 10,000 operating hours.

The price of a used machine depends on its type, size, condition, and number of recorded operating hours. Specific resale values are available from auctioneers and manufacturers of earthmoving equipment. The condition and remaining useful life of used equipment should be determined by an expert.

Operating and Maintenance Costs

Purchases of fuel, oil, tires, lubricants, and filters and any expenses associated with routine maintenance are considered operating costs. Expenditures on fuel account for approximately 90% of operating costs. The expense of operating dozers, loaders, and landfill compactors varies according to type and make; the manufacturer should, therefore, be consulted for specific estimates. Generally speaking, direct operating costs are $3.00 per hour. The skill of the equipment operator, the type of waste handled, topography, and soil conditions also affect operating costs.

Maintenance costs, parts, and labor also vary widely but can be approximated by spreading one-half the initial cost of the machine over its anticipated useful life (10,000 hrs.). To make these costs more predictable, most equipment dealers offer lease agreements and maintenance contracts. Long downtimes usually associated with major repairs can be reduced by taking advantage of programs offered by most equipment dealers.

High operating costs are frequently associated with low initial costs of the equipment and vice versa. The purchaser should, therefore, require that equipment bids include estimated operating costs.

Actual operating and maintenance expenses should be determined during site operation by use of a cost accounting system. This information can be used to identify areas where costs may be reduced; excessive fuel consumption, for example, may mean the machine needs adjustment or that operating procedures should be modified. Data from the cost accounting system can be used to more accurately predict operating and maintenance costs.

Characteristics and Uses of Completed Landfill

Reclaiming land by filling and raising the ground surface is one of the greatest benefits of sanitary landfilling.

CHARACTERISTICS

The designer should know the purposed use of the completed sanitary landfill before he begins to work. Unlike an earth fill, a sanitary landfill consists of cells containing a great variety of materials having different physical, chemical, and biological properties. The decomposing solid waste imparts characteristics to the fill that are peculiar to sanitary landfills. These characteristics require that the designer plan for gas and water controls, cell configuration, cover material specifications (as determined by the planned use), and the periodic maintenance needed at the completed sanitary landfill.

Decomposition

Most of the materials in a sanitary landfill will decompose, but at varying rates. Food wastes decompose readily, are moderately compactible, and form organic acids that aid decomposition. Garden wastes are resilient and difficult to compact but generally decompose rapidly. Paper products and wood decay at a slower rate than food wastes. Paper is easily compacted and may be pushed into voids, whereas lumber, tree branches, and stumps are difficult to compact and hinder the compaction of adjacent wastes.

Car bodies, metal containers, and household appliances can be compacted and will slowly rust in the fill with the help of organic acids produced by decomposing food wastes. Glass and ceramics are usually easily compacted but do not degrade in a landfill. Plastics and rubber are resilient and difficult to compact; rubber decomposes very slowly, most plastics not at all. Leather and textiles are slightly resilient but can be compacted; they decompose, but at a much slower rate than garden and food wastes. Rocks, dirt, ashes, and construction rubble do not decompose and can be easily worked and compacted.

Density

The density of solid waste in a landfill is quite variable. One that is well constructed can have an in-place density as great as 1,500 lbs. per cubic yard, while that of poorly compacted solid waste may be only 500. Generally, 800 to 1,000 lbs. per cubic yard can be achieved with a moderate compactive effort. Soft and hard spots occur within the fill as a result of different decomposition rates and compaction densities. Density influences such other characteristics as settlement and bearing capacity.

Settlement

A sanitary landfill will settle as a result of waste decomposition, filtering of fines, superimposed loads, and its own weight. Bridging that occurs during construction produces voids. As the waste decomposes, fine particles from the cover material and overlying solid waste often sift into these voids. The weight of the overhead waste and cover materials helps consolidate the fill, and this development is furthered when more cover material is added or a structure or roadway is constructed on the fill.

The most significant cause of settlement is waste decomposition, which is greatly influenced by the amount of water in the fill. A landfill will settle more slowly if only limited water is available to decompose the waste chemically and biologically. In Seattle, where rainfall exceeds 30 in. per year, a 20-ft. fill settled 4 ft. in the first year after it was completed. In Los Angeles, where less than 15 in. of rain falls per year, 3 years after a landfill had been completed a 75-ft. high area had settled only 2.3 ft., and another section that had been 46 ft. high had settled a mere 1.3 ft.

Settlement also depends on the types of wastes disposed of, the volume of cover material used with respect to the volume of wastes disposed of, and the compaction achieved during construction. A fill composed only of construction and demolition debris will not settle as much as one that is constructed of residential solid wastes. A landfill contructed of highly compacted waste will settle less than one that is poorly compacted. If two landfills contain the same types of wastes and are constructed to the same height, but one has a waste-to-cover volume ratio of 1:1 and the other a ratio of 4:1, the first will settle less. Because of the many factors involved, a fill may settle as much as 33%.

Settling can produce wide cracks in the cover material that expose the wastes to rats and flies, allow water to infiltrate, and permit gas to escape. Differential settling may form depressions that permit water to pond and infiltrate the fill. Settling may also cause structures on the landfill to sag and possibly collapse;

the underground utility lines that serve these buildings or traverse the site may then shear. Because every landfill settles, its surface should be periodically inspected and soil should be added and graded when necessary.

Bearing Capacity

The bearing capacity of a completed sanitary landfill is the measure of its ability in pounds per square foot to support foundations and keep them intact. Very little information is available on the subject, but a few investigators place the bearing capacity of a completed landfill between 500 and 800 lbs. per square foot; higher values have, however, been noted. Since there is no definite procedure for interpreting the results of solid waste bearing tests, any value obtained should be viewed with extreme caution.

Almost without exception, the integrity and bearing capacity of soil cover depend on the underlying solid waste. Most bearing strength tests of soil are conducted over a short period; several minutes for granular materials to a maximum of 3 days for clay having a high moisture or air content. During the test, the soil adjusts to its limits under the load imposed and conditions of confinement. Solid waste, on the other hand does not follow this pattern of deformation but continues to alter its structure and composition over a long period of time. Natural soils, which are not as heterogeneous as solid waste, produce test values that fall within a predictable range. Moreover, repeated tests of the soil will produce similar results; similar relationships have not been established for solid waste.

Landfill Gases

Landfill gases continue to be produced after the landfill is completed and can accumulate in structures or soil, cause explosions, and stunt or kill vegetation. Placement of a thick, moist, vegetative, final cover may act as a gas-tight lid that forces gases to migrate laterally from the landfill. If the site is converted into a paved parking lot, this may also prevent the gases from venting into the atmosphere. Design of gas controls should, therefore, conform with the planned use of the completed fill.

Corrosion

The decomposing material in a landfill is very corrosive. Organic acids are produced from food, garden, and paper wastes, and some weak acids are derived from ashes. Unprotected steel and galvanized pipe used for utility lines, leachate drains, and building foundations are subject to severe and rapid pitting.

All structural materials susceptible to corrosion should be protected. Acids present in a sanitary landfill can deteriorate a concrete surface and thus expose the reinforcing steel; this could eventually cause the concrete to fail.

USES

There are many ways in which a completed sanitary landfill can be used; it can, for example, be converted into a green area or be designed for recreational, agricultural, or light construction purposes. The landfill designer should evaluate each proposal from a technical and economic viewpoint. More suitable land is often available elsewhere that would not require the expensive construction techniques required at a sanitary landfill.

Green Area

The use of a completed sanitary landfill as a green area is very common. No expensive structures are built, and a grassed area is established for the pleasure of the community. Some maintenance work is, however, required to keep the fill surface from being eroded by wind and water. The cover material should be graded to prevent water from ponding and infiltrating the fill. Gas and water monitoring stations, installed during construction, should be periodically sampled until the landfill stabilizes. Gas and water controls and drains also require periodic inspection and maintenance.

If the final cover material is thin, only shallow-rooted grass, flowers, and shrubs should be planted on the landfill surface. The decomposing solid waste may be toxic to plants whose roots penetrate through the bottom of the final cover. An accumulation of landfill gas in the root zone may interfere with the normal metabolism of plants. This can be avoided by selecting a cover material having a low water-holding capacity, but this type of soil provides poor support for vegetation. On the other hand, a moist soil does not allow decomposition gas to disperse and consequently gas venting must be considered.

The most commonly used vegetation is grass. Most pasture and hay grasses are shallow-rooted and can be used on a landfill having only 2 ft. of final cover, but alfalfa and clover need more than this. The soil used for final cover influences the choice of vegetation. Some grasses, such as tall meadow oat grass, thrive well on light sand or gravelly soils, while others, such as timothy grass, do better in such heavier soils as clays and loams.

Climate also influences the selection of grasses. Bermuda is a good soil binder and thrives in southern States. Perennial rye does best where the climate is cool and moist and winter is mild; it roots rapidly but dies off in 2 to 3 years if shaded. Redtop and bent grass thrive almost anywhere except in drier areas and the extreme south. The selection of the grass or mixture of grasses depends, therefore, on climate, depth of the root system, and soil used for cover material. Mowing and irrigating requirements should also be considered. In general, it is not advisable to irrigate the landfill surface, because the water may infiltrate and leach the fill.

Agriculture

A completed sanitary landfill can be made productive by turning it into pasture or crop land. Many of the grasses mentioned above are suitable for hay production. Corn and wheat usually have 4-ft. roots, but the latter occasionally has longer ones. The depth of the final cover must, therefore, be increased accordingly.

If cultivated crops are used, the final cover should be thick enough that roots or cultivating do not disturb its bottom foot. If the landfill is to be cultivated, a 1- to 2-ft. layer of relatively impermeable soil, such as clay, may be placed on top of the solid waste and an additional layer of agricultural soil placed above to prevent the clay from drying out. Excessive moisture will also be prevented from entering the fill. Such a scheme of final cover placement must also provide for gas venting via gravel trenches or pipes.

Construction

A foundations engineering expert should be consulted if plans call for structures to be built on or near a completed sanitary landfill. This is necessary because of the many unique factors involved; gas movement, corrosion, bearing capacity, and settlement. The cost of designing, constructing, and maintaining buildings is considerably higher than it is for those erected on a well-compacted earth fill or on undistrubed soil.

The most problem-free technique is to preplan the use of islands to avoid settlement, corrosion, and bearing-capacity problems. Ideally, the islands should be undisturbed soils that are bypassed during excavating and landfilling operations. Settlement would then be governed by the normal properties of the undisturbed soil. Alternatively, truck loads of rocks, dirt, and rubble could be laid down and compacted during construction of the landfill at places where the proposed structure would be built.

The decomposing landfilled waste can be excavated and replaced with compacted rock or soil fill, but this method is very expensive and could prove hazardous to the construction workers. The decomposing waste emits a very putrid smell, and hydrogen sulfide, a toxic gas, may be present with methane, an explosive gas. These two gases should be monitored throughout the excavating operation. Gas masks may have to be provided for the workmen, and no open flames should be permitted.

Piles can also be used to support buildings when the piles are driven completely through the refuse to firm soil or rock. Some of the piles should be battered (angled) to resist lateral movement that may occur in the fill. Another factor to consider is the load imposed on the piles by solid wastes settling around them. The standard field penetration resistance test is used to determine the strength of the earth material in which the piles are to be founded. During this test, penetration will be resisted by the solid waste, but as the refuse decomposes and settling occurs, it may no longer resist and will more likely create a downward force on the pile. There are no data for established procedures for predicting this change in force.

Several peculiar problems arise when piles are used to support a structure over a landfill. The decomposing waste is very corrosive, so the piles must be protected with corrosion-resistant coatings. It may be very difficult to drive the piles through the waste if large bulky items, such as junked cars and broken concrete, are in the fill where the structure is to be located. The fill underlying a pile-supported structure may settle, and voids or air spaces may develop between the landfill surface and the bottom of the structure. Landfill gases could accumulate in these voids and create an explosion hazard.

Light, one-story buildings are sometimes constructed on the landfill surface. The bearing capacity of the landfill should be determined by field investigations in order to design continuous foundations. Foundations should be reinforced to bridge any gaps that may occur because of differential settling in the fill. Continuous floor slabs reinforced as mats can be used, and the structure should be designed to accommodate settlement. Doors, windows, and partitions should be able to adapt to slight differential movement between them and the structural framing. Roads, parking lots, sidewalks, and other paved areas should be constructed of a flexible and easily repairable material, such as gravel or asphaltic concrete.

Consolidating the landfill to improve its bearing capacity and reduce settlement by surcharging it with a heavy layer of soil does not directly influence the decomposition rate. If the surcharge load is removed and the structure is built before the waste has stabilized, settlement will still be a problem, and the bearing capacity may not be as great as expected.

None of the methods for supporting a structure over a landfill are problem-free. A common difficulty is keeping landfill gases from accumulating in the structure. Even buildings erected on undisturbed islands of soil must be specially designed to prevent this from developing. A layer of sand can be laid over the proposed structural area and then be covered by two or more layers of polyvinyl chloride sheeting. An additional layer of sand can then be emplaced. If the bottom layer of sand is not saturated, it will act as a gas-permeable vent, and the sheeting will prevent the gas from entering or collecting under the structure. The top layer of sand protects the sheeting from being punctured.

Another approach is to place an impermeable membrane of jute and asphalt under all below-grade portions of the structure. A gravel or sand layer must underlie the jute-asphalt membrane and be vented to the atmosphere. The most reliable method is to construct a ventilated false basement to keep gas from accumulating.

Utility connections must be made gas proof if they enter a structure below grade. If the building is surrounded by filled land, utility lines that traverse the fill must be flexible, and slack should be provided so the lines can adjust to settlement. Flexible plastic conduits are more expensive than other materials but would probably work best, because they are elastic and resist corrosion. Gravity waste-water pipelines may develop low points if the fill settles. Liquid wastes should be pumped to the nearest sewer unless the grade from the structure to the sewer prevents low points from forming. Shearing of improperly designed water and waste-water services caused by differential settlement can occur where they enter the structure or along the pipeline that traverses the fill.

Recreation

Completed landfills are often used as ski slopes, toboggan runs, coasting hills, ball fields, golf courses, amphitheaters, playgrounds, and parks. Small, light buildings, such as concession stands, sanitary facilities, and equipment storage sheds, are usually required at recreational areas. These should also be constructed to keep settlement and gas problems at a minimum. Other problems encountered are ponding, cracking, and erosion of cover material. Periodic maintenance includes regrading, reseeding, and replenishing the cover material.

REGISTRATION

The completed landfill should be inspected by the governmental agency responsible for ensuring its proper operation. Following final acceptance of the site, a detailed description, including a plat, should be recorded with the proper authority in the county where the site is located. This provides future owners or users with adequate information regarding the previous use of the site. The description should, therefore, include type and general location of wastes, number and type of lifts, and details about the original terrain.

Management

ADMINISTRATIVE AGENCY

The responsibility for operating a sanitary landfill is normally determined by the community administrative structure involved, and it must do so in the light of its own circumstances.

Municipal Operations: In most municipal operations, administrative responsibility is assigned to the department of public works, one of whose divisions manages the solid waste program. As the scope of this division's activities increases, it is desirable to subdivide the division into functional sections. Regardless of organizational structure, collection and disposal plans and operations must be coordinated to achieve satisfactory and economical solid waste management.

Special Districts: Many states have enabling legislation that permits the formation of special-purpose districts, which can include solid waste disposal districts. These districts are advantageous in that they can serve may political jurisdictions and may have provisions for levying special taxes. Before any special district is considered, the state laws applicable to them should be investigated.

County Operations: A sanitary landfill administered by a county may have advantages over a municipal operation. A county operation could serve a number of incorporated and unincorporated areas using existing governmental apparatus, and it might allow comprehensive planning for a larger geographic area. Other advantages are economy of scale and greater availability of land.

Private Operations: Many sanitary landfills are operated successfully by private industry under a contract, franchise, or permit arrangement. In contract operations, the municipality contracts with the operator to dispose of its solid waste for a fixed charge per ton or load. The municipality usually guarantees that the contractor will receive a certain minimum amount of money. Franchises usually grant the operator permission to dispose of wastes from specified areas and charge regulated fees. Permits allow the operator to accept wastes for disposal without regard to source.

Private operations may be beneficial to municipalities that have limited funds, but the community must not shirk its responsibility for proper solid waste disposal. Of the three methods, contract operations generally give the municipality the best guarantee that solid wastes will be disposed of properly because standards can be written into the contract. Franchises usually provide the next best control of operation.

ADMINISTRATIVE FUNCTIONS

An administrative agency is responsible for proper solid waste disposal, including planning, designing, financing, cost accounting, operating, recruiting and training, informing the public, and establishing minimum disposal standards.

Finances: Sanitary landfill capital costs include land, equipment, and site improvements. Operating costs include salaries, utilities, fuel, and equipment maintenance. There are several sources of funds to meet capital and operating costs. The general fund, derived from taxes, normally cannot provide enough money to meet capital costs but is often used to pay for operating expenses. There are advantages to using the general fund for this purpose. The administrative procedures and extra cost of billing and collecting are eliminated. Since all the taxpayers help pay for the sanitary landfill, they are more likely to use the sanitary landfill rather than an open dump.

Using general funds for landfill operations does, however, have disadvantages. Cost accounting and other administrative procedures may be so relaxed disposal costs are difficult or impossible to determine, and users may have to be monitored. It may also be extremely difficult for solid waste management operations to get money from the general fund because of the low priority often assigned to them.

General obligation borrowing is a common method of financing the capital costs of a sanitary landfill. This type of bond generally carries a low interest rate but is easily marketed because it is secured by the pledge of real estate taxes and because all of the real estate within the taxing district serves as security for the borrowed funds. State statutes usually limit the amount of debt a community can incur. If the debt is already substantial, this method may not be available. In some cases, general obligation bonds are retired with revenues generated by the landfill operation; this minimizes the ad valorem taxes necessary for bond retirement.

Revenue bonds differ from general obligation bonds in that they are secured only by the ability of the project to earn enough to pay the interest and retire the bonds. In this case, fees must be charged to landfill users in amounts necessary to cover all capital and operating expenses. It is necessary to set the fees high enough to accumulate a surplus over and above debt service needs in order to make the bonds attractive to prospective purchasers. This method of financing requires that the administering agency follow good cost accounting procedures, and it allows the agency to be the sole beneficiary of cost saving procedures. In addition, the producer of solid waste is forced to pay the true cost of its disposal.

User fees are primarily a source of operating revenue, but a municipality might also employ them to generate funds for future capital expenditures. The fees can be adjusted to cover not only the operating and capital costs of present landfills but also to provide a surplus for acquiring land and equipment. Fees do not provide the capital outlay needed to start a sanitary landfill.

Although fees necessitate more work and expense because of the weighing, billing, and collecting involved, these requirements provide an insight into the management and operation of the landfill. Commercial haulers are usually billed on a per ton basis. Since the individual loads from homes are small, the users are charged on a per load basis to reduce weighing and bookkeeping. Because fee operations require that collection vehicles be recorded at the gate, this provides an additional control over wastes received at the landfill.

Operational Cost Control: A primary duty of administration is to monitor and control the cost of operation. Cost accounting isolates the detailed expenses of ownership and operation and permits comparison of costs against revenues. The important costs of operation include: wages and salaries, maintenance of and fuel for equipment, utilities, depreciation and interest on buildings and equipment, and overhead. Basic data for cost accounting include the amount of waste disposed of at the fill, either by the ton or cubic yard. A cost accounting system recommended for use at a sanitary landfill has been developed by the Office of Solid Waste Management Programs.

Performance Evaluation: In most cases, there is a control agency at the state or local level that determines if the operation is being conducted in a manner that safeguards against environmental pollution. To ensure a sanitary operation, the administrative agency should conduct its own performance evaluation. This should be done at the administrative, not the operating or supervisory level, and its requirements should be at least as stringent as those of the higher control agency. While operating and supervisory personnel should know that these inspections will occur at specified frequencies, they should not know the exact day. This will help ensure a more representative inspection.

Personnel: To secure and retain competent employees, the administration must have a systematic personnel management plan. First a job description should be prepared for each position at the sanitary landfill. A typical list of positions for a large operation might include: (1) administrative tasks (management, accounting, billing, engineering, typing, filing); (2) operating tasks (weighing, operating equipment, spreading, compacting, excavating, hauling, road maintenance, dust control, maintaining equipment, traffic control, vector control, litter control, site security).

Once the job areas are defined, management must determine how many employees are needed; there may be some overlapping responsibilities. For instance, a small sanitary landfill may need only one operator to handle all its equipment. As the size of the operation increases, a division of labor will become necessary for sustained efficiency.

Governmental operations normally will have a civil service system that defines hiring and career-advancement procedures. In this case, management's responsibility is to write good job descriptions and interview applicants. A potential employee should understand the job fully before he is hired. If he is expected to perform other duties during emergencies, he should be fully apprised of this fact. Management must evaluate the ability of potential employees to comprehend and perform their tasks before they are hired.

Private operators may have more latitude in their employment practices. They should also interview and evaluate applicants as to interest in the job, ability to do the work, and potential for increased responsibility. Once an employee is hired, management must see that he is trained properly. Such training should emphasize the overall operation of the landfill, safety, and emergency procedures. Employees responsible for more critical and complex tasks are given more intensive training. Employees should thoroughly understand work rules as well as procedures for handing out reprimands and submitting grievances.

Wages must be comparable with similar employment elsewhere. Larger operations may increase employee satisfaction by providing lunch room and locker facilities at the site. It is desirable to have on-the-job training, insurance plans, pension plans, uniforms, paid holidays and vacation, and sick leave programs.

Public Relations: Public relations is one of the manager's most important administrative functions. Solid waste disposal sites represent an extremely emotional issue, particularly to those who live in the vicinity of a proposed site. Many sites are acceptable from an environmental control aspect but are vigorously opposed by citizens who associate them with old-fashion open or burning dumps. Convincing the public of the advantages of a sanitary landfill is a tedious process but can be accomplished by explanation and education. The program should begin early in the long-range planning stages and continue after operations begin. Public information should stress that at a sanitary landfill the waste is covered daily, access is restricted, insects and rodents are controlled, and open burning is prohibited.

Examples of properly operated sanitary landfills that have been accepted near residential areas should be pointed out. Benefits to be derived by using the completed site as a park or playground, for example, should be emphasized. The media available to the solid waste manager are not limited to radio, television, billboards, and newspapers, but include collection vehicles, collectors, disposal facilities, and billing receipts. Help provided by community organizations can do much to increase public support. Extensive "stumping" by elected and appointed officials in support of a proposed solid waste disposal system is invaluable if the speakers are knowledgeable and have sufficient aids to help them, such as slides, films, and pamphlets.

The single most important factor for winning public support of a solid waste disposal system is an elected or appointed official who firmly believes that it is acceptable and needed. A person willing to accept the challenge of developing short-and long-range plans and to see that they are properly implemented is invaluable. Once these plans are developed and implemented, the disposal system must be operated in a manner that upholds the high performance of which it is capable.

A comprehensive solid waste management plan should be developed, preferably on a regional basis. Detailed design and operating plans should cover a 10-year period and long-range, land-use planning should be developed for 20 years. Appropriate locations for sanitary landfill sites can then be identified, based on the needs of the area to be served. These sites can be zoned for waste disposal or other usage that will discourage development of a residential area. The regional approach to planning and implementation is especially desirable because it often is more economically feasible for all concerned. Land suitable for sanitary landfilling is usually scarce or nonexistent within the jurisdiction of a large city. Smaller communities nearby may be able to provide the land and thus be able to dispose of their own solid wastes in an acceptable manner.

A key aspect of public relations is the procedure for handling citizen complaints. Deficiencies in operating methods or employee courtesy should be investigated and acted on promptly. If this practice is followed, citizens will be less hostile toward the operation, and employees will become more conscientious.

A sanitary landfill represents a positive and relatively inexpensive step communities can take to provide a safe and attractive environment. By proper design, operation, and management, sanitary solid waste disposal can be provided.

PART II

SPECIAL SUBJECTS AND STUDIES

Sanitary Landfill Facts

The material in this chapter is taken from PB 204,403 published in 1970.

PLANNING A SANITARY LANDFILL

A sanitary landfill is an engineering project. When sound engineering principles are applied, the result will be a successful and efficient operation. Most operational problems can be prevented in the initial development stages. This is easier and more economical than correcting the defects once the operation has begun.

The first step toward the ultimate goal of establishing a sanitary landfill operation is, of course, initial planning. Preliminary planning develops the basic groundwork for the actual engineering phases of site selection, design, and operation. Advanced planning should include consideration of a competent designer; a public information program; a survey of solid waste practices and possible sites; methods of financing; ultimate use of the completed site; and site zoning arrangements.

Competent Designer: Engineering knowledge and experience in sanitary landfill site selection, design, and operation are essential requirements of the individual or agency chosen to develop the sanitary landfill. If the planning or operating agency does not have this engineering experience and competence, every effort should be made to obtain the services of the best engineering consultant available.

Although a sanitary landfill is considered the most inexpensive of the methods of disposal, it is a mistake to assume that a successful operation requires little skill or knowledge of design and operation. The engineer or consultant is important; this is a poor place to attempt to economize. The money spent for the services of a competent designer will bring returns in a sanitary landfill operation that is successful and acceptable to the public.

Information Program: Unfortunately, many people associate impressions of open burning dumps with sanitary landfills. As a result the planning of a sanitary landfill usually meets with public opposition unless the operating agency has conducted acceptable operations elsewhere. In many communities, public acceptance of a sanitary landfill site is the most important factor in deciding whether it will exist.

Preliminary planning should include an active public information program to explain to the public what comprises a sanitary landfill operation and what benefits can be expected.

In gaining public support the designer will find it helpful to have the final use of the landfill area determined in advance. An architectural rendering or a model of the completed site as a park, playground, golf course, or other planned use, is a good public relations tool.

When opposition to the proposed sanitary landfill is exceptionally strong, the operating agency can use a temporary pilot operation to illustrate a good sanitary landfill while simultaneously soliciting newspaper and TV support and possibly even hiring professional public relations services for the program.

Operations must be exemplary in order to gain public support. The public will soon discover any discrepancies between the public information program and actual operations.

Other Considerations: The responsible officials in the preliminary planning phase must decide how the initial cost and the operating costs of the sanitary landfill will be financed.

These officials should also investigate the amount and reliability of available data concerning the quantity and characteristics of the solid wastes to be handled. If sufficient and reliable data necessary for proper site selection and design are not available, the area to be served by the sanitary landfill must be surveyed to procure the necessary information.

If at all possible, the ultimate use of the completed landfill site should be decided during the initial planning stage. Knowing the final use of the site permits the designer to plan more effectively and gains public support for the project.

Zoning restrictions have sometimes interfered with the development of an area for a sanitary landfill. Many legal problems can be avoided if preliminary planning includes arrangements for zoning potential areas for sanitary landfill operations and ultimate site use.

SELECTING A SITE

An important engineering step toward establishing an acceptable sanitary land-fill operation is site selection. As with the preliminary planning phase, proper site selection can eliminate many future operational problems. The factors to be considered when selecting a sanitary landfill site will require technical know-how and experience, and so it bears repeating that a well qualified individual or agency should be responsible for site selection.

Land Requirement: The land area; or, more important, the volume of space required; is primarily dependent upon the character and quantity of the solid wastes, the efficiency of compaction of the wastes, the depth of the fill, and the desired life of the landfill. Data on the quantity and character of residential, commercial, and industrial solid wastes to be landfilled are therefore necessary for estimating the space required. In estimating volume requirements, volume reduction of the solid wastes due to compaction must be considered. The desired life of the landfill is another major factor in determining the total volume required.

The volume requirement for a sanitary landfill should be determined on the basis of the specific data and information for each individual project. As an estimate, however, using a waste generation rate of 5.3 pounds per person per day, solid waste density of 1,000 pounds per cubic yard, and one part earth cover to four parts waste, a population of 10,000 people would require 15 acre-feet of space per year.

Zoning Restrictions: A survey conducted by the American Public Works Association indicated that a high percentage of cities are restricted by their zoning ordinances in the acquisition of disposal sites. Consequently, before a full-scale investigation of a potential site is undertaken, all zoning ordinances should be reviewed and cleared or changed to eliminate any legalities that could prevent or indefinitely hold up the use of a particular parcel of land for a sanitary landfill. Advance planning to zone the potential landfill site areas for sanitary landfill operation can circumvent many of these problems.

Accessibility: The site should be easily reached by trucks via highways or arterial streets. Sites requiring trucks to travel through residential areas will normally draw many complaints. Such sites should be avoided or selected to minimize residential travel.

The roads to the site should be of width and construction adequate to handle all sizes of trucks when fully loaded, during all weather conditions. Such problems as narrow bridges, low underpasses, and steep grades on the access routes should be investigated. Since the site should be accessible at all times, it is desirable to have several access routes so that if one route is temporarily unusable the site can still be used.

Haul Distance: The haul distance is an important economic factor in selecting the sanitary landfill site. The economic distance to the site will vary from locality to locality depending upon capacity of collection vehicles, hauling time, and size and methods of the collection agency. The larger the quantity of refuse hauled per trip and the shorter the hauling time due to express roads, freeways, etc., the greater the distance the solid wastes can be hauled for the same cost.

Cover Material: The availability of cover material is another economic factor to consider, for the cost of hauling cover material to the site can be excessive. A site that has cover material close by will keep these costs at a minimum.

The field investigation of the potential site should include soil analysis to determine the suitability and the quantity of soil available for cover material. Soil with good workability and compaction characteristics is the most desirable cover material. A well graded soil has these qualities and is a good cover material.

Geology: The potential danger of ground and surface water pollution resulting from the landfill cannot be overlooked. Solid wastes ordinarily contain many contaminants and often infectious materials. Serious health hazards or nuisances can result if these pollutants are permitted to enter water supplies. Site selection should include a geological investigation of the site, possibly in conjunction with the cover material field investigation, to determine the potential of either ground or surface water pollution. The groundwater table must be located and information obtained on the historical high groundwater level and on the general movement of the groundwater.

Geological investigation should also examine the topography of the site itself and the surrounding area to determine potential flooding conditions during heavy rains and snow melts. Special attention should be given to low-lying sites that might be drainage basins for surrounding areas. Surface water drainage and flooding can quickly erode the cover material and the refuse fill.

Sites located near rivers, streams or lakes also deserve careful scrutiny. Generally, a landfill should not be located in a flood plain because of the water pollution hazard, and because these sites can become unusable both during and after floods. Sanitary landfills that are located in such areas require special engineering design.

Climate: In some locations, climate is important in site selection and may even dictate the method of operation. In an extremely cold locality, a site requiring excavation of trenches and cover material may become a problem because of freezing during the winter months. However, a site can be used in a wintery locale if the trenches and cover material are excavated during the summer months to carry the operation through the winter period.

In areas receiving considerable rainfall, a low-lying site may be undesirable because of flooding and muddy working conditions. In rainy areas, a desirable site would be high in relation to the surrounding area and have good drainage features. In windy locales, a site surrounded by natural windbreaks will help to contain loose paper and minimize any dust problems.

Fire Control Facilities: Although there is little chance of fire at a sanitary landfill operated in accordance with good practices, suitable fire protection should be provided. Fires can usually be extinguished by smothering with a blanket of earth, but all sites should also have water available for fire control. Fire control facilities are especially important if residential or commercial structures are relatively close and in extremely dry areas where the fire could spread quickly and do extensive damage.

DESIGNING A SANITARY LANDFILL

The design and operational steps during development of the sanitary landfill are not distinct entities. Basic knowledge and experience in the operational aspects of a sanitary landfill are necessary for the design phase. In essence, the design phase develops the plan of operation. It consists primarily of determining the operational plan and preparing the necessary detailed plans and specifications for construction and operation. Good plans and specifications are essential for estimating costs, for obtaining bids, and for operational control and inspection.

Plans: Detailed plans should be prepared showing the existing topography and the designed contours of the completed landfill. As mentioned, it is extremely helpful when designing the final ground elevations, if the use of the completed landfill has been previously determined.

The plans should show the overall program for landfilling, the drainage features, groundwater table, location of the cover material, and the wet weather operation site. The plans should also detail all construction features such as access roads, personnel and equipment facilities, scales, fencing, signs, waterlines and other utilities.

Specifications: The plans should be complemented with a set of specifications for construction and operation. Construction specifications cover construction materials, workmanship, and equipment. Operating specifications detail the method of operation, including weighing the wastes, cross-sectioning the site at definite time intervals, thickness of cover material, depth of lifts and cells, compaction, wet weather procedures, amount, type, and size of equipment, and personnel.

OPERATING A SANITARY LANDFILL

The appearance of the sanitary landfill during operation cannot be overly stressed. The operation is the only phase of the project seen by the public.

Consequently, public acceptance of the plan, design, and operation will be based solely on the operation. A well operated sanitary landfill is the goal of the planner, the designer, and the operator. Each must have a thorough knowledge of all the factors in achieving this goal.

Supervision: A clean, orderly, and economic operation requires constant and competent supervision. It is also important to employ experienced or adequately trained personnel to operate the sanitary landfill.

Operating Records: For continuing evaluation and future planning, detailed records should be kept of incoming material: the weights, the type, and the origin. Any deviation from the plan of operation should be recorded. Topographic surveys of the landfill should be made regularly to determine the rate of space utilization. The incoming-material data and the topographic surveys can be used to determine the amount of compaction, efficiency, land use, and operation efficiency, and to estimate the degree of decomposition and eventual settlement. Good cost-accounting records should be maintained, including the initial cost of the land and equipment, and the operating cost of the labor, equipment, equipment maintenance, depreciation, etc. These data are necessary for budgetary planning for determining the cost rates for users, and for comparison with other operations, justifying expenditures, and estimating the efficiency of operation.

Directions: Sanitary landfills, particularly those open to the public, need directional signs and markers on nearby highways to help speed traffic movement. At the entrance to the site a large legible sign should be posted to inform the public of the hours of operation, cost of disposal, and rules and regulations (such as, "only covered trucks permitted"). At large sanitary landfill operations, signs should also be used on the site to direct the users to the unloading area.

On-Site Roads: The on-site roads to the unloading area should be of all-weather construction and wide enough to permit easy two-way truck travel. Road grades should be designed for the largest fully loaded trucks to travel at a reasonable rate. It is particularly important at large sites that traffic in and out of the area flow smoothly.

Methods: Sanitary landfilling consists of the basic operations of spreading, compacting, and covering. Two general methods have evolved: the area method and the trench method. Some schools of thought also include a third, the slope, or ramp, method. In some operations, a slope or ramp is used in combination with the area or trench methods. For this reason, the three methods will be described: area landfill, trench landfill, and the ramp, or slope, method.

In an area sanitary landfill, the solid wastes are placed on the land; a bulldozer or similar equipment spreads and compacts the wastes; then the wastes are covered with a layer of earth; and finally the earth cover is compacted. The area method is best suited for flat areas or gently sloping land, and is also used in quarries, ravines, valleys or where other suitable land depressions exist. Normally the earth cover material is hauled in or obtained from adjacent areas.

In a trench sanitary landfill, a trench is cut in the ground and the solid wastes are placed in it. The solid wastes are then spread in thin layers, compacted, and covered with earth excavated from the trench. The trench method is best suited for flat land where the water table is not near the ground surface. Normally the material excavated from the trench can be used for cover with a minimum of hauling. A disadvantage is that more than one piece of equipment may be necessary.

In the ramp or slope method (a variation of the area and trench landfills), the solid wastes are dumped on the side of an existing slope. After spreading the material in thin layers on the slope, the bulldozing equipment compacts it. The cover material, usually obtained just ahead of the working face, is spread on the ramp and compacted. As a method of landfilling, this variation is generally suited to all areas. The advantage of utilizing only one piece of equipment to perform all operations makes the ramp or slope method particularly applicable to smaller operations. The slope or ramp is commonly used with either area or trench sanitary landfill.

Compaction: Solid wastes should be placed at the top or base of the working face, spread in layers about 2 feet thick, and compacted. If a slope or ramp is used, better compaction will normally result if the wastes are spread and compacted from the base upwards.

The degree of compaction is dependent on the character of the solid wastes, the weight and type of compacting equipment, and the number of passes the equipment makes over the material. The actual density of the landfill can be determined from operating records and data. The degree of compaction is a useful tool to determine the rate of space usage, expected life of the landfill, and the overall efficiency of the operation.

Working Face: The size of the working face of the sanitary landfill operation is determined by the rate of unloading of incoming vehicles. The working face should be as narrow as possible to minumize the exposed area, but not so small as to interfere with the unloading operations and the movement of landfill equipment.

A minimum width of the working face should be approximately twice the width of the tractor to allow the tractor to move from side to side thus compacting the entire exposed surface.

Depth of Cells: Cell depth is the thickness of the solid wastes layer measured perpendicular to the working slope where the equipment travels. The depth of cells is determined largely by the size of the operation, the elevation desired for the completed fill, the depth of the trench or depression to be filled, and in some cases, the amount of cover material available. Eight feet is generally recommended as a maximum single cell depth because deeper cells usually result in fills that have excessive settlement and surface cracking. However, the cell depth of presently operated sanitary landfills varies from 2 feet to 15 feet or more.

Cover: The compacted solid wastes must be covered at the conclusion of each day, or more frequently if necessary, with a minimum of 6 inches of compacted earth. A well-graded soil having good workability and compaction characteristics is a most desirable cover material. If a well-graded soil is not available on the site, it will be necessary to adjust the covering procedures to the type of cover material available or to haul in a suitable cover material. The cover is necessary to prevent insect and rodent infestation, blowing paper, fires, the attraction of wildlife, and the release of gas and odors.

For daily cover a minimum of 6 inches of compacted soil is recommended. For intermediate cover on lifts which will not have additional lifts placed on them within a year, a minimum of 12 inches of compacted soil is recommended. A minimum of 2 feet of compacted soil is recommended for the final cover. The final cover should be placed over the fill as soon as possible to help assure that wind and water erosion does not expose the wastes. Where trees will be planted on the completed fill, a depth of 3 or more feet of compacted earth has been found necessary.

Large Items: Large bulky items such as car bodies, refrigerators, water heaters, and tree stumps, can be handled routinely with other solid wastes at large sanitary landfills that use heavy equipment. At small sanitary landfills where light equipment is normally used, special provisions may be necessary to handle bulky items.

A separate unloading area or an alternate site operated in a sanitary manner should be utilized for the disposal of bulky items that cannot be handled routinely with other solid wastes.

Blowing Paper: In an American Society of Civil Engineers survey of sanitary landfill operations, the operating problem most frequently reported was blowing paper. The common method of controlling blowing paper is with a combination of permanent and portable fences. It is important, therefore, that the designer consider the prevailing wind direction when designing the operation. Unfortunately, under certain wind conditions paper may blow up and over the fences, so that fences do not provide complete control. Prompt compaction and covering and daily pick up of loose paper should be practiced to control wind-blown paper.

Maintenance: Routine maintenance will be required to maintain a clean, orderly and acceptable operation and site. It is important, particularly at public sanitary landfills, to cut grass and weeds, pick up scattered paper, maintain good access roads, control dust, and maintain immaculate employee and public facilities.

Drainage: Ponding on the landfill surface will result in excessive seepage into the landfill and must be prevented. Precautions must be taken to prevent run-off water from eroding the cover material and exposing the wastes. Adequate drainage therefore is essential both during the filling operation and for the completed landfill. Good drainage will usually require periodic regrading of the site, and the use of culverts or grassed waterways. It is recommended that the slope of the surface of the completed fill should be a minimum of 1%. Since the landfill will undergo uneven settlement, it may be necessary to design the original slope for more than 1% to maintain a 1% slope after settlement. To prevent erosion, however, steep slopes should be avoided.

Winter Operations: Experience has shown that with good planning and proper operating techniques, a sanitary landfill can be operated even in the severe winters of the northern states. If the trench method is used, the trenches should be excavated before the cold weather. It may be necessary to stockpile cover material and cover it with straw, leaves, or other material to prevent freezing. The material should be piled loosely with minimum compaction. All snow and ice should be removed from the trenches before use; snow fences can protect the access roads. A well-contructed, heated tractor cab enables the operator to work efficiently during the cold weather.

Wet Weather Operation: Wet weather can seriously hamper the operations of a sanitary landfill by making the soil too soft, mucky, or slippery for equipment operation. Wet weather can also seriously interfere with trenching, covering, and general traffic flow to and from the working area. For these reasons, all-weather access roads and adequate drainage should be provided.

In many cases it is advantageous to stockpile materials such as concrete rubble, broken asphalt pavement, or stone for use on the site roads during wet weather. This will minimize the cost of constructing and maintaining hard-surface roads to the unloading area. It is also desirable to provide a temporary wet weather landfill area adjacent to the all-weather road. Such sites are used only during the wet weather periods when the normal working area is not accessible.

Particular attention must be given to landfills when the trench method is being used. If pumping or good drainage is not provided, the trenches will fill with water, resulting in possible ground or surface water pollution and complete shut-down of the operation.

Salvage Operation: To ensure clean and orderly sites and to prevent landfills from looking like open dumps, salvage operations should be prohibited at all sanitary landfill sites. The American Society of Civil Engineers has stated that the most objectionable disposal sites from the standpoint of appearance are generally those where the salvage activity is the greatest.

PUBLIC HEALTH ASPECTS

Vector Control: In a properly operated and maintained sanitary landfill insects and rodents are not a problem. Well-compacted wastes and cover material are the most important factors in achieving vector control. Six inches of compacted earth cover is recommended for preventing the emergence of houseflies from the fill. Good compaction of the cover material also discourages rodents from burrowing through the cover material. Good housekeeping and daily covering of the solid wastes are musts for vector control.

Water Pollution: Under certain geological conditions, the burial of solid wastes is a real potential for chemical and bacteriological pollution of ground and surface waters. Several investigations of the pollution of groundwater from landfills have indicated that if a landfill is intermittently or continuously in contact with groundwater, it can become grossly polluted and unfit for domestic or irrigational use.

Proper planning and site selection, combined with good engineering design and operation of the sanitary landfill, can normally eliminate the possibility of either surface or groundwater pollution. Some common preventive measures are: (1) locating the site at a safe distance from streams, lakes, wells, and other water sources; (2) avoiding site location above the kind of subsurface stratification that will lead the leachate from the landfill to water sources, i.e., fractured limestone; (3) using an earth cover that is nearly impervious; (4) providing suitable drainage trenches to carry the surface water away from the site.

Air Pollution: Air pollution caused by smoke should not occur. Burning is not permitted at a properly operated sanitary landfill. If an accidental fire does occur, it should be extinguished immediately.

Dust: In dry weather, dust may constitute a nuisance at a sanitary landfill operation. Dust at the unloading area can be controlled by sprinkling the unloading area and the deposited refuse with water. Other dust control measures are the planting of grass or other vegetation on the finished fill and the application of water, road oil, or calcium chloride to the access roads.

Odors: Odors are usually the result of gases from anaerobic digestion of putrescible material. They are generally considered a nuisance but can be a public health hazard. The best control for odors is rapid and continuous coverage of solid wastes during the day and sealing surface cracks of the completed area of the landfill to prevent emissions of large concentrations of odorous gases.

Wildlife: Birds, particularly gulls, and other wildlife are common at open and burning dumps, but there is little exposed food to attract wildlife at sanitary landfills. Most good sanitary landfill operations are free from these nuisances; however, there is no guarantee that all sanitary landfills will be completely free of wildlife. If the site is kept clean, and the solid wastes covered promptly with earth, gulls and other wildlife will be at a minimum.

Gas Production: Gases produced within a sanitary landfill consist chiefly of methane, nitrogen, carbon dioxide, hydrogen, and hydrogen sulfide. Methane gas is explosive and can be a hazard if accumulated in enclosed spaces. At landfills where methane and other gases are generated, the gases should be dissipated into the atmosphere and prevented from concentrating in sewers or other structures located on or near the site.

Hazardous Materials: Although it is not common or recommended practice, hazardous materials such as sewage solids, radioactive wastes, pathologic wastes, explosive materials, and chemicals can be disposed of at sanitary landfill sites under special conditions. The special provisions for handling and disposing of these materials will depend on local conditions. Individual handling and disposal may be necessary using a special area separate from the main operation. The particular requirements should be considered during the design phase so that they may be included in the operational specifications.

EQUIPMENT

A wide variety of equipment is on the market today from which to select the proper type and size needed for an efficient operation. The size, the type, and the amount of equipment required at a sanitary landfill depend on the size and method of operation and to some degree on the experience and preference of the designer and equipment operators.

Types: The most common equipment used on sanitary landfills is the crawler or rubber-tired tractor. The tractor can be used with a dozer blade, trash blade, or a front-end loader. A tractor is versatile and can normally perform all the operations: spreading, compacting, covering, trenching, and even hauling the cover material. The decision on whether to select a rubber-tired or a crawler-type tractor, and a dozer blade, trash blade, or front-end loader, must be based on the conditions at each individual site.

Other equipment used at sanitary landfills are scrapers, compactors, draglines, and graders. This type of equipment is normally found only at large sanitary landfills where specialized equipment increases the overall efficiency.

Size: The size of the equipment is dependent primarily on the size of the operation. Small sanitary landfills for communities of 15,000 or fewer, or sanitary landfills handling 46 tons of solid wastes per day or less, can operate successfully with one tractor of the 5 to 15 ton range.

Heavier equipment in the 15 to 30 ton range or larger can handle more waste and achieve better compaction. Heavy equipment is recommended for sanitary landfill sites serving more than 15,000 people or handling more than 46 tons per day.

Amount: Sanitary landfills servicing 50,000 people or fewer, or handling about 155 tons of solid wastes per day or less, normally can manage well with one piece of equipment, but provisions must be made for standby equipment. It is preferable that a second piece of equipment be purchased and used for re-placement during breakdown and routine maintenance periods of the regular equipment. Arrangements can normally be made, however, with another public agency or private concern for the use or rental of replacement equipment on short notice in case of a breakdown of the regular equipment.

At large sanitary landfills serving more than 100,000 people, or handling more than 310 tons of solid wastes per day, more than one piece of equipment will be required. At these sites, specialized equipment can be utilized to increase efficiency and minimize costs. In the table a general guide is given for the selection of the type, size, and amount of equipment for various sizes of sanitary landfills.

Average Equipment Requirements

Population	Daily Tonnage	No.	Equipment Type	Size in Lbs	Accessory*
0 - 15,000	0 - 46	1	Tractor crawler or rubber-tired	10,000 - 30,000	Dozer blade Landfill blade Front-end loader (1- to 2-yd)
15,000 - 50,000	46 - 155	1	Tractor crawler or rubber-tired	30,000 - 60,000	Dozer blade Landfill blade Front-end loader (2- to 4-yd) Multipurpose bucket
		*	Scraper Dragline Water truck		
50,000 - 100,000	155 - 310	1 - 2	Tractor crawler or rubber-tired	30,000 or more	Dozer blade Landfill blade Front-end loader (2- to 5-yd) Multipurpose bucket
		*	Scraper Dragline Water truck		
100,000 or more	310 or more	2 or more	Tractor crawler or rubber-tired	45,000 or more	Dozer blade Landfill blade Front-end loader Multipurpose bucket
		*	Scraper Dragline Steel-wheel compactor Road grader Water truck		

*Optional. Dependent on individual need.

FACILITIES

A small sanitary landfill operation will usually require only a small building for storing hand tools, equipment parts, etc., and a shelter with sanitary facilities for the employees. A single building may serve both purposes.

A large sanitary landfill operation should have a maintenance and storage ga-rage for equipment and an administration building. If the scales are not adja-cent to the administration building, a scale house may also be needed. Sani-tary facilities should be available for both employees and the public. In addition, it is recommended that locker rooms and showers be provided for the employees.

COSTS

The cost of a sanitary landfill consists of the initial investment for land, equipment, and construction features, and the operating costs.

Initial Investment

The magnitude of the initial investment depends on the size and sophistication of the landfill. A typical breakdown of the major items that normally constitute the initial investment is as follows:

1. Land
2. Planning and designing
   a. Consultant
   b. Solid wastes survey
   c. Site investigation
   d. Design, plans, specifications
3. Site development
   a. Land development — clearing, landscaping, drainage features, etc.
   b. Access roads
   c. Utilities — water, electricity, telephone
   d. Fencing, signs
4. Facilities
   a. Administration
   b. Equipment maintenance
   c. Sanitation
   d. Weight scales
5. Equipment — tractor, scraper, etc.

Generally, the major portion of the initial investment is for the purchase of the land and equipment. Often a sizable part of the initial investment for land and equipment can be recovered through the development or use of the land and the salvage value of the equipment.

If funds are not available for the proposed investment, consideration should be given to leasing land or equipment, or both, to spread the cost over the life of operation.

Operating Cost

The operating cost of a sanitary landfill depends on the cost of labor and equipment, the method of operation, and the efficiency of the operation. The principal items in operating cost are:

1. Personnel
2. Equipment
   a. Operating expenses – gas, oil, etc.
   b. Maintenance and repair
   c. Rental, depreciation, or amortization
3. Cover material – material and haul costs
4. Administration and overhead
5. Miscellaneous – tools, utilities, insurance, maintenance to roads, fences, facilities, drainage features, etc.

Wages ordinarily make up about 40 to 50% of the total operating cost. Equipment equals 30 to 40%; cover material, administration, overhead, and miscellaneous amount to about 20%.

The operating costs per ton versus the amount of solid wastes handled in tons and the population equivalent may be charted (Figure 8.1).

FIGURE 8.1: SANITARY LANDFILL OPERATING COSTS

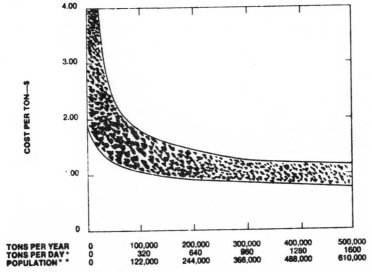

TONS PER YEAR	0	100,000	200,000	300,000	400,000	500,000
TONS PER DAY*	0	320	640	960	1280	1600
POPULATION**	0	122,000	244,000	366,000	488,000	610,000

* Based on 6-day work week.
** Based on national average of 4.5 lbs per person per calendar day.

Source: PB 204,403, EPA, 1970

The operating cost of a small operation handling less than 50,000 tons per year varies from $1.25 to approximately $5.00 per ton. This wide range is primarily due to the low efficiency of the smaller operations which are usually operated on a part-time basis.

Full-time personnel, full-time use of equipment, specialized equipment, better management, and other factors that lead to high efficiency are possible at large sanitary landfill operations. The increased efficiency results in lower unit cost of disposal. The unit cost of a large landfill handling more than 50,000 tons per year will generally fall between $0.75 to $2.00 per ton.

To compare the true cost of sanitary landfilling with that of incineration or composting, it is essential that the costs and returns of the initial investments and the hauling costs be considered along with the total disposal costs including the disposal of incinerator residue and noncompostable materials. The hauling costs of a collection system that uses the sanitary landfill disposal method may be higher than the hauling costs of a system using incineration or composting, since sanitary landfills are generally located farther from the waste-generating area than are incinerators or compost plants. A sanitary landfill, however, may increase the value of a plot of unusable land by converting the site to a playground, golf course, park, etc., thereby obtaining a major investment cost advantage over incineration and composting.

COMPLETED SANITARY LANDFILL

Decomposition: Little information is available on the decomposition of buried material in a sanitary landfill. It is extremely difficult to predict the time required for complete decomposition. Many items, particularly paper, have been found unchanged in landfills that had been completed for 15 to 25 years. The rate of decomposition is primarily dependent upon the moisture content and generally takes place at a very slow rate.

Decomposition of the wastes will result in the production of gases, principally methane, carbon dioxide, nitrogen, hydrogen, and hydrogen sulfide. The rate of gas production will usually reach a peak within the first 2 years and then slowly taper off.

Methane gas causes the most concern because of its explosive character. Precautions should be taken that will prevent the gas from concentrating in sewers or other structures located on or near the landfill.

Settlement: Settlement of the landfill is dependent on the depth of the fill, composition, compaction of the material, moisture content, and other factors. Studies have indicated that approximately 90% of the ultimate settlement will occur in the first 5 years. The final 10% will occur over a much longer period. As a rough indication of the amount of settlement that might occur, several Los Angeles area sanitary landfills, 90 to 110 feet deep, have settled 2.5 to 5.5 feet in 3 years.

Underground Fires: Although underground fires rarely occur in a completed landfill, the possibility does exist. All underground fires should be dug up and extinguished. The cell construction of a sanitary landfill helps to confine and restrict the spread of the fire should one occur.

Maintenance: Completed landfills generally require maintenance because of differential settlement. Maintenance consists primarily of resloping the surface to maintain good drainage and filling in small depressions that result from uneven settlement.

Uses: Completed landfills have been used for recreational purposes; parks, playgrounds, or golf courses. Parking and storage areas or botanical gardens are other final uses. Because of settling and gas problems, construction of buildings on completed landfills generally has been avoided; in several locations, however, one-story rambling-type buildings and airport runways for light aircraft have been constructed directly on sanitary landfills. In such cases, it is important for the designer to avoid concentrated foundation loading which can result in uneven settlement and cracking of the structure. The designer must provide the means to allow the gas to dissipate to the atmosphere and not into the structure. Multi-story buildings can be built over completed landfills, using steel and concrete pilings, and special engineering design.

ADVANTAGES AND DISADVANTAGES

Advantages

1. Where land is available, a sanitary landfill is usually the most economical method of solid waste disposal.
2. The initial investment is low compared with other disposal methods.
3. A sanitary landfill is a complete or final disposal method as compared to incineration and composting which require additional treatment or disposal operations for residue, quenching water, unusable materials, etc.
4. A sanitary landfill can be put into operation within a short period of time.
5. A sanitary landfill can receive all types of solid wastes, eliminating the necessity of separate collections.
6. A sanitary landfill is flexible; increased quantities of solid wastes can be disposed of with little additional personnel and equipment.
7. Submarginal land may be reclaimed for use as parking lots, playgrounds, golf courses, airports, etc.

Disadvantages

1. In highly populated areas, suitable land may not be available within economical hauling distance.
2. Proper sanitary landfill standards must be adhered to daily or the operation may result in an open dump.
3. Sanitary landfills located in residential areas can result in extreme public opposition.
4. A completed landfill will settle and require periodic maintenance.
5. Special design and construction must be utilized for buildings constructed

on completed landfill because of the settlement factor.

6. Methane, an explosive gas, and the other gases produced from the decomposition of the wastes may become a hazard or nuisance problem and interfere with the use of the completed landfill.

Special Studies of
Fabricated Landfill Cells

The material in this chapter was taken from a 1970 report of the U.S. Department of Health, Education, and Welfare entitled *Special Studies of a Sanitary Landfill.*

1964-1965

Two years were spent in the preparation and study of the landfill cells described in this report. They exist at the Spadra Landfill No. 2, operated by the Los Angeles County Sanitation Districts. The purposes for which these cells were built were:

Test Cell A— Seattle rainfall pattern replication
Test Cell B— Turf development and irrigation
Test Cell C— Maintenance of aerobic environment
Test Cell D— Refuse encapsulation in polyethylene membrane
  to measure gas production

Compaction ratios from 2.1 to 2.2, and in-place density of 1,000 lbs./yd.^{3}, were achieved for the test cells. Cell A, receiving the Seattle rainfall equivalent plus an extra 55 in. (for a total of 87 in. of water), did not show percolation into the leach collection cans. Cell B, after receiving 113 in. of applied irrigation water, produced leach in the collection can located 7 ft. below the surface. Normal turf development was readily achieved and maintained on Cell B.

The greatest settlement, nearly 2 ft. in 17 months, occurred in aerobic Cell C, whereas the two anaerobic Cells A and B settled 0.5 and 0.4 ft., respectively during the same period. Extensive settlement in Cell C produced cave-ins with holes measuring 3 ft. by 4 ft. that extended to the bottom of the cell. The cave-ins were caused by a combination of oxidation, heavy rainfall and surface flooding.

In anaerobic Cell A, the major gas constituents by volume have been fairly steady over the past year at 60% carbon dioxide and 40% methane. Oxygen, hydrogen and nitrogen were present in varying amounts. In Cell B, the gas composition was affected by movement of air from Cell C when the blower was in operation. The major gas components were carbon dioxide, nitrogen and methane. Cell C was aerobically operated and the gas composition was dependent upon the duration of the blower operation. The chief gas components at the upper level of the cell were nitrogen (70 to 80%) and carbon dioxide (10 to 20%). Slightly lesser amounts existed at the lower level, but oxygen averaged about 10%. Methane was minimal when the blower was in operation.

The temperature at the 10-ft. depth in anaerobic Cell A was about $100°$F. for the first 5 months, and then gradually decreased to $71°$F. over the balance of the test period. The temperature behavior at the bottom depth was similar. The temperature in Cell B declined from an early peak of $120°$ to $70°$F. Although intended to be an anaerobic cell, its performance was influenced by passage of air from Cell C notwithstanding a compacted, 5-ft. wide, continuous earth barrier. The aerobic Cell C supported a $193°$F. temperature at mid-depth as much as 174 days following cell construction. Bottom temperatures reached peaks sufficiently high to destroy thermistors. Smoke emanations with fire were noted on a few occasions. The cell temperature was affected by the aeration cycle.

Cell D, intended for determining quantitative studies of gas production, was unsuccessful although constructed with extreme care by professional plastic fabricators. The polyethylene envelope was not able to store gas. Coring and side cutting of the five original, 4+ yr. old, anaerobic test cells demonstrated that only minor decomposition of the solid wastes had occurred. Moisture analyses on a dry weight basis for numerous core samples ranged from 5.3 to 42.9%, considerably less than computed values at the time of construction.

Sanitary Landfill Site

Selection: This investigation was conducted at Spadra Landfill No. 2, operated by the County Sanitation Districts of Los Angeles County.

Preparation: Preparation of the site on which the test cells were to be constructed included clearing away of walnut trees, excavation of the cells, placement of access wells, and installation of the facilities required before placement of the refuse.

Cell Excavation: It was decided to position 4 cells in an area adjacent to the entrance to the landfill, as close as possible to the Weighmaster's office as well as a source of power. This area was of a gently sloping nature, so that it was necessary to resort to both cut and fill operations to form the 4 cells. Cells A and B were formed by cutting into undisturbed earth. Cells C and D were formed in well compacted earth. Construction of the cells was undertaken by the District personnel, utilizing bulldozers and scrapers. Cell D failed in its purpose. When completed, the 3 test cells were fully below finished grade. End slopes, established to permit easy entry and exit of the equipment, were about one on two, and side slopes were about one on one-half. The result was an in-line series of 3 cells having the appearance of inverted truncated pyramids, with tops and bottoms in essentially parallel planes.

All cells had bottoms measuring approximately 50 ft. on a side and tops measuring approximately 70 ft. by 130 ft. Their average depth was approximately 20 ft. That portion of each cell utilized for research purposes was the mass rising vertically above the bottom area.

Access Well: In the center of each cell there was erected an access well to provide outlets for gas collection lines, leach collection lines, and electrical leads, and a means of human access for observing bottom drainage (if any), the taking of internal humidity and temperature measurements, and collection of leach.

Each access well consisted of a steel pipe 44 in. diameter by ¼ in. thick by 18 ft. long, with numerous openings cut into the side for admission of the aforementioned conduits emanating from within the cell. The earth bottom of each test cell provided a suitable foundation for the access well. Since the access wells were but 18 ft. long, and since it was the intention to carry the cells to a finished depth of 21 ft., it was necessary to build a 3-ft. high wooden extension on top of each of them. Each structure was fitted with a hinged, locked cover. Each access well was sealed off from the atmosphere by covering the wooden super-structure with an air-tight, neoprene-coated nylon tarpaulin.

All gas conduits and electrical leads were carried outside of the enclosure and housed in a wooden box flush with grade for convenience in taking samples, and so that the internal environment would be unchanged during the sampling process. A 6-in. high concrete and aluminum berm was placed around each access well to prevent surface drainage from reaching the access well.

Power Supply: It was necessary to bring in power from the nearest lines strung along the adjacent highway. New lines were strung from there to a temporary pole provided by the Districts to furnish 6 kw, 220 v-3 phase current. To serve the research site, a panel board was erected and fitted with control and time clock equipment for the blower, and a transformer to provide the single phase current for the vacuum pump and irrigation controls. Underground lines in rigid conduits carried the single phase current to 4 different locations within the test site.

Refuse and Soil

Refuse Source: All of the refuse placed in the cells originated in the residential districts of the adjoining communities of Pomona, San Dimas, Claremont and LaVerne.

Refuse Characteristics: In addition to accepting refuse from only the residential areas of the communities named in the preceding section, further control was exerted to make certain that only typical domestic refuse consisting of paper, grass and garden trimmings, garbage and miscellaneous inert material was placed in the cells. Further, such materials as industrial wastes, lath and plaster, tree logs and stumps, and broken concrete, were generally excluded from the cells. The solid waste placed in the cells was assumed to have the same composition as determined at the start of the earlier project, about 65% paper, 25% garden trimmings, 5% garbage and 5% inerts by volume. In the laboratory, the average moisture content for the entire mass of trucked refuse was determined to be 31% on a wet weight basis (44.8% dry weight basis).

Soil Characteristics: The top soil of the entire Spadra site comprises a thin layer of organic clay. It was skinned off and stockpiled for use elsewhere. The subsoil consists of a decomposed shale. It is this material which was used for final cover on the top of Cells B and C.

Cell Construction

Description of Cells: In Cell A, the refuse was placed continuously until the full depth (19 ft.) was reached. As the refuse was being placed, sufficient water was added to bring the moisture content to 97.4% on a dry weight basis. The refuse placed was subjected to the standard compaction procedure. To bring the overall depth to 21 ft., a 2-ft. thick earth cover was placed. Since this cell was to be used as a basis for studying the effect of simulated rainfall, particularly with regard to rainfall penetration, it was necessary to provide an earth cover that would permit water penetration. That portion of the earth cover having the same dimensions as the bottom of the cell was therefore imported from a Pomona construction site.

Laboratory tests showed the material to be a "sandy silt" with 54% passing through a No. 4 sieve and 60% passing through a No. 200 sieve. The dry density was 102 lbs./ft.^{3}. The coefficient of permeability, assuming 75% degree of compaction, was 50 ft./yr. For application of the simulated rainfall, irrigation piping was laid just beneath the top surface to service individually controlled Rain Bird nozzles located one at each corner and one in the center. The amount of water applied was in simulation of the Seattle, Wash., rainfall.

In Cell B, the refuse was placed continuously until the full depth (19 ft.) was reached. As the refuse was being placed, sufficient water was added to bring the moisture content to 73.3% on a dry weight basis. The refuse placed was subjected to standard compaction procedure. To bring the overall depth to 21 ft., a 2-ft. thick earth cover was placed. Since this cell was to be used as a basis for studying the effect of maintaining a high quality, golf course type turf, particularly with regard to penetration of irrigation water, it was necessary to provide a top soil favorable to turf growth. This was done by mixing "Loamite," a lignin-organic base material containing approximately 45% lignin, 85% organic matter and 1% nitrogen, with the native topsoil. The amount used was

10% by volume. An automatic sprinkler system was installed to insure that the turf would be properly irrigated.

An "Irrometer" system was installed, consisting of two pairs of tensiometers tied in electrically with a solenoid valve. The tensiometers were installed in pairs, one 3 in. below the surface and the other 6 in. below the surface. When an unsatisfactory soil-moisture relationship was reached at any of the four tensiometers, irrigation would automatically begin and continue until the proper soil-moisture condition was obtained at all tensiometers. Bermuda seed was selected and chicken guano was used as a fertilizer to help produce the turf. The irrigation piping was laid just beneath the top surface, and individually-controlled Rain Bird nozzles were located one in each corner and one in the center.

Before the refuse could be placed in Cell C, a system of piping by which air could be admitted to the completed cell was installed. This system consisted of 4-in. diameter VC perforated Wedge-Lock pipe laid in trenches 12 in. deep by 12 in. wide. The network was made up of 3 parallel 48-ft. lines on 24-ft. centers crossed at right angles by 7 lines on 6-ft. centers. The outside periphery of the network was a closed loop. A near-vertical 4-in. galvanized steel line was installed to convey the air from the blower mounted at ground surface to the cell aeration system. The refuse was then placed continually until the full depth (19 ft.) was reached. As the refuse was being placed, sufficient water was added to bring the moisture content to 80.0% on a dry weight basis.

The refuse was subjected to standard compaction procedure. To bring the overall depth to 21 ft., a 2-ft. thick top cover was placed. To prevent movement of forced air through the earth cover and the atmosphere, an impervious membrane was stretched over the cell 1 ft. below the surface, i.e., at mid-depth of the cover. The membrane used was a white, 6-mil thick polyethylene. It was expected that movement of air through the cell would tend to dry out the refuse. For this reason, a network of perforated ½-in. diameter PVC spray pipe was laid on top of the refuse, immediately under the top cover. The layout used was similar to that described for the air piping. So that the cell gases could be recirculated during blower operation, a 6-in. diameter VC Wedge-Lock pipe was laid on top of the cell, connecting the housing on top of the center access well to the blower intake.

The wooden extension to the center access well for this cell was constructed so that it could be reduced easily in height since considerable settlement of the cell surface was expected. A Buffalo Forge Company industrial exhauster was selected for supplying air to the cell. The blower was rated at 1,000 cfm against a 6-in. static pressure at 2,345 rpm. The blower's inside surfaces were treated to prevent corrosion. A valved manifold was provided at the intake to mix fresh air with recirculated gases in any desired proportion. A time clock was wired into the electrical system so that the operating cycle of the blower could be varied.

Volumes: Only refuse trucks (packers) of known volume were permitted to unload their refuse at the test site. The volumetric capacity of each packer was obtained from the municipality which owned it. The volume of each excavation in which refuse was to be placed was surveyed and computed through use of the prismoidal formula.

Weights: Each truck that entered the Spadra site was weighed. The Weighmaster issued a receipt on which was recorded the truck number, the total weight, the tare weight, and the net tonnage of refuse carried by the truck. The truck was then routed to the test site. The field representative of the research staff was stationed at the site to direct the unloading of each truck and placement of the refuse. The representative also recorded the receipt number and the truck number as it unloaded, and at conclusion of the day's work the entire listing of receipt numbers was checked against the Weighmaster's record to make certain that only those tonnages were included on the record that actually reached the test site.

A bulldozer and scraper was normally used to transport and level the earth that was to be used for top cover. The permeable soil cover for Cell A was imported by truck as described previously. All of the water used in the construction of the refuse cells was metered. From the known gallonage, the weight of the water added was computed.

Construction Summary: All of the data pertaining to the cell construction are presented in the following table.

Cell Construction Summary

Line	Cell Data	A	B	C
1	Date Started	6-15-64	6-25-64	7-15-64
2	Date Completed	7-14-64	7-14-64	8-07-64
3	Working Days to Replace Refuse in Cell	11	12	15
4	Cubic Yards of Refuse Trucked to Cell[2]	7,195	7,449	7,202
5	Pounds of Refuse Trucked to Cell[2]	3,482,340	3,649,980	3,442,560
6	Delivered Trucked Density, Pounds Per Cu Yd[3]	484	490	478
7	Volume of Cell, Cubic Yards[4]	3,468	3,495	3,291
8	Fill Density, Pounds Per Cubic Yard[5]	1,004	1,044	1,046
9	Gallons of Water Added[6]	151,071	85,547	99,969
10	Pounds of Water Added	1,259,932	713,462	833,742
11	Pounds of Water Present in Trucked Refuse[7]	1,079,525	1,131,494	1,067,194
12	Total Pounds of Water in Cell	2,339,457	1,844,956	1,900,936
13	Percent Moisture of Cell, Dry Weight Basis[8]	97.4	73.3	80.0

Notes:

1. Calculations exclude final fill covers.

2. Actual truck volumes and scaled weights

3. $\dfrac{\text{Line 5}}{\text{Line 4}}$

4. Determined by field measurements

5. $\dfrac{\text{Line 5}}{\text{Line 7}}$

6. Measured by water meter.

7. Determined by laboratory tests of representative samples

8. $\dfrac{(\text{Line 5} \times 31\%) + \text{Line 10}}{\text{Line 5} - (\text{Line 5} \times 31\%)} \times 100$

Moisture content of refuse on wet basis = 31%

On line 6 of the table, the density of the refuse as delivered to each cell is shown and is seen to be uniform. On line 7 are presented the volumes of the excavations. On line 8 are shown the calculated cell densities. These densities were virtually the same for all cells.

The working time required to build the 3 cells was longest for Cell C. Many man days of hard, physical labor were required for placement of the aeration lines and related equipment. The compaction ratio is usually considered to be the trucked volume of the refuse divided by the in-place volume of the same refuse. A recent survey of sanitary landfill practices demonstrated that 70% of all operating landfills responding to inquiry achieved a compaction ratio of from 2:1 to 3:1 by various procedures. However, the method of calculation used was generally not specified.

The compaction ratios achieved in the earlier study by this Group by the various construction techniques employed varied from 1.29:1 to 2.12:1. It is emphasized that the trucked volumes used in determining the ratios represented known, "pre-compacted" values. The compaction ratios achieved in this study were 2.06:1 for Cell A, 2.13:1 for Cell B, and 2.18:1 for Cell C.

Mensurative Equipment: While the cells were being constructed to their finished surface elevation, it was necessary to install the equipment which would make possible the measurement of internal and external temperatures, internal moisture and cell settlement, and provide for collection of gas and leach samples. Figures 9.1 through 9.3 are diagrams of each cell showing placement of all equipment.

Thermistors: To measure the internal temperatures of each cell, 3 general purpose, bead-type thermistors were buried in the refuse as the cell was constructed. These thermistors were located at distances of 4 ft., 10 ft., and 16 ft. above the bottom surface. The thermistors were selected to operate in a corrosive atmosphere over the full range of expected temperatures. They and their leads were protected by enclosure in $3/8$-in. diameter copper tubing. Each thermistor was fitted with 50-ft. Teflon-coated leads to reach from the thermistor location into the access well and up to ground surface. A fourth thermistor was installed near the bottom of the access well and was taped to a conventional mercury thermometer for comparison of readings.

Even with these precautions, thermistors were lost, apparently because of corrosion of leads or because of tearing of leads with settlement. The first losses occurred in Cell C at the bottom and mid-depth due to excessive temperatures after 193 days. The last loss occurred in Cell B at the bottom depth after 233 days. Temperatures were obtained by measuring the resistance in the Thermistor with a "Thermistor Thermometer" and referring the resistance to calibration curves prepared in the laboratory before installation.

Thermometers: An electrically driven recording thermometer using 7-day charts was located with the sensing device mounted in a shaded area at the office of

FIGURE 9.1: CROSS SECTION OF CELL A

NOTE: All leads continue up the access well to the instrument box

No Scale

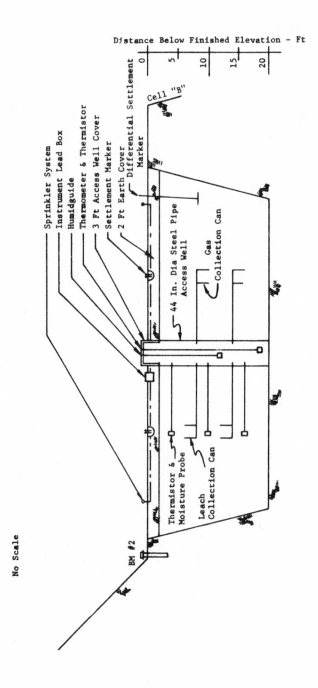

Source: PB 196,148, 1970

FIGURE 9.2: CROSS SECTION OF CELL B

NOTE: All leads continue
up the access well to the
instrument box. Leach
cans are in a spiral at
2 ft intervals.

No Scale

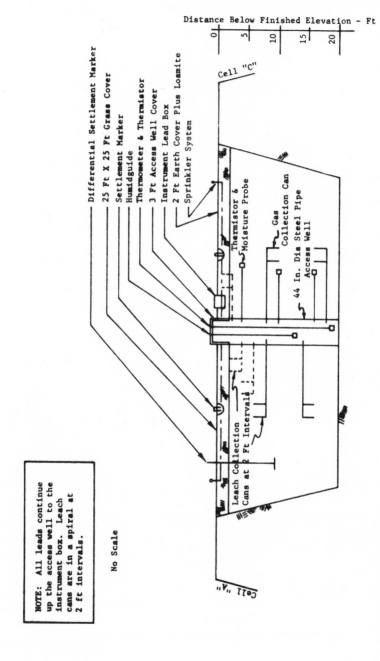

Distance Below Finished Elevation - Ft

Differential Settlement Marker
25 Ft X 25 Ft Grass Cover
Settlement Marker
Humidguide
Thermometer & Thermistor
3 Ft Access Well Cover
Instrument Lead Box
2 Ft Earth Cover Plus Loamite
Sprinkler System

Cell "C"

Thermistor &
Moisture Probe

Gas
Collection Can

44 In. Dia Steel Pipe
Access Well

Leach Collection
Cans at 2 Ft Intervals

Cell "A"

Source: PB 196,148, 1970

FIGURE 9.3: CROSS SECTION OF CELL C

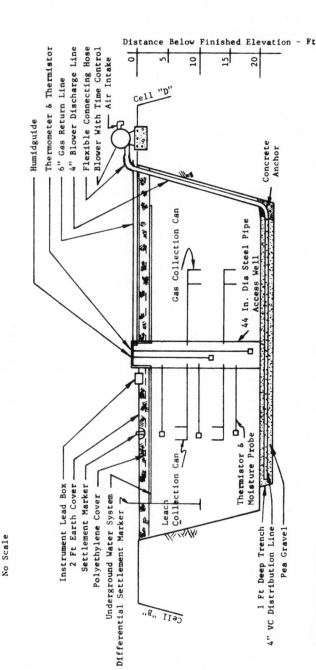

NOTE: All leads continue up the access well to the instrument lead box

No Scale

Source: PB 196,148, 1970

the Weighmaster at the entrance to the Spadra site. The recording thermometer was calibrated against a standard laboratory thermometer, and a maximum-minimum thermometer was installed near it as a constant check on the recorded temperatures.

Moisture Probes: To secure the internal moisture content of each cell, 3 moisture probes were buried in the refuse next to the thermistors as the cell was constructed. The purchased probes consisted of 2 stainless steel, wire mesh, cylindrical electrodes, set concentrically in plaster-of-Paris. Each probe was fitted with a 50-ft. lead of heavy duty, laminated wire. The soldered joint was protected with an epoxy resin. It was expected that moisture readings could be obtained by taking readings with a conductivity bridge and referral of the readings to calibration curves prepared by the supplying laboratory. However, for the conditions under which the probes were used, it proved impossible to take readings which could be converted into meaningful humidity valves. Even in the laboratory, calibration readings proved unreliable.

Gas and Leach Collection Cans: As the cells were constructed, half sections of 55-gal. steel drums were located within Cells A and C, 2 with open end up for the collection of leach and 2 with closed end up for the collection of gas. In Cell B, 9 half drums with open end up were installed in a descending spiral pattern between top and bottom of the cell for tracking vertical penetration of irrigation water. Also, 2 half drums were installed with open end down for gas collection. These are hereinafter referred to as "leach collection cans" and "inverted collection cans."

To protect the cans against corrosion, they were given a bitumastic coating before placement. Copper tubing was used to convey any leach and the expected gas from the cans to the center access wells. Leach lines were valved at entrance to access wells. Gas lines were carried on up to ground surface where they terminated in compression stop cocks housed in a wooden box flush with grade.

The cans were installed within the fill with the copper outlet tubing so placed as to allow for future settlement. Gas samples were obtained at approximately 6 and 12 ft. above the bottom. The take-off tubes from the leach collection cans were at the same distance above the bottom. No gas collection lines were lost.

Gas Analysis: A standard, glass, gas collector was installed between the terminal of the copper gas line and portable vacuum pump. To take a sample, the valve on the end of the gas collection line was closed, the pump was started, and the system back to the closed valve was evacuated. The valve was then opened, permitting movement of the gas from the cell into the collection system, and the pump was run for 5 minutes before the sample to be used for analysis was sealed in the gas collector. The 5 minute purge used was determined through experimentation. All timing was done by stopwatch in the interest of uniformity. Less than 24 hours elapsed between the times of sample collection and sample analysis.

Settlement Bench Marks: A survey monument was established in undisturbed earth at one end of the longitudinal axis of the test cells. Also, 4 survey markers consisting of 2-in. capped pipes set in concrete were established 90° apart and 15 ft. from the center-line of the access well on the surface of each cell. To measure differential settling within a cell a steel settlement plate was installed 10 ft. above the bottom within each cell. Each plate was approximately one foot square, to which was welded a 3/4-in. diameter steel pipe of sufficient length to reach above the finished surface elevation.

Cell Activity

External Climatic Factors: The total rainfall on the test site for the period of study (to December 31, 1965) has been 28.7 in.

Application of Water: Beginning in July, 1965, an effort was made to correlate the total amount of water applied (irrigation plus rainfall) with the required amount in accordance with Seattle rainfall. Approximately 16 in. were applied which was 0.7 in. more than require. Even with the flooding which took place in December, 1964, (55 in.) plus the water applied since that time (30 in.) no leach was collected.

The Bermuda grass was planted on top of Cell B on August 25, 1964. Careful and frequent hand watering was required (normal for any new lawn) until a study stand was obtained. It was refertilized on October 9. It was not until October 16 that the tensiometers could be given control of the watering cycle. The first cutting was made on October 30. A third application of fertilizer was made on February 25, 1965. On March 4, a broad leaf weed killer was applied as part of the weed control measure exercised over the entire research site. Since that time, an excellent turf has been maintained. The total irrigation water applied for the period of study was 84.2 in. The total rainfall plus irrigation on Cell B was thus 112.9 in.

These amounts have produced leach only from the top collection pan. The actual amount withdrawn was about 100 ml. of a typical dark green, odorous liquid. The entrapment of water percolating downward through a medium into a collection pan is not a certainty, and there is always the danger of the pan being bypassed in spite of efforts to preserve the continuity of the medium inside and above the pan. However, since 2 leach collection cans were set, and since leach only appeared in the top can, it is assumed that percolation of the applied water has not yet occurred to a depth of more than 7 ft.

Settlement: The settlement of the surface of the cells, due to compaction of the the refuse was periodically measured by survey. Settlement was also influenced by the unusually heavy rains of November, 1965. The settlement data indicate that the greatest settlement, nearly 2 ft. in 17 months, has occurred in aerobic Cell C. In the two, full-size anaerobic cells, settlement of 0.50 ft. has occurred in Cell A and 0.40 ft. has occurred in Cell B. Cell C developed several longitudinal settlement fissures adjacent to the natural earth, approximately 30 ft.

long and $1/2$ in. wide. These fissures were filled with earth and were not a particular problem.

Cave-ins in Cell C did prove to be quite a problem. The first occurred in October, 1965, simply as the result of natural oxidation. The cave-in produced a hole in the cell measuring 3 ft. by 4 ft. and extending to the bottom. Two more cave-ins followed, one on November 26 and one on December 11, but these were hastened by the very unusual rains of that period. These cave-ins occurred at the periphery of the cell and served as funnels to channel surface runoff to the bottom of the cell. The result was an inundation of all aeration lines . Backfilling with clean earth repaired the cave-ins.

The settlement of the bottom half of Cell A and Cell B lagged behind the settlement of the top half by 0.10 ft. The differential settlement between the top half and the bottom half of Cell C was 0.26 ft. In other words, the lower portion of the cell settled 1.59 ft. resulting in increased "equivalent" density of the bottom fill material. The upper portion of the cell followed the lower portion down and actually compressed 0.26 ft. additional to give a total surface settlement of 1.85 ft. Thus, the density of the upper portion of the fill material was virtually unchanged. It is expected that this differential would become greater as the depth of fill increased and/or as the settlement plate location is lowered.

Gas Production: In Cell A, the chief component of the gas has been carbon dioxide at top and bottom levels. This gas component decreased rapidly at the start, and then tapered off to a fairly steady 60% over the last year. Methane increased rapidly at the start, and then less rapidly to a fairly steady 40% over the last year. Since Cell A was operated under anaerobic conditions with liberal application of water, these quantities are not considered unusual. Oxygen, hydrogen and nitrogen were all present in varying minor amounts.

Cell B was constructed also to operate under anaerobic conditions, and it was separated from Cell A by a 5-ft. thick wall of undisturbed earth. However, with the blower in operation, a slight billowing of the tarpaulin covering the center access well could be seen, and later on the odor of decomposing organic material was noticeable when one was standing on Cell B. It was thus evident that some of the air being sent into Cell C was moving through the earthen barrier into Cell B. Analyses showed that carbon dioxide, methane and nitrogen were the major components. Because of the passage of air into Cell B, oxygen was always present and in significant quantities.

The gas composition data for Cell C could not be generalized. In this cell, intermittent aeration and accompanying recirculation of the gas produced within the cell was practiced. Also, fresh make-up was added at all times, usually by positioning the flap valve in the intake line at 45°. With the blower in operation for extended periods, the chief gas components by volume at the upper level were carbon dioxide (10 to 20%) and nitrogen (70 to 80%), and at the lower level were carbon dioxide (8 to 15%), nitrogen (70 to 75%) and oxygen (5 to 15%). These ranges were due to the facts that the blower was operated on varying on-off cycles and the air was admitted through the piping system underlying the cell.

The blower was off at times either by choice when oxidation would proceed too rapidly and fire would break out, or by reason of breakdown of equipment. The heavy rains of November, 1965, caused motor failure necessitating removal and repair, and it was found that by December the methane was rising rapidly at the lower level and to a lesser extent at the upper level, accompanied by a decrease in nitrogen. Oxygen almost disappeared at the upper level, but held up at the lower level to a surprising degree.

1966

Existing Cells A, B and C

External Climatic Factors: The total rainfall on the test site for the full period of study (to December 31, 1966) has been 43.3 in. The total rainfall for 1966 was 14.6 in.

Application of Water: The required annual amount of water to be applied to Cell A to simulate Seattle rainfall is 42.52. The actual amount of water applied during the year was 28.70 in. irrigation water plus 14.59 in. rainfall for a total of 43.29 in.

Since no leach has been withdrawn from even the top collection can after application of more than 10 ft. of water over 28 months, it appears to be a reasonable assumption that percolating water is bypassing the collection cans. A coring program was initiated on August 22, at which time all cells were cored at opposite corners and samples were taken at 2 ft. depth increments. The samples were sealed immediately and transported to the laboratory where their moisture contents were determined.

The moisture content at one cell location varied from 45 to 60% on a wet weight basis or 82 to 147% on a dry weight basis; and at a second location varied from 32 to 64% on a wet weight basis or 47 to 180% on a dry weight basis. Averaging all figures, the respective moisture contents were 53 and 117%. The computed moisture content of the cell at the time of construction was 97% on a dry weight basis indicating that the applied water has effectively increased the moisture content. If only the bottom half of the cell is considered, from which moisture is not readily drawn through capillarity and subsequent evaporation, the average figure increases to 131% on a dry weight basis, indicating effective downward percolation of the applied water.

The actual amount of water applied during the year to Cell B was 41.57 in. of irrigation water applied on demand by the tensiometer equipment plus 14.59 in. rainfall for a total of 56.16 in. This was very adequate to maintain an excellent turf cover on top of the cell.

At the time of construction, this Cell B had had 9 half drums with open end up installed within it in a descending spiral pattern between top and bottom for tracking vertical penetration of the percolating irrigation water. Leach was withdrawn from the top collection can only, despite application of some 14 ft. of water. Suspecting that the collection cans were being bypassed by the percolating water, this cell was also cored at opposite corners on August 22. The moisture content at one cell location varied from 22 to 44% on a wet weight basis or 28 to 79% on a dry weight basis; and at the second location varied from 26 to 59% on a wet weight basis or 34 to 142% on a dry weight basis.

Averaging all figures, the respective moisture contents were 43 and 80%. The computed moisture content of the cell at the time of construction was 73% on a dry weight basis, indicating that the applied water has had a slight effect on the cell. If only the bottom half of the cell is considered, the average figure decreased to 66% on a dry weight basis, and a behavior just the reverse of Cell A was observed. There were several reasons for this. First, the addition of water to Cell B was controlled by two pairs of tensiometers, each pair consisting of a unit installed 3 in. below the surface and another unit installed 6 in. below the surface. When an unsatisfactory soil-moisture relationship was reached at any of the four tensiometers, the spray system was activated and irrigation took place until the proper soil-moisture condition was obtained at all tensiometers.

Ideally, only enough water was to be applied at one time to take care of the turf demand, with no excess left to percolate down through the cell. Second, the top cover for Cell B was carefully made up by combining "Loamite" with native soil to produce a material which would hold moisture rather than permit its passage. On the contrary, Cell A was covered with an imported sandy silt which would readily permit passage of surface water through it. Third, air introduced into Cell C is known to penetrate into Cell B and would have a drying out effect at least in the lower portion of the cell. Fourth, the collection pans do not appear to entrap moisture effectively. These reasons partially explain and justify the non-entrapment of leach.

Cell C had been subject to flooding on several occasions for various reasons during its first 18 months of existence, principally channeling of surface waters into crevices and cave-ins, and moisture determinations made on core samples could not be considered meaningful. Nevertheless, the cell was cored along with Cells A and B and moisture data obtained. The data did suffice to indicate that at the lower depths the cell was drying out and that the moisture content should be increased before a condition could be reached which would slow down or stop bacterial activity. Water was therefore admitted to Cell C through the spray piping built into the cell at the time of construction. Between early September and mid-October, 12,800 gal. were added at regular intervals in small increments.

Settlement: The settlement of all cells was periodically measured by survey. During the year Cell A settled an additional 0.24 ft., Cell B 0.32 ft. and Cell C 0.64 ft. Cell A and B have each settled a total of 0.75 ft. and Cell C has settled a total of 2.50 ft. or 3.33 times as much. The rate of settlement of the surfaces of all cells has been fairly uniform with few exceptions.

The differential settlement between the top half and bottom half of each cell increased during the year. In Cell A the differential is 0.15 ft., in Cell B 0.25 ft., and in Cell C 0.51 ft. This is simply indicative of an increase in the "equivalent" density of the bottom fill material. Additional cave-ins occurred during the year in Cell C, and numerous fissures developed on the surface of all three cells, but especially C. The cave-ins were backfilled as soon as possible and the fissures were packed with sand.

Gas Production: Cell A continued over the entire year to produce a gas high in carbon dioxide and methane at top and bottom levels. Oxygen and nitrogen were present in varying minor amounts. A trace of hydrogen appeared in only 9 samples. There has been no marked change in the gas composition from what it was over the last half of 1965.

Cell B also continued to produce a gas high in carbon dioxide and methane at top and bottom levels. And again, because of air from Cell C moving into Cell B, oxygen was always present in quantities much higher than found in Cell A. The presence of oxygen is not normally compatible with the presence of methane, and yet the technique as well as the equipment used was thoroughly checked often enough for them not to be suspect. It is to be noted that the gas composition changed greatly when the blower serving Cell C was put into operation for the first time in the year early in April, and that 3 months elapsed before a steady state analysis was reached. At the close of the year, the analysis was much the same as at the close of 1965.

As stated in the preceding paragraph, the blower was put back into service early in April, and the immediate effect on the gas composition was evident. The nitrogen content increased greatly, accompanied by a decrease in carbon dioxide and methane, all as expected. While oxygen also increased as anticipated, there remained considerably more methane than expected.

It is emphasized that for the last 9 months of the year the blower was in continuous operation: on 0.5 hour and off 3.5 hours to December 1 and then on 0.5 hour and off 1.0 hour. The data obtained during that time have been very consistent, more so than during any other operating period when blower operation was either changed or shut down. The effect of increasing the blower "on" time on December 1 is reflected in the last sample taken on December 28 when, at the upper level, the carbon dioxide and methane decreased and the oxygen and nitrogen increased. The new cycle had little effect on the cell bottom environment.

Cell Temperatures: During the year, Cell A at mid-depth experienced a range of but 11°F., from 64°F. in the winter to 75°F. in the summer, a high insufficient to expect any great amount of bacterial activity. The frequent application of water apparently serves to cool the landfill mass. The same may be said of Cell B, wherein a range of but 15°F. was experienced, from 66°F. in the winter to 81°F. in the summer. In Cell C, the temperature of the upper level dropped during the first 3 months, while the blower was shut down for repairs, from 111°F. to 91°F. Then, with restarting of the blower, the temperature rose gradually to a high of 114°F.

Thermistors in Cell C at mid-depth and bottom levels were lost some time ago. To obtain bottom temperatures, a thermometer immersed in a water bath was suspended in the access well. As shown, the thermometer readings are consistently higher than the thermistor readings at the upper level. This condition existed since the air was introduced at the bottom of the cell and greatest oxidation would occur at that level. When Cell C was cored, those core samples which appeared unusually warm were checked with a thermometer immediately upon their being brought to the surface. These spot temperatures were seen to be considerably higher on occasion than the temperatures routinely taken by thermistors.

New Cell D

Construction: The research program had, as one of its announced purposes the construction of a large volume, gas-tight cell to be used for quantitative study of gas production.

Since previous efforts to study gas production by encapsulating a large mass of refuse within an impervious polyethylene membrane failed, it was decided to make a new approach and seal the refuse within a steel enclosure. For this purpose, there was purchased a 10,000 gal. underground storage tank, 95 ft. i.d. by 28 ft. high, manufactured from ¼-in. A-36 steel. To minimize corrosion the tank was give a resinous inside coating and was covered with an asphalt paint on the outside. The tank is shown on Figure 9.4.

The tank was installed at a site adjacent to existing Cell C and, in fact, on the site of former Cell D which failed in its purpose. A standard clamshell-type bucket was used to take out the old refuse, sand, and plastic membrane until there had been formed an open pit 28.5 ft. deep measuring about 12 ft. x 14 ft. at the bottom and 36 ft. x 36 ft. at the top. A 3-ft. layer of refuse was placed at the bottom and this in turn was covered by ¼-in. thick plywood, both to provide a cushion for the tank and protection for the tank bottom.

A crane was used to lower the tank into the hole and hold it in a vertical position while an insulating layer of refuse was placed around it. The vertical free-standing tank in its final position extended 3 ft. above ground level. Dirt was packed around the above-ground projection to form a sloping berm. The tank was then ready for filling with refuse.

A 6 in. layer of sand was placed in the bottom of the tank. Some 31,090 lbs. of refuse as delivered to the tank in weighed packers were then placed in the tank. The refuse was typically domestic, having been collected from homes in

FIGURE 9.4: ASSEMBLY DIAGRAM CELL D

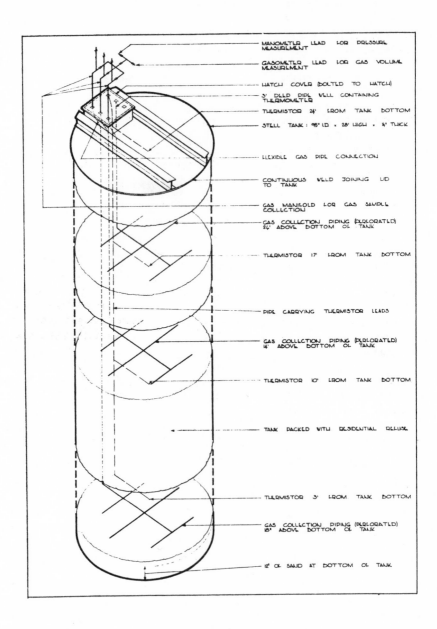

Source: PB 196,148, 1970

Pomona. From spot sampling of the refuse, the breakdown by volume was 42.7% paper, 38% grass and garden clippings, 3% plastic, 5% glass, 7% metal and 5% dirt. During placement of the refuse, a system of perforated piping was installed to permit withdrawal of gas at top, bottom and mid-depth (or to add water), and thermistors were installed at similar locations. Also during placement of the refuse, sufficient water was added to bring the moisture content to 69.9% on a dry weight basis. Since compaction was limited within the confines of so small an area, the resulting in-place density was a low 634 lbs./yd.^{3}.

The top of the tank was sealed by a continuous, external weld. After the cover was welded in place, field personnel entered the tank through a manhole to paint the inside of the weld with a protective sealant. Additional refuse and a top layer of dirt were then laboriously added through the cover manhole to fill the tank. Flexible, neoprene hoses connected the pipes carrying the thermistor leads and the gas pipes to the hatch nipples, and the hatch was then bolted down. A plastic gasket in combination with a liquid sealant was used to make the hatch gas tight.

All joints and welds were brushed with a fluorsene soap solution and the tank was tested by placing it under a pressure of 1 psi by pumping compressed air into it. After holding the pressure for 30 minutes, the pressure was released and the tank was considered sealed under zero pressure, confirmed by a water manometer. The gas manifold was immediately connected to a wet test cell, later replaced by a gasometer, for measurement of all gas produced by the decomposing refuse.

Performance: For approximately the first month, the exterior gas manifold was directly connected to a wet test cell. All valves were open, permitting measurement of all gas produced within the cell. The discharge line from the wet test cell was submerged to maintain a positive pressure on the entire system. Within 3 days, 39.3 ft.^{3} of gas had been produced and measured, and this volume proved to be 98% of that which would be produced. During these 3 days, the internal pressure (in. water) of the cell dropped from the initial reading of 12.0 to 6.5, and then to zero 6 days later. At that time, the wet test cell was permitted to discharge into the atmosphere.

Because gas production had fallen off to almost immeasurable quantities, the wet test cell was replaced after 33 days with a laboratory-built gasometer which would permit storage of gas and more accurate volume determinations. However, by the end of the second month, all gas production ceased.

The tabulated data show a decline in temperature at all levels; from 88° to 78°F. at the bottom, from 100° to 83°F. at the bottom quarter, from 93° to 87°F. at mid-depth, and from 100° to 78°F. at the top quarter. Using the gas collection piping at the top of the cell as a spray system, 450 gal. of water were added on the 62nd day to raise the moisture content of the refuse and improve the environment necessary for bacterial activity. The decision to add water was prompted, of course, by the stoppage of gas production. The addition of water not only did not result in a step-up of gas production, but also served to decrease cell temperatures at a still faster rate and put the entire cell under a vacuum. Negative pressures were first observed in the 98th day and existed until the 145th day.

Temperatures remained low through the end of the period covered by this progress report and it is not expected that significant gas quantities will be produced until temperatures come back up to at least 90°F. The high percentage of cellulose packed into the cell will also markedly limit the rate of gas production.

1967

Cells A, B, and C

External Climatic Factors: The total rainfall at the test site for the full 3.5 yr. period of study (to December 31, 1967) has been 62.1 in. The total rainfall for 1966 was 18.8 in.

Application of Water: The required annual amount of water to be applied to simulate the Seattle rainfall was 42.52 in. The actual amount of water applied to Cell A during the year was 21.37 in. irrigation water plus 18.77 in. rainfall for a total of 40.14 in.

There was a water supply reservoir located on top of a high hill adjacent to the research site. On September 3, this reservoir accidentally overflowed, and the water cascaded down the hill and onto the surfaces of Cells A and B. Based on flood markings, the minimum amount of water estimated to have entered Cell A was 3,750 gal. The minimum amount of water estimated to have entered Cell B was 2,450 gal.

The coring program initiated on August 22, 1966, for the purpose of determining the moisture content of the cells, was continued. The cells were cored in February and again in November, and samples were taken at 2-ft. depth increments. The top cover and the subgrade were also sampled. The samples were sealed immediately and transported to the laboratory where their moisture content was determined.

The moisture content of the cell as a whole, on a wet weight basis, remained virtually unchanged during the interval between corings despite the application of 29.8 in. water. On a dry weight basis, the moisture content increased 10%. By the end of the year, the moisture content of the earth cover was considerably higher than that of the top layer of refuse, indicating the ready capillary rise of water from the top layer of refuse for subsequent evaporation from the bare cell surface. The moisture content of the subgrade, 2 ft. below the landfill, was considerably less than that of the bottom layer of refuse, when sampled in November, indicating slow movement of water into the ground.

The actual amount of water applied during the year to Cell B was 49.58 in. of irrigation water applied on demand by the tensiometer equipment (and including the aforementioned reservoir drainage) plus 18.77 in. rainfall for a total of 68.35 in. This was adequate to maintain an excellent turf cover on top of the cell.

Cell B received 61.2 in. water between corings. The picture presented by analysis of the core samples is as follows. The moisture content of the cell as a whole on a wet or dry weight basis remained virtually unchanged, and the moisture content of the subgrade when sampled in November was considerably less than that of the bottom layer of refuse, again indicating slow movement of water into the ground. However, the moisture content of the earth cover was little different from that of the top layer of refuse.

Considering that Cell B received more than twice the amount of water applied to Cell A (on call from the tensiometer control equipment), and considering that the top cover of Cell B was especially prepared to resist passage of applied water, the relationship is reasonable. The average moisture contents in November for the designated cell portions (as noted above in Cell A) again indicate a downward transfer of water as in Cell A, and again show that the depth with the highest moisture content was between 8 and 14 ft. below the surface in February.

Cell C received no water during the year other than normal rainfall of 18.8 in. The cell has continued to exhibit a loss of moisture. The moisture content of the cell as a whole decreased from 46.5 to 39.1% on a dry weight basis. In contrast to Cells A and B, the driest material is found in the bottom portion (16 to 18 ft.) in both February and November, a condition to be expected since the forced air is introduced into the fill from the air ducts located beneath the fill. For the same reason, there is little difference in the moisture contents of the bottom portion of the cell and the subgrade.

Settlement: The settlement of all cells was periodically measured by survey. During the year, Cell A settled an additional 0.57 ft., Cell B 0.51 ft. and Cell C 1.14 ft. As shown, Cells A and B have each settled a total of approximately 1.30 ft. and Cell C has settled a total of 3.75 ft. or nearly three times as much. The rate of settlement of all cells has been fairly uniform with the few exceptions probably caused by expansion of the adobe cover soil.

The bench marks used to measure settlement are concrete monuments originally set flush with the cell surface. There are four at each cell, located about 12 ft. from the access well on N-S and E-W diameters. The reported settlement refers to the average movement of these benchmarks. There are portions of the cells that have settled to a greater and lesser extent. In Cell C, for instance, the surface settlement around the access well is more than 5 ft.

The differential settlement between the top half and bottom half of Cells A and B increased during the year. In Cell A the differential is now 0.35 ft., and in Cell B it is 0.46 ft. The differential in Cell C remained 0.51 ft. This is simply indicative of an increase in the "equivalent" density of the bottom fill material. While there were no serious cave-ins during the year, surface fissures continued to develop and these were filled in as soon as possible.

Gas Production: Cell A continued over the entire year to produce a gas high in carbon dioxide and methane at top and bottom levels. Oxygen and nitrogen were present in varying minor amounts. There was no hydrogen. There has been no marked change in the gas composition from what it was during 1966.

Cell B also continued to produce a gas high in carbon dioxide and methane at top and bottom levels. And again, because of air from Cell C moving over 25 ft. through an adobe soil wall into Cell B, oxygen was generally present in quantities up to 4%, whereas the Cell A value was generally less than 1%. The continuing presence of oxygen is not normally compatible with the presence of methane, and yet the technique as well as the equipment used were thoroughly checked and appeared to be satisfactory.

The gas analyses for Cell C correlated blower operation. The blower steadily supplied air at desired on-off scedules throughout the full year. The cycle of on 0.5 hour and off 1.0 hour started on December 1, 1966, was continued to September 26, 1967. On that date the cycle was changed to on 1.0 hour and off 0.5 hour. The change was made simply to determine what the effect of more air would be in the gas composition and temperatures.

The data indicate there was little immediate or long-time change in the analysis of the gas taken from the lower portion of the cell. Oxygen values remained in the range of 17 to 20%, carbon dioxide in the range of 1 to 6%, and nitrogen in the range of 73 to 77%. While it was expected that methane would disappear, small amounts persisted. Difficulties were encountered in obtaining valid gas samples from the upper portion of the cell during this interval of 3 months. Methane, for instance, was found in quantities that appeared unreasonably high.

Cell Temperatures: During the year, Cell A at mid-depth experienced a range of 24°F. from 58°F. in the winter to 82°F. in the summer. In Cell B, the temperature range was 22°F. from 60°F. in the winter to 82°F. in the summer. Thermistors in Cell C at mid-depth and bottom levels failed in 1966. To obtain internal temperatures, thermometers immersed in water baths were suspended in 2-in. diameter pipes which, in turn, were set into the shafts established by the coring operation.

The mid-depth temperatures are seen to be consistently higher than bottom temperatures due to the fact that the air introduced into the bottom of the cell has a cooling effect. By the end of November, after 2 months of increased blower operation, the temperature had risen as high as 162°F. When Cell C was cored in November, the core temperatures at depths of 8 to 12 ft. on the North side confirmed this value. However, core temperatures on the South side of the cell were much lower through the middle portion ranging from 106° to 130°F.

Cell D

Performance: Gas production within the cell totalled less than 1 ft.^{3} between mid-July and the end of August, 1966. There was no gas produced from that date until February 22, 1967. During this interval, the tank was observed to be under a partial vacuum, indicating there was no gas leakage taking place. Beginning on that date and to year's end, 1,919 ft.^{3} were measured, equivalent to 26.3 ft.^{3}/yd.^{3} of refuse.

During this period of gas production, temperatures within the cell rose slowly and reached optimum values for bacterial activity throughout the tank by June 12. During the last 6 months, the temperatures (by thermistors) ranged from 92$^°$ to 120$^°$F. At the end of August, a thermometer was placed in a water bath and lowered into a 2-in. diagram sealed pipe originally affixed within the top cover plate of the cell. This thermometer thus reads the temperature existing at the top level of the refuse in the tank, about 3 ft. below ground level.

Preliminary Conclusions

With this investigation now two-thirds through its scheduled time, some preliminary conclusions can be drawn from the data presented.

(1) The Seattle rainfall pattern (about 40 in./yr.) has brought about a slow percolation of water through the test cell and into the subgrade.

(2) The golf course irrigation pattern (about 62 in./yr.) has brought about a slow percolation of water through the test cell and into the subgrade.

(3) The principal gases present in the anaerobic cells have been carbon dioxide and methane and in the aerobic cell, carbon dioxide, oxygen, and nitrogen.

(4) Gas production within the 10,000 gal. sealed tank during the last, most active 10 months totalled 1,880 ft.^{3}, equivalent to 25.8 ft.^{3}/yd.^{3} of refuse.

(5) The surface settlement of the aerated cell, over the 3.5 yr. test period, has been nearly 3 times that of the anaerobic cells.

(6) The growth of Bermuda grass has been successfully maintained for 3.5 yr. on an anaerobic landfill with an earth cover of 2 ft.

1968-COMPLETION

The purposes of the field investigation, utilizing landfill cells having a depth of approximately 20 ft. and an earth cover of 2 ft., were to (1) study the percolation through the landfill as a result of application of sufficient water to maintain a golf course type turf, (2) study the percolation through the landfill as a result of application of sufficient water to simulate the rainfall pattern of a temperate climate (Seattle), (3) study the effects of aerating a landfill, (4) measure settlement of both aerobic and anaerobic landfills, (5) study the quality of gas produced in the landfills receiving the various treatments, and (6) determine the volume of gas produced by a known quantity of refuse decomposing under anaerobic conditions.

Data were developed as a result of the construction of model landfills and their treatment under selected environmental conditions. Practical application of the reported data requires detailed knowledge of individual landfill conditions, existing or proposed, best known to the responsible authorities.

(1)   Initial landfill compaction ratios from 2.1 to 2.2, and an in-place density of 1,000 lbs./yd.^{3} were achieved for the Test Cells A, B and C. The in-place density for Cell D was 634 lbs./yd.^{3}.

(2)   Cell A, receiving the Seattle rainfall equivalent of 184 in. plus an extra 30 in. (for a total of 214 in. of water) exhibited some percolation into the subgrade as evidenced by a 7% increase in the percent moisture of the subgrade over that of undisturbed soil at similar depth. At the close of the project, the differential was 12.5%

(3)   Cell B, receiving 392 in. of applied irrigation water, exhibited greater percolation into the subgrade as evidenced by a 15% increase in the moisture content of the subgrade over that of undisturbed soil at similar depth. At the close of the project, the differential was 41%.

(4)   The growth of Bermuda grass was successfully maintained on an anaerobic landfill with a top earth cover of 2 ft. especially prepared to favor turf growth.

(5)   The greatest settlement of 4.25 ft. occurred in aerobic Cell C. The two anaerobic cells each settled 2.20 ft.

(6)   In anaerobic Cells A and B, after ageing 2 years, the major gas constituents by volume were carbon dioxide and methane in almost equal amounts (nearly 50%). Oxygen and nitrogen were present in small, varying amounts.

(7)   Cell C was aerobically operated and the gas composition was dependent upon the duration of the blower operation. The gas samples obtained during aeration were characteristically high in nitrogen and oxygen, and low in carbon dioxide and methane.

(8)   The maximum temperature reached in anaerobic Cell A was 108°F. after 79 days. Over the final 2 years of the over 4 year study the temperature ranged between 53°F. and 88°F.

(9)   The maximum temperature reached in Cell B was 120°F. after 31 days. Over the final 2 years of the over 4 year study the temperature ranged between 60° and 90°F. Although intended

to be an anaerobic cell, its performance was influenced by the passage of air from aerobic Cell C notwithstanding a 5-ft. wide, continuous adobe-shale barrier.

(10) The maximum temperature reached in Cell C was 193°F. after 174 days. Over the final 2 years of the over 4 year study the temperature ranged between 90°F. and 164°F. Bottom temperatures reached peaks high enough to destroy thermistors. Smoke emanations with fire were noted on a few occasions. The cell temperature was affected by the aeration cycle.

(11) A cell similar in construction to Cell A or B, but smaller, intended for quantitative studies of gas production, was unsuccessful although constructed with extreme care by professional plastic fabricators. The polyethylene envelope was not able to store gas.

(12) The maximum temperature reached in Cell D was 117°F. after 368 days. Over the final 2 years, the temperature ranged between 67°F. and 120°F.

(13) 73 yd.^{3} of refuse packed into an underground sealed and instrumented steel tank produced 2,027 ft.^{3} of gas, or 27.7 ft.^{3}/yd.^{3} of refuse, over 907 days. Virtually all the gas was produced between the 230th and 600th day.

(14) Final examination of the cell materials during the coring operation showed the aerated Cell C refuse to be well decomposed except for plastics and other inerts. In contrast, the anaerobic Cells A and B refuse was easily identifiable.

(15) Based on the original cell depth of 20 ft., the volume reduction achieved through aeration amounted to 21.5%. The volume reduction achieved in the anaerobic cells was 11.5%.

(16) Epoxy-coated steels supplied by factory specialists provided protection against severe corrosion. Stainless steel thermistors, copper conduits, Teflon-coated leads, galvanized pipe, and asphalt-coated steel were found to be inadequate for this type of investigation. All seriously deteriorated or failed because of high temperatures, corrosion, or strain exerted by differential settlement.

Summary Report

Percolation: Cells A and B were constructed for the purpose of studying percolation resulting from (1) the application of water in accordance with the Seattle rainfall pattern of 1961 and (2) the application of water necessary to support a golf-course like turf. In both cases, efforts to measure moisture content of the landfill material by moisture probes and percolation by entrapment of water in collection lysimeters or cans were unsuccessful. A program of cell coring, with cores subjected to laboratory analysis for their moisture content, was initiated in August, 1966.

Water was applied manually to Cell A, the intent being to duplicate the established Seattle monthly increments. The schedule was immediately upset in 1964 when unintentional flooding took place, and again in Semptember 1967 when an adjacent reservoir overflowed. Nevertheless, the Seattle rainfall total was closely approximated in 1966, 1967 and 1968. The amount applied in 1965 was reduced to compensate for the 1965 flooding.

The water applied to the turf on top of Cell B was automatically controlled by tensiometers, beginning in October 1964. Irrigation proceeded in normal manner except for brief periods when the tensiometers needed repair. In September 1967 the reservoir overflow placed an unwanted volume of water on the cell, and from July through October 1968 faulty operation of the tensiometers placed considerable unnecessary water on the cell.

The amount of water applied to Cell B during 1968 was from 1.75 to 2.75 times the amount applied in previous years. This is not considered particularly damaging to the investigation since any landfill or golf course turf could be subjected to unexpected flooding.

The total amounts of water applied to Cells A and B were approximately 214 in. and 392 in., respectively. As stated above, the effect of this water on the moisture content of the cells and the possible movement of water down through the cells and into the subgrade was checked by coring in the cells in August, 1966, February and November 1967, and every 3 months thereafter in 1968. Core samples taken at 2-ft. depth increments were placed in sealed containers immediately and transported to the laboratory where their moisture contents were determined. Moisture contents on a dry weight basis have been averaged for bands consisting of the top 6 ft., the middle 8 ft., and the bottom 6 ft.

The top band of Cell A always had the lowest moisture content of the 3 bands. With two exceptions, the earth cover exhibited still lower moisture content. A combination of the upward rise of the water through the cover by capillarity with subsequent evaporation, and of downward movement of the water through the cell, would account for this. At least during the final year of the project, the moisture content of the middle band was considerably greater than the bottom band, indicating great capacity of the fill material to retain water. Of greatest interest and importance is the fact that the moisture content of the subgrade varied only -4% +7% from an average of 31% over the entire time, and was only 7% more than the native soil samples taken from equivalent depth. The indication is that little water has percolated into the tight, adobe-shale subgrade.

The picture presented by the data of Cell B is not quite as clear. In this case, there were 2 cores in which the moisture content of the top band was not less than any other band. The top earth cover had the least moisture content in all cases. There was no consistency in the relationship of the moisture content of the middle band to the bottom band. It is significant that the moisture content of the subgrade averaged 39%, or about the same as Cell A, until the

September-December period of 1968 when it averaged 77%. This increase correlates with the excessive amounts of water applied to the surface in July, August, September and indicates that under such an unusual condition there was appreciable percolation into the subgrade.

Cell C of course was kept in a drier condition by reason of aeration. Attention is called to the fact that to prevent movement of air through the cover into the atmosphere, an impervious membrane was stretched over the cell 1 ft. below the surface. Because of the varied off-on cycle of the blower, as well as extended on and off periods, the data do not fall into any pattern permitting rational explanation. As expected, the bottom band which received the full benefit of the air admitted was always much drier than the middle band and, over the final year, was the driest band.

Over the last 6 months, the average moisture content of the bottom band was only 34%. The average moisture content of the subgrade was 30%. Sampling of the subgrade was discontinued after June, 1968 to avoid further damage to the air gridwork. Since Cell C received only rainfall totalling 72 in., most of which should have been stopped by the membrane, plus about 8 in. applied through the subsurface spray piping between September and October 1966 to purposely increase the moisture content, it may be concluded that no percolation into the subgrade took place.

Gas Quality: Samples of the gaseous environment within Cells A, B and C were taken on a regular basis over the entire period of the investigation until August 1968. By then, the original field installation had deteriorated to the point where gas samples were suspect. For instance, many of the gas samples from the anaerobic Cell A were analyzing as air. Replacement of some of the copper leads in the access well, and overhauling of the chromatograph equipment including column replacement, did not correct the situation. Earlier, brief gaps in the data were generally caused by operating difficulties with the analytical equipment.

The gas components determined were carbon dioxide, methane, nitrogen, oxygen, and hydrogen. The peak concentrations of nitrogen and carbon dioxide occurred early in the study, followed by a buildup in the concentration of methane. This change in the concentration of gas constituents with time was clearly evident.

In Cell A, carbon dioxide concentrations gradually decreased over the first 2 years from approximately 85 to 55% and then held at approximately 50% over the final 2 years. Conversely, methane built up from approximately 5% at the start to approximately 45% after 2 years, with little change occurring after that time. Nitrogen was never a major component in the gas samples taken from Cell A.

Cell B was similar to Cell A as far as construction was concerned. It did receive nearly twice as much water as Cell A. More important, there was abundant evidence that some of the air applied to Cell C was able to move through the undisturbed, 5-ft. thick adobe-shale barrier separating the 2 cells and into Cell B. This was true especially during the first 2 years or so when the aeration equipment was able to function normally on a planned program. The carbon dioxide decreased over the first 6 months from approximately 85 to 50% at the upper level, and from approximately 70 to 40% at the lower level.

Over the last 2 years the concentrations at both levels were comparable at 50%. Methane built up at each level over the first 2 years from approximately 1 to 40%, and then held fairly constant over the balance of the time at approximately 45%. Nitrogen was a major component only during the first 1.5 years, reaching concentrations of 55%.

The data of Cell C cannot be grouped in the above described fashion, for the on-off blower periods and the blower cycle used governed the gas composition more than the elapsed time. In general, when the blower was operating, the analysis would come up to expectations: oxygen as high as 20%, nitrogen as high as 80%, carbon dioxide as low as 1%, and methane as low as 0.5%.

Many combinations of on-time and off-time were used, and it was ultimately found that an on-time of 1.0 hour and an off-time of 0.25 hour resulted in the maintenance of a satisfactory cell environment. Early in the investigation, when the fill material was fresh, a combination of even shorter on-time and longer off-time would result in too rapid oxidation accompanied by high temperatures, smoke, occasional fire and odor problems.

Settlement: The bench marks used to measure settlement were concrete monuments originally set flush with the cell surface. There were 4 at each cell, located about 12 ft. from the access well on N-S and E-W diameters. The reported settlement refers to the average movement of these benchmarks. There were portions of the cells that settled to a greater extent. In Cell C, for instance, the surface settlement around the access well was over 6 ft. The surveys were conducted weekly at the start for about the first 3 months, biweekly for the next 3 months, and then at approximately monthly intervals.

Cells A and B each settled a total of 2.20 ft. and Cell C settled a total of 4.25 ft. The fact that the aerobic Cell C settled more than anaerobic Cells A and B is due to the greater reduction in volume of refuse through oxidation of the organic matter present. There was little identifiable matter in the December corings of Cell C other than plastic, rubber, some metal, scorched paper, and highly decomposed rags.

Gas Production: The gas production of Cell D was the only purpose for which it was constructed. This cell consisted of a 10,000 gal. underground steel storage tank, 95 in. i.d. x 28 ft. high x ¼ in. thick, which was packed with refuse, instrumented, and carefully sealed. The amount of gas produced was 2,027 ft.^{3} over a 907-day period. This is equivalent to 27.7 ft.^{3}/yd.^{3} of refuse.

The initial release of gas occurred within the first 3 days following packing and sealing of the tank. Only 1 ft.^{3} was produced in the following 50 days, and then none until the 230th day. This long period of non-production could have been due to acidification or low temperatures unfavorable to bacterial action. By the time gas production ceased, the temperatures within the tank were less than 90°F. and ultimately dropped to the low seventies. The pickup in gas production accompanied a rise in temperature.

Gas production might also have been delayed until the tank was fully stabilized as an anaerobic unit. After packing, the tank was tested for leakage by admitting compressed air, and the unit was initially aerobic. A manometer was fitted into a gas line and was used as a constant check to make certain there were no leaks in the tank or piping.

Temperatures: All cells reached maximum temperatures very early in the study. Cell A reached 108°F. after 79 days, Cell B 120°F. after 31 days, Cell C 193°F. after 174 days, and Cell D 117°F. after 368 days. Over the final 2 years, temperatures in Cell A ranged between 53° and 88°F., in Cell B between 60° and 90°F., in Cell C between 90° and 164°F., and in Cell D between 67° and 120°F. Cell D, during the final year, never rose above 92°F.

Progress Report — 1968

External Climatic Factors: Monthly average air temperatures and daily rainfalls were obtained from the Pomona Weather Station records. The total rainfall at the test site was 9.4 in.

Application of Water: The required annual amount of water to simulate the selected Seattle rainfall of 1961 is 42.52 in. The actual amount of water applied during the year was 33.94 in. irrigation water plus 9.39 in. rainfall for a total of 43.33 in.

The actual amount of water applied during the year was 145.28 in. of irrigation water plus 9.39 in. rainfall for a total of 154.67 in. Faulty operation of the tensiometer equipment resulted in the application of far more water than necessary during July, August, and September for support of the Bermuda grass. The coring program initiated on August 22, 1966 for the purpose of determining the moisture content of the cells was continued. The cells were cored every 3 months beginning in March, 1968 and samples were taken at 2-ft. depth increments. The top cover and subgrade were also sampled when feasible.

The moisture content of the core profile averaged 50% on a wet weight basis during the year, an increase of 5% over the previous year. The moisture content of the subgrade was again less than that of the bottom layer of the refuse in all but a single case, indicating very slow movement of water into the ground or greater water capillarity of the refuse than the ground. At the bottom of the table are shown the average moisture contents for the top portion of the cell (2 to 6 ft.), the middle portion (8 to 14 ft.), and the bottom portion (16 to 20 ft.). The band with the highest moisture content was between 8 and 14 ft. below the surface.

The moisture content of the core profile averaged 50% on a wet weight basis, the same as Cell A despite the application of nearly 3.5 times as much water. The moisture content of the subgrade was generally 10 to 25% less than that of the bottom layer of refuse, again indicating slow movement of water into the ground. However, the moisture content of the earth cover was little different from that of the top layer of refuse, especially after application of the excessive amounts of water during the summer months. Considering the greater application of water to Cell B, and that the top cover of the cell was prepared for the growing of turf, the relationship is reasonable.

The average moisture contents of the designated cell bands again indicate a downward transfer of water as in Cell A, and, with the exception of the June cores, again show that the highest moisture content was in the 8 to 14 ft. band. Direct observation of core samples taken at the bottom at the Fall coring showed a condition of saturation. Cell C received no water during the year other than the normal rainfall of 9.39 in. The moisture content of the core profile averaged 40% on a wet weight basis. In contrast to Cells A and B, the driest material was always found in the bottom band, a condition to be expected since the forced air was introduced into the landfill from air ducts located beneath the fill. Sampling of the subgrade was discontinued because of the danger of striking the air ducts.

The cores of Cell C demonstrated an advanced stage of decomposition over Cells A and B. Paper and paper products were frequently scorched, grass with the original green color was rarely seen, and there was much unidentifiable material.

Settlement: The settlement of all cells was periodically measured by survey. During the year, Cell A settled an additional 0.89 ft., Cell B 0.93 ft., and Cell C 0.51 ft. This was the first year in which settlement of the aerated Cell C lagged behind Cells A and B. Cells A and B settled nearly twice as much as Cell C, thereby reducing the settlement of Cell C from what had been 3 times as much as Cells A and B to twice as much. Cells A and B each settled a total of approximately 2.20 ft., and Cell C settled a total of approximately 4.25 ft.

The differential settlement between the top half and the bottom half of all cells increased during the year. In Cell A the differential was 0.70 ft., in Cell B 0.86 ft., and in Cell C 0.64 ft. This is simply indicative of an increase in the "equivalent" density of the bottom fill material.

Gas Quality: Cell A continued to produce a gas high in carbon dioxide and methane at top and bottom levels. Oxygen and nitrogen were present in varying minor amounts. There was no hydrogen. Cell B also continued to produce a gas high in carbon dioxide and methane at top and bottom levels. Oxygen and nitrogen were present in varying minor amounts. There was no hydrogen.

Heavy rains in March caused a cave-in around the access well of Cell C and permitted surface water to move down along the casing and into the aeration channels thereby effectively blocking air passage. This difficulty was later compounded by the collapse of the main air line because of corrosion. In August, the main air line was relocated to discharge directly into the center access well, and any aeration was achieved by passage of air through existing openings or ports in the access well casing and into the cell.

Because of the mistaken belief that air passage was being blocked by flooded ducts, the collapse of the air line was not discovered for about 3 months and consequently the blower was not operated for this period. Values of carbon dioxide and methane were predictably high during the long off period of the blower. Conversely, oxygen and nitrogen values were high during the blower on periods.

Cell Temperatures: To obtain the internal temperatures of Cells A and B (following failure of thermistors), thermometers were suspended in ¾-in. diameter water-filled pipes which, in turn, were set into the shafts established by the coring operation. The system was the same as that installed for Cell C in 1967. All of the temperature readings are correlated with the date on which they were taken and the total elapsed time in days following completion of each cell.

In Cell A, the temperature range was $40°F.$, from $60°F.$ in the winter to $100°F.$ in the summer. In Cell B, the temperature range was $28°F.$, from $62°F.$ in the winter to $90°F.$ in the summer. The excessive amounts of water applied apparently had a cooling effect. In Cell C, the temperature range at a depth of 4 ft. was $43°F.$, from $76°$ to $119°F.$ At the 10-ft. depth, the range was $59°F.$, from $84°$ to $143°F.$ With the blower operating in the normal manner, temperatures at the 10-ft. depth were much higher than at the 4-ft. depth. With the blower off, the temperature differential was slight.

Gas Production: Gas production within the cell totalled less than 100 ft.^{3}, with less than ¼ of it being collected over the final 8 months. There was virtually no gas produced over the last 6 months. Frequent checking insured that there were no leaks in the system.

The last thermistor in the tank failed. A hole was drilled as close as possible to the tank wall. A ¾-in. diameter water-filled pipe was placed in this hole, and a thermometer was lowered into the pipe to a depth of 14 ft. Still available was a thermometer installed in an internal pipe at a depth of 4 ft. The temperature at the 14-ft. depth ranged from $76°$ to $92°F.$ The temperature at the 4-ft. depth (inside of the tank) ranged from $59°$ to $88°F.$

Site Planning for Landfills

The material in this chapter was taken from a 1973 report entitled "Site Planning and Future Use for Sanitary Landfill" prepared by the Illinois Institute for Environmental Quality.

The two commonly used methods of dealing with solid wastes are incineration and the sanitary landfill. Incineration is a relatively efficient operation, but requires a large capital investment with continued high operational expenditures.

FIGURE 10.1: DIAGRAM OF SANITARY LANDFILL OPERATION

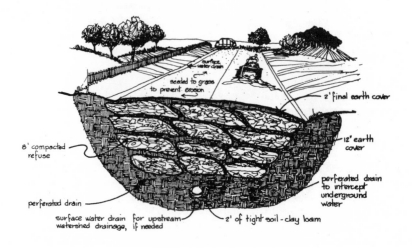

surface water drain

seeded to grass to prevent erosion

2' final earth cover

8' compacted refuse

12" earth cover

perferated drain to intercept underground water

perferated drain

surface water drain for upstream watershed drainage, if needed

2' of tight soil - clay loam

Until the more ambitious refuse treatment ideas, such as resource recovery, are made practical, the most workable method for communities of all sizes is the sanitary landfill. In any event there will always be an unwanted residual which must be taken to a landfill.

The modern sanitary landfill process entails the depositing of refuse on or in the land in a compacted and systematic manner and covering the refuse with a blanket of earth. The resulting landform is a resource that can become a ball park, a sledding mound, an amphitheater, farm land, or some other welcome addition or continuation of the landscape.

FIGURE 10.2: POTENTIAL USE OF A COMPLETED LANDFILL FOR RECREATION

However, more than technical considerations are necessary to make the sanitary landfill site a desirable part of the community. Other considerations are essential in gaining community acceptance. These include:

> Perceptual and visual problems which are concerned with the appearance of the site during and after utilization, including such annoyances as dust, blowing refuse, unsightly views, traffic from hauling trucks, and damages to neighboring streets and roads.

> Operational aspects which fail to consider the relationship of the site to the surrounding land uses.

> The need to commit the site to valuable land uses before, during, and after the use of the site as a sanitary landfill.

SITE PLANNING PROCESS

A planned sanitary landfill site is concerned with developing the best final use concurrent with minimizing the negative effects associated with the filling operation. A good plan takes advantage of site operation characteristics and directs the waste filling process into a dual role of filling land areas and of creating new landforms and use areas. In addition, it is concerned with the impact of the operation and the new land use on the adjacent lands. In order to accomplish these objectives, an analysis of the influencing factors should be completed as soon as possible to determine the best methods of reducing the normal conflicts associated with the operations, the most appropriate use, and the proper action for accomplishing this land use. This analysis is called site planning.

PLANNING AND DESIGN SEQUENCE

A planned fill and development process of a sanitary landfill site evolves from three basic planning phases: collecting and recording information; analysis of this data to determine pertinent and influential factors; and formulation of the operations plan, and the development plan, and associated detailed plans.

The first step in developing a plan for operation and future development is to gather information pertinent to the operation and future use. Information concerning the site and the environment, also social, political, and economic considerations, must be obtained. The plan proposals will reflect the degree of detail and accuracy of this survey information.

Following is a list of important planning data. Much of the required information can be obtained from various maps in local planning offices, from United States Geological Survey maps, and from soil survey maps. However, data such as groundwater and operational characteristics are not normally available, but must be obtained to produce a functional plan. Site and area inspections to collect data, of course, would be mandatory.

Site Survey Data
  Property line survey
  Easements and rights-of-way
  Location of utilities; structures; and roads, indicating type of surface, volume of traffic, and classification of road (arterial, collector, minor)
  Contour maps with 2 or 5 foot intervals with slopes indicated
  Aerial photograph (1" = 400' scale) if available
  Relationship of the site to surrounding terrain
  Surface conditions such as rock outcroppings
Soils Data
  Depth of topsoil and subsoil
  Soil types and locations
  Description of the soil classification, grain size distribution, permeability, compactability, and other pertinent properties
Geological Data
  Type of geological formation
  Location and lithology of bedrock
  Aquifer recharge locations
  Sand and gravel deposits

Hydrological Data
    Surface runoff rates and patterns
    Groundwater location, rate and direction(s) of flow
    Wells, streams, ponds, and other water development
    Floodplain designations
Vegetative Data
    Existing ground flora
    Location of wooded areas
    Types of vegetation
Climatic Data
    Wind velocities and direction
    Rainfall data
Land Use Data
    Zoning and land use maps
    Existing land uses adjacent to and in the general area of the site
    Development trends (patterns of expansion)
    Access and transportation arteries
Perceptual Data
    Views into the site
    Areas of most probable visual conflict
    Areas of noise generation and most probable conflict

The second step is the analysis of the collected data to determine the potentials of the site, effect on the operation and future potential uses, and the factors (functional and visual) that will require specific solutions in the planning proposals.

Analysis of this information should be followed by a review of the equipment and operational factors to determine their patterns and capabilities as influenced by the site. These factors should include: type of excavating and landfilling equipment; type of landfill method or methods to be used; anticipated general filling patterns; area required for storage, maintenance weighing, and administration; sources and types of wastes to be received, and an estimate of daily quantity of wastes to be received; and types of daily, intermediate, and final cover to be used.

These factors will have some effect on the selection of land use, especially in relation to creating land forms, but they may be altered somewhat, in light of environmental factors, such as views, and in accord with the land use chosen.

Unless the land use had been previously selected, the next step is to study the environmental conditions, analyze these conditions in relation to the site and operational factors and select an appropriate use. A development plan designating the land use and land forms is then drafted. From this plan, detailed operational plans will be formulated, which should include: points of entrance to and exit from the sanitary landfill site and to and from the operating area of the sanitary landfill, interior roads and ramps, devices for controlling litter, screening plans for controlling access to the sanitary landfill site, and grading plans for access and visual control.

The plan must also include drainage facilities, structures, walls, cribbing, surface protection devices, or any other devices as are necessary to comply with applicable water quality standards. Weighing facilities, buildings for administration, maintenance, and storage, fire protection facilities, utilities, salvage operations, fill areas and borrow areas must also be provided. Also indicated are planting plans for screening and visual control, grading plans indicating depth of excavations and final elevations of fill areas. Areas must be indicated where fill will not be deposited.

SITE PLANNING GUIDELINES

The responsibility of designers and operators of sanitary landfills extends beyond the primary function of disposing of waste in an efficient and safe manner. The sanitary landfill is a part of the environment which affects people and their lives, and can influence the neighborhood and the community.

It has become apparent that detailed planning of sanitary landfill operations is essential if a degree of compatibility of the industry in the urbanizing landscape is to be achieved. As urbanization of the landscape proceeds, there are increasing social pressures bearing on landfill operators to improve their appearance and operating practices. Man is becoming increasingly aware of the necessity of maintaining and improving the quality of his environment. As this awareness spreads, it is important that the landfill operator pay serious attention to improving his public image in the community.

The purpose of this section is to provide suggestions and standards to serve as a general guide and as a check list for creating landfills that are compatible within the community. It is not the intent of these standards to serve as negative restrictions on the designer and operator.

Image

The development of a positive image for a sanitary landfill operation is important in establishing community acceptance. The image of a landfill is formed by the impressions of the public as they travel past an operation, from the experiences of neighboring landowners, by persons who enter the landfill site, and by the reputation and publicity given to the individual operators.

Two basic considerations are essential in developing a positive image. First, good management and compliance with state regulations and federal guidelines will ensure a safe, efficient and economical operation. Second, creating a harmonious relationship between site features and operations with the surrounding landscape can be achieved through good design based on functional and visual principles.

To please the public, the landfill must work well and look good. A good design will provide physical improvements outside and inside the operating site which will be conducive to creating an environment which is acceptable to the public. Potential solutions and suggested alternatives for good site design will focus on four areas:

(1) Site Organization — Primary relationships of operational activities and site elements

(2) Landform Design — Emphasis on visual and functional aspects of berms, cut banks, and stockpiles

(3) Site Details — The coordination of site elements with special emphasis upon individual features

(4) Planting Design — Arrangement and planting techniques

The following discussion will provide specific examples and ideas which can be applied to both new and existing sanitary landfill sites in order that they may become positive elements in the community.

Site Organization

In analyzing a sanitary landfill site, generally four zones exist.

FIGURE 10.3: FOUR ZONES OF A SANITARY LANDFILL

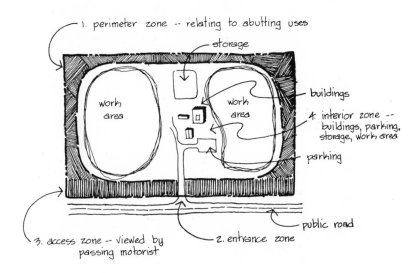

While these four zones act as a total unit in a landfill operation, each will be discussed separately so that specific solutions can be indicated.

Perimeter Zone: The perimeter zone of the property is important in developing a site. It is the area adjacent to the surrounding land uses which can affect the attitude toward the operation, and therefore must receive the intensive treatment at the beginning of the landfill operation in order to avoid any undesirable effects.

The primary functions of the perimeter are to provide a safety barrier for any of the public tempted to enter the site and to minimize atmospheric nuisances such as noise, dust, and blowing paper and debris from the interior working area.

Visually, the perimeter can serve as a screen between the public and work area, preventing undesirable views of the storage facilities and working portion of the site. The perimeter can also be the first area of the site ready for rehabilitation and use by the public, if such rehabilitation occurs concurrently with the operation.

FIGURE 10.4: PERIMETER ZONE SERVES AS A SCREEN OR BARRIER

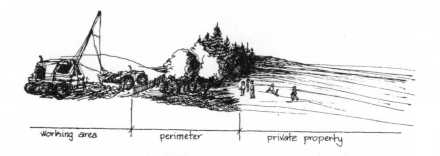

working area   perimeter   private property

The simplest way to eliminate or minimize objections at the perimeter is with screening or barrier structures. There are three main techniques available.

Plant Materials — By the use of heavy mass planting of evergreen and/or deciduous trees and shrubs, undesirable views into the interior working area can be prevented. Plant screens in the perimeter zone will also aid in reducing dust problems by means of filtering the dust and reducing wind velocity. Dense trees and shrubs can reduce wind velocity by up to 10 mph.

FIGURE 10.5: PLANTING IN PERIMETER ZONE FOR SAFETY

Also, noise created by operating equipment within the site can be reduced by up to 10 decibels by dense vegetation along the perimeter. Any existing vegetation on the perimeter should be disturbed as little as possible, since its effect is immediate.

FIGURE 10.6: PLANTING IN PERIMETER ZONE FOR NOISE AND WIND REDUCTION

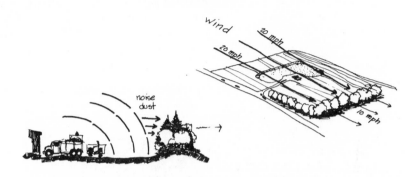

FIGURE 10.7: PLANTING IN PERIMETER ZONE CAN REDUCE NOISE

Earth Berms — Topsoil should be removed prior to filling and used for final cover of the landfill waste. It can be stockpiled and graded into earth berms along the perimeter to provide a barrier against views and access by individuals into the site. To be completely effective they should be at least six feet high.

FIGURE 10.8: EARTH BEAMS USED FOR SCREEN SCREENING

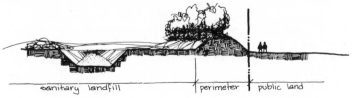

Screens and Fences — Screening and fencing of wood or other materials along the perimeter might be employed only as a temporary measure until vegetation matures. The major advantage of fences is that they will provide an immediate barrier against views and access, as well as immediate control in reducing dust and noise emissions.

**FIGURE 10.9:   FENCING PROVIDES IMMEDIATE CONTROL AND SCREEN-
ING ALONG PERIMETER ZONE**

Even with the use of plant screens, earth mounds, and fences, some paper and trash are bound to blow on or off the site. Daily pickup must be a part of the operating routine. Crews should clean up all loose material on the site daily as well as all material on adjoining properties and access routes that could in any way be connected with the fill process. This would probably include picking up trash thrown out of car windows and other loose refuse not connected with the operation. The public must have no cause to complain about the operation.

Entrance Zone: The entrance to the sanitary landfill site is the access point between the public area and the interior of the site. The entrance should be readily identifiable and safe. Good sight distances, acceleration and deceleration lanes, and proper turning radii will help assure safety. Allowing a generous open space at entrances, and setting buildings back from the road can help define the entrance space. This space can be reinforced with plant materials, subtle grading with gentle mounds, entrance signs, and site lighting, to add to the visual quality of the entrance.

Access Zone: The portion of the site adjoining the public road has a very important image potential. This zone is more likely to establish opinion of the operation than any other zone because it receives the most exposure. It should, therefore, appear organized, and like the perimeter zone, function to provide a safety barrier for preventing uncontrolled entrance by the public, as well as minimizing atmospheric nuisances, such as noise, dust and blowing paper. This zone can also serve as a screen between the public and work area, preventing undesirable views of the working portion of the site.

FIGURE 10.10: VIEW INTO SITE WITH NO SCREENING IN ACCESS ZONE

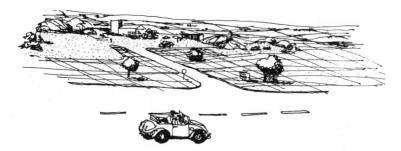

If the working area of the landfill has progressed far enough into the interior of the site, the access zone could provide limited reuse potential of the landfill site. Again, the operator might view this as a public service, providing an asset to the community. Uses such as ballfields, bicycle and walking pathways, or even picnicking could be developed.

FIGURE 10.11: POSSIBLE USE OF AREAS WHERE LANDFILLING IS COMPLETED

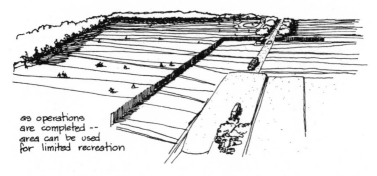

as operations
are completed --
area can be used
for limited recreation

Interior Zone: The interior zone of the site consists of the landfill working area and related facilities, such as buildings, storage areas, roads, and parking. These facilities must function properly in order to avoid any dangerous situations for both workers on the site, trucks transporting waste, and visitors to the site. Also, if properly designed, visual and air pollution problems can be eliminated or minimized that otherwise could not be solved by solutions in the other three zones.

The following suggestions should be considered as possible solutions to potential problems in this zone and creation of a positive image.

Buildings — (1) Buildings and structures for administration and weighing of trucks should be conveniently located in respect to the entrance road. They should be located relatively close to the entrance in order to avoid both trucks and automobiles from having to drive across the landfill site and possibly interfere with operational activities of the site.

(2) It may not be necessary to locate buildings for administration and weighing near those structures for maintenance and storage. By separating these uses, any unnecessary conflict can be avoided. This will depend primarily on the size of the site and operational practices.

Working Area — (1) If individuals are permitted to deposit waste materials, separate areas should be provided with possibly a container or some other type of structure where material can be deposited conveniently. The area should be separated from the main flow of truck traffic in order to avoid accident or injury.

(2) Although burning is prohibited in sanitary landfill operations, fires may occur accidentally or spontaneously, therefore provisions should be made on the site for fire control.

(3) Adequate control and separation should be provided between the immediate work area and adjacent land uses as well as the entrance, interior roads, and buildings.

(4) The greater the distance between the work area and surrounding land uses, the less potential for nuisances such as dust, noise, and blowing paper. It would be desirable if the work area was no closer than 500 feet to residences, but if this is not possible, the perimeter area should be developed immediately with earth mounds, planting, or fencing to minimize these problems.

FIGURE 10.12: SEPARATION OF LANDFILL OPERATION FROM RESIDENTIAL AREA

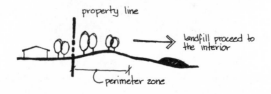

(5) Control of gases produced by decomposing solid wastes can be provided by venting gases to the atmosphere and burning, or by constructing impermeable soil barriers of clay to prevent gas migration.

(6) Moveable litter fences should be used to control blowing paper in the immediate vicinity of the working face.

As a general rule, trench operations which are perpendicular to the wind direction require less litter fencing because the solid waste tends to be confined within the walls of the trench. At a very windy trench site, a four foot snow fence may suffice.

FIGURE 10.13: TRENCH OPERATIONS PERPENDICULAR TO PREVAILING WIND TO MINIMIZE BLOWING LITTER

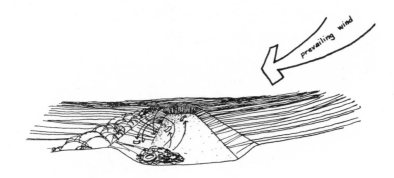

Blowing paper may be more of a problem in area type operations, where a six to ten foot litter fence may be desirable downwind of the working face.

FIGURE 10.14: PORTABLE LITTER FINCES MAY BE NEEDED TO MINIMIZE BLOWING LITTER

(7) Proper grading and drainage should prevent runoff from reaching the active working area, thereby causing surface and groundwater pollution. The best preventive is to direct the flow around the site, leaving internal drainage as the only concern.

When storm runoff cannot be diverted around the site, provisions for adequate storm drainage through the site will have to be provided, such as impermeable open channels, or underground pipes.

Runoff from the site flowing toward the working area should be intercepted with shallow diversion ditches or low mounds running parallel to the face and 50 to 100 feet away from the face.

**FIGURE 10.15: DIVERSION DRAINAGE DITCHES TO PREVENT SURFACE
WATER FLOW INTO FILL AREA**

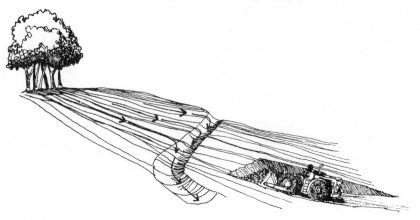

The water diverted in this manner should flow to natural drainage systems, and should not be allowed to remain standing on the site.

(8) Siltation of streams and water bodies within the site, as well as adjoining the site, should be prevented by proper grading and vegetative cover.

Interior Roads and Parking —

    (1)   All vehicular movement patterns within the site should reflect the dimensional requirements for trucks and similar large vehicles. For instance, a minimum inside radius of 40 feet is necessary for single unit trucks to turn properly.

    (2)   All major vehicular surfaces, such as access roads, parking areas, and weighing area, should be paved to prevent dust problems.

    (3)   Fences, plant screens, and mounds along roads and near buildings will also minimize dust and blowing papers and reduce noise.

    (4)   Since roads within the work area cannot be permanently

paved, these surfaces should be treated frequently with oil or water to control dust.

(5)   Major access roads within the site could be depressed in order to reduce noise and dust.

FIGURE 10.16: DEPRESSING MAJOR ROADS WILL REDUCE DUST AND NOISE

road →

(6)   Parking for the public and/or workers should be separated and controlled in order to eliminate conflict with the flow of trucks in and out of the site.

Landform Design

The earth's surface is fundamental to any landscape design in two ways. First, it is the foundation upon which the future design will be built. It receives the most wear and tear and in turn requires the most care and maintenance. And secondly, it is the medium in which all plants live and grow.

In designing a sanitary landfill site, landform design takes on a third purpose. The mounds of unwanted waste can become the material to create new, large scale landscape elements seldom feasible in other types of development. Here is a raw material in quantities that make many ventures possible. Ski slopes can grow in areas flat as the eye can see. Lookout points and hiking trails spring from the prairie. Earth formed amphitheaters and play fields can be created. Tree and grass covered hills of former waste material can screen out views of industrial and urban growth, protecting remnants of open space and nature areas, and turning them into private wild places in the middle of urbanization.

FIGURE 10.17: LANDFORMS OFFER MANY POTENTIAL USES

There are two general approaches in landform design to consider. The first, the natural landform, takes its key from the surrounding topography. These forms are smooth, rounded, and irregular. If the landscape is rolling, the new forms should follow and possibly accentuate these existing patterns. If the site is flat and some interest is desired, earth forms could be gentle and low, but not startling or out of proportion to the eye. The strongest existing forms in the area must be identified, and the new landforms related to the entire landscape. These forms might be appropriate where the landfill site would be developed for open space, parks, campgrounds, or wildlife areas.

The second approach is the architectural landform. It is usually marked by strong, regular, and straight lines that are obviously man-made. This approach is usually more appropriate in urban areas where the site might be developed for an amphitheater, race track, or a series of open play fields.

In both approaches, simplicity of design is essential. The topography of the existing natural forms will dictate the final form, whether it be a natural or architectural approach. It is necessary to carefully consider and analyze the features inherent to the site and the surrounding landscape, whether vegetation or landform, which will assist in making the final landform of the site appear harmonious to the surrounding environment.

In the discussion of site organization, the use of earth mounds offered various solutions to reducing noise and dust problems, providing control, and eliminating undesirable views of the working area. In designing landforms for these purposes, as well as relating to future uses of the site, the following factors must be considered.

Use: Uses, such as roads and buildings, require certain minimum and maximum grades in order to properly function. Therefore, it may be necessary to cut or fill certain parts of the site before landfilling operations begin. Any uses or activities planned for the site after completion of the landfill will also have specific grade (slopes) limitations, which must be realized in order that the site may be utilized for its intended purposes.

General gradient ranges for specific uses and site facilities are as follows:

Truck farm	2-4%	Softball fields	1%
Nursery	2-4%	Tennis courts and	
Single family	2-15%	other paved courts	1%
Riding club	2-10%	Recreation apparatus	
Country club	2-10%	areas	1-10%
Golf course	2-15%	Parking areas	1-5%
Tree farm	2-20%	Minor streets	1-12%
Campsites	2-20%	Sidewalks	1-8%
Hunting camp	2-20%	Driveways	1-10%
Game preserve	2-30%	Picnic areas	2-8%
Regional park	2-50%	Archery range	2-10%
Open space	2-50%	Hiking trails	2-25%
Buildings	0-10%	Sled slopes	5-15%
Football fields	1%	Ski slopes	10-50%

Drainage: Proper surface and subsurface drainage must be provided on and around the site to afford maximum protection for structures and other uses on the landfill site and adjoining land. All surfaces, whether paved or planted should have a minimum slope of 0.5% to prevent water from ponding, especially over fill areas where minimum slopes should not be less than 2%. Maximum slopes for drainage will depend upon the capability of the soil to resist erosion, which is related to the amount and density of vegetation cover and the type of soil, such as clay, sand, or silt. For instance, soils which have a heavy vegetative cover will resist erosion more than those that may be barren or covered with sparse grasses.

Stability: Where steep cut or fill exist or will be made, the soil may have to be formed in such a way as to provide a stable surface. Depending upon the type of soil, maximum angles are possible for each individual soil type.

In creating landforms along the perimeter zone and within the interior of the landfill, maximum slopes will to a large degree depend upon the stability of the soil used.

Plant Growth: In order to provide optimum conditions to encourage existing growth and establish new growth, it will be necessary to replace topsoil over the fill areas. This topsoil should be stripped and stockpiled prior to filling operations. Proper grading will be necessary in providing adequate topsoil, as well as providing proper drainage for plants to grow.

Where existing vegetation will remain for screening purposes, elevations cannot be changed without seriously injuring or killing plants. Existing trees will have the best opportunity for survival if the grade from the base of the trunk to the drip line of the branches remains intact, without cut or fill.

Property Boundary: The landforms must blend with existing conditions at the boundaries of the site in order to provide a smooth contour of the land.

FIGURE 10.18: GRADING OF LANDFILL PERIMETER

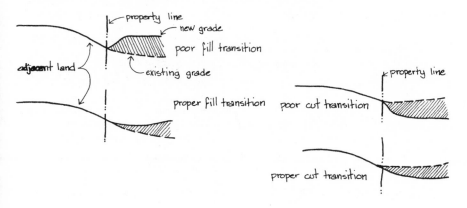

Settling: A major concern with landform creation is the problem of settlement. Although the refuse receives considerable compaction as it is deposited, a fairly high degree of settling does occur during the first two to five years. After the first two years, the land should settle enough to establish the necessary grades. Additional earth fill will be required to make level most playing court surfaces and areas requiring a relatively level grade. Less organized recreation can easily accommodate minor shifts in the surface grade with little interference with activities.

Play shelters and other light buildings can be accommodated on floating foundations. If possible, areas requiring buildings should be designed before the fill operation starts, so that these areas can be left unfilled or filled with concrete, demolition debris, or earth fill to provide a sturdy, safe foundation.

Depth of Cell: Cell depth is the thickness of the solid waste layer measured perpendicular to the working slope where the equipment travels. The depth of cells is determined largely by the size of the operations, the desired elevation of the completed fill, the depth of the trench or depression to be filled, and in some cases, the amount of cover material available. Eight feet is generally recommended as a maximum single cell depth because deeper cells usually result in fills that have excessive settlement and surface cracking. However, landfills are operating successfully at fill depths of approximately 20 feet.

Quantity of Cover Material: Since the compacted solid wastes must be covered at the end of each working day with at least six inches of soil, temporary landforms will have to be provided near the working face. Depending on what method of filling is used, quantity of cover material will vary. For instance, with the area method, solid waste is usually placed over existing grades, requiring cover material to be brought in or removed from other sections of the site. With the trench method, usually adequate cover material can be excavated. In all cases, topsoil should always be removed and stockpiled as earth mounds and used when necessary for cover.

Equipment: Availability of adequate and satisfactory earth moving equipment will influence the quantity of soil that can be moved and its appearance.

Site Details

Unfortunately, site details are often considered to be extras. These details, however, are what make the difference between good and poor design. In a sanitary landfill, where public acceptance is vital, details are especially important.

Selection and application of site details must be properly coordinated and must solve site problems to result in a unified development. Emphasis should be placed on simply detailed and easily interpreted design solutions and quality of workmanship. Design integrity and construction quality, tempered with imagination, can add much interest to essential site elements: signs, materials, roads, buildings, and lighting.

Materials: The structural materials requiring attention on the site are mainly those used in fencing and screening for controlled access at the entrance. Those chiefly used are stone, wood, metal and brick. Choice is usually influenced by the price of materials in the area. However, it is usually a good idea to stick to materials native to the area. If the land is to become part of an existing park system, use of fencing and site details in the part will help associate the site with its future use.

The idea is to make the site and all of its elements fit as gently as possible into the land and the landscape. The same material should be used consistently all over the site. Salvage materials, such as wood or used utility poles should be incorporated when possible, both for economical reasons and as a step towards wise reuse of refuse.

Service Buildings: The service buildings are usually temporary, but they should receive some attention since they are or can be visible to the public. Use of one or two compatible colors throughout, preferably deep earth tones, will make them less obvious. Although, no major investment would be desired for plantings, inexpensive fast growing shrubs, vines, or annual seeds or plants could be used to make the buildings more attractive.

Road Construction: Road construction on the site may vary in materials, although all sites must provide stable, all weather roads. Factors to consider in choosing paving materials are climate, projected life of the site, daily truck traffic, and future road needs. If concrete or asphalt with gutters is used, the road system should be incorporated as a part of the site drainage system, if possible. On access roads within the working area of the site, some used oil products can be placed on the road as a covering to reduce dust in the summer.

The entrance road may or may not be considered part of the final design plan, but if it could be utilized, it would be more economical. On large sites, more than one entrance road system may be used in the life of the site.

Lighting: The intent of site lighting is to produce an adequate degree of lighting to insure safety. Since the landfill is generally not used past daylight hours, extensive site lighting is not necessary except as a discouragement to intruders around buildings and maintenance areas. Also, some minor lighting may be included at the entrance for safety.

Planting Design

A sanitary landfill is a large area. It should not be managed as a garden with attendant mowing, watering, pruning, etc. Plants should be chosen for their ability to take care of themselves and arranged in a straightforward and utilitarian manner rather than as decorations. Landfills need not be decorative; in fact, such treatment would attract attention to what should best go unnoticed.

Plants are only incidentally attractive. Their function is to make the earth habitable for all life. They break the wind, cast shade, hold the mineral soil with their roots, improve the soil with the nutrients and organic matter of their fallen leaves, remove CO_2 from the atmosphere, and provide all the oxygen and food for animal species.

Plants serve five important functions in a sanitary landfill. They can be used to: screen unsightly areas, improve visual quality of the site, control dust, control and minimize noise, and control erosion.

In selecting plants, one should be aware of plant characteristics that will best serve the needs. There are several general guidelines to follow:

(1)   The plant should be hardy in the local area.

(2)   The plants should be fast growing where quick effects are desirable.

(3)   The plants should be selected on the basis of local soil conditions. Some plants will do well in wet soils, others in dry soil, and others in poor soil.

(4)   The plants should be of a form that will provide effective screening or control. For instance, columnar trees or low growing plants require special consideration for screening purposes.

(5)   The plants should require a minimum amount of maintenance.

Screen plantings will be located primarily in the perimeter and access zones of the landfill. Depending on the amount of space available, the screen can be deep or narrow, in straight lines or irregularly spaced, or curving. Density of the individual plants and their spacing is of little importance in a deep screen. But, these two characteristics become increasingly critical as a screen is narrowed, even to a single row.

FIGURE 10.19: TYPES OF SCREEN PLANTINGS

deep screen does not rely on density and spacing of plants

narrow screens require dense and close spacing of plants

Variation in lineal arrangement can be accomplished by introducing a variety of species into the planting scheme. To be of maximum benefit, plant materials should be installed prior to the landfilling operation and be of sufficient size and density to achieve relatively quick results. Token or cosmetic plantings of small size and wide spacings provide minimum screening and thus the basic reason for the plantings cannot be achieved. By using a combination of plant materials a quicker and more attractive screen can be achieved. The following figure illustrates several screening considerations.

FIGURE 10.20: SCREENING CONSIDERATIONS

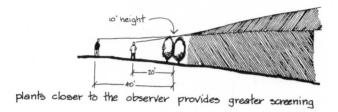

plants closer to the observer provides greater screening

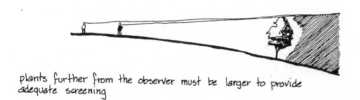

plants further from the observer must be larger to provide adequate screening

The effectiveness of screening will depend upon the height of the plants and the distance between the observer and the plant screen. The closer the plants to the observer, the greater the visual screen. Plants further from the observer must be larger to provide a similar effect.

Trees with high branching characteristics will not screen out undesirable views at ground level. If the ground slopes up behind the trees, effective screening may be provided. Areas that slope down from behind the plants, can be screened effectively by lower plants, such as shrubs.

Not all areas require "instant" screening. For example, when a particular section of the site will not be disturbed for a period of time, smaller and less expensive plants can be installed far in advance of any anticipated use, thus providing a mature and effective screen when the need arises.

In addition to screens, plants can be used to enhance the entrance zone. They can also have some effect on noise abatement and can definitely be used to control dust, both around the building area and the working area. For example, trees planted adjacent to areas where dust is stirred up, such as along access roads, will help contain the dust in a relatively small area. Plants can be the best means of preventing erosion. Leaves above and the roots below the ground of a dense stand of plants minimize and may even eliminate the removal of soil particles by falling raindrops and by flowing surface water. Any kind of plant cover (even noxious weeds) will provide this service. At the same time and in a similar way, plants also prevent the full force of the wind from reaching the ground and thereby minimize soil erosion by wind. In both cases, the denser the vegetation, the more effective it is. For immediate effect, grasses and herbs provide the best solution.

Plant Life Forms: Basically, six kinds of life forms or combinations of life forms are appropriate for landfill sites. Each has its own characteristic qualities and appearance.

(1) Grasses and herbs can be quickly established from seed and may be annual (die at the end of one year) or perennial (grow again each year for several or many years).

(2) Shrubs can be planted as seeds, seedlings, or specimens. They are many-stemmed woody plants which, if hardy, will send forth new growth each year from the previous year's growth.

(3) Trees are usually single stemmed woody plants which attain a height in excess of 15 feet. They can be planted as seeds, seedlings, saplings, or specimens.

(4) Vines are herbaceous or woody plants which cling to or twine around any available objects including other plants. Some species are rampant growers and can be used for quick soil cover and to hide or disguise a fence or building.

(5) Trees and grasses are sometimes combined as in parks and grazed woodlands.

(6) Trees and shrubs are the more natural combination which also include young trees and herbaceous plants. There are numerous variations of species, sizes, and relationships, but typically three or more layers of plant heights exist at one time.

Shrubs and grasses are not found growing in combination except as a transitional stage which will ultimately become woodland. Vines may be found playing a minor role in all situations.

Plant Lists: Since the selection and placement of plant materials must be carefully analyzed in respect to local conditions and purposes, it is recommended that the landfill operator consult individuals experienced in this area, such as landscape architects, local forestry agents from the Department of Conservation, or representatives in the Department of Agriculture.

Sources of Plant Materials: Several sources for plant materials exist. The primary source is the vegetation existing on the site which should be retained wherever possible, and for as long as possible. Judicious design and operation can minimize disruption of natural plant cover, especially that which exists in the perimeter and access zones. Some stands of woodland may be retained continuously in an undisturbed state to form a nucleus of the post operative land use. Other woodlands, hedgerows, thickets, meadows, etc., will temporarily screen and prevent erosion and weed growth until displaced by filling operations. This is the most inexpensive source.

Another source of plants is the simple regeneration of native plants existing on the site. It is the least costly and can be a most successful planting technique, although knowledge of the germination requirements of different species is essential. On bare soil, the first year will usually produce a crop of so-called weedy annuals. Among them will probably be some tree and shrub species, and if given enough time, the weeds will be shaded out.

The process can be speeded up, however, simply by mulching the bare soil with an organic mulch. This soil treatment encourages the perennials and woody plants, and dramatically, discourages the annuals. Natural generation of larger, slower growing, more expensive, and/or hardier species can be encouraged in this way, even beneath species which have been planted for more immediate effect.

Planting Schedule: The primary considerations with respect to determining planting season are temperature and moisture. Seeding operations for grasses can take place during late summer or early fall which will ensure enough moisture for fast germination. The plants will then be strong enough to withstand winter conditions.

Planting of deciduous plant material can take place any time during dormancy and as long as the soil is workable. Fall planting is advantageous in drier soils. Conifers and broadleaf evergreens can be planted during late August and early September. Root growth is strong at this time and the roots will be established before winter sets in.

Planting with Seed — There are a few trees, especially black walnut and oaks, which can be started successfully in the field direct from seed.

Planting with Cuttings — There are some trees and shrubs, usually fast growing bottomland species which can be rooted from cuttings in the field. This list includes cottonwoods, willows, sycamores, green ash, currant, and some shrub dogwoods.

POTENTIAL USE

Before a site is used as a sanitary landfill, some initial decisions should be made as to how the site can be used after the landfill is completed. The potential use of the site will influence the operating practices. The operating practices influence the success and potential use of the site.

There are many potential land uses that can be developed on a completed sanitary landfill. Theoretically, any of the major land uses —residential, institutional, industrial, commercial, recreational-open space, agricultural— could be considered for final use. Any of these possible uses will require careful consideration and analysis in determining their feasibility.

Landfills which are unplanned in terms of potential use, usually require extensive corrective work later. This means, in terms of creating usable land, maximum effort with minimum results. It means that landfill operations proceed with little or no recognition of essential land development criteria, thereby creating whatever land characteristics that may occur from unplanned operations. Unplanned operations, more often than not, result in: the misplacement of waste materials and stockpiles useful in building and shaping land, excavation of shallow areas, shaping of narrow fragmented and other irregular shaped unusable land, and burying of useable cover material.

Planned development involves investigating the characteristics of both the natural resource and the landfill operation to determine the most efficient way to develop the maximum potential of the site. Areas where the greatest amount of usable land can be shaped with the least effort or with available material are noted. Potential drainage problems are indicated and resolved during the course of the planning; and, suitable access to the site is determined and maintained throughout the landfill operations.

In considering potential uses for a sanitary landfill site, three possible conditions exist. First, the site could be used prior to the landfill operations. In some cases, land may be purchased by the landfill operator who has no intention of filling the site immediately. This assures the operator of having at his disposal a readily available location for sanitary waste disposal. Use of the site prior to filling would provide facilities which would be flexible and temporary in nature. Second, the site might be used for certain types of activities concurrent with landfill operations.

Again, uses would have to be flexible and temporary, but could provide desirable facilities in the community. And thirdly, the final use of the site after completion of the landfill. These uses would be permanent. All three conditions will be discussed in relation to suggested specific uses of the site later in this section.

Land Use Selection

The greatest limitation placed on a sanitary landfill for any potential use is the capability of the soil to physically support buildings and structures. Due to varying degrees of settlement, a completed landfill site cannot physically support any land use requiring a fairly high degree of subsoil stability. Many subsoil support problems can be overcome, but in general, such solutions are intricate, expensive, and justifiable only in exceptional circumstances.

FIGURE 10.21: INSTABILITY OF LANDFILL

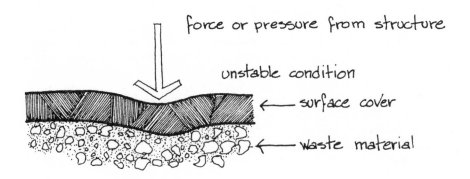

force or pressure from structure

unstable condition

← surface cover

← waste material

In such land use types as residential, industrial, or commercial, where extensive footings and foundations for buildings are essential, it appears questionable whether a sanitary landfill should be used.

For example, industrial and commercial facilities require firm foundations. Most require service connections, gas, water, sewerage, etc., that cannot tolerate non-uniform settlement. Vehicular service to heavy industries located on fill sites would suffer, as the weight and frequency of railroad and large truck deliveries could not be accommodated without excessive settlement. The same may be implied for residential, and many institutional uses, such as educational facilities and civic centers.

There are exceptions, of course. There are examples of large structures having been constructed upon completed sanitary landfill sites. The new ice hockey stadium in Pittsburgh, Pennsylvania, is but one of several examples. But, it must be remembered that the footings for such large structures extend through the fill and rest on bedrock.

Three general categories of land uses are most acceptable for landfill sites. These include recreational-open space, agricultural, and limited types of institutional land. Recreational-open space and agricultural uses are the most acceptable, since they are not only able to tolerate the limitations imposed by the fill site, but are also most readily able to accept and benefit from those assets afforded by the sanitary landfill site.

The final use of the site will depend upon many conditions, such as location, size of property, and slope. Even the most efficient physical adaptation of any particular site is subject to change; for example, it may be affected by zoning ordinances and changes in other public policies. Also, whenever changes in the demand for different types of land use occur, the operator may want to reexamine his proposals for development. The ability for anticipating demands for the future will vary with the amount of time involved between starting the landfill operation, and finally implementing the development.

The time and rate for a sanitary landfill site to be filled is dependent upon many variables. The time it takes will depend upon the size of the site and the daily volume of refuse expected. The rate will depend upon the operating practices, primarily, how well the waste material is compacted. If material is compacted to 1,000 lbs./yd.^{3}, the volume disposed of in a year would occupy approximately 19 acre-feet for a population of 10,000 people.

From the start, filling activities should be undertaken in conjunction with proposed development plans, regardless of how distant the completion date. Provisions for concurrent or temporary reuse of the land at the completion of each filling stage, as an interim step before final development, will be an important consideration for stabilization and patterns of filling operations.

Recreation — Open Space

The final transition of a sanitary landfill site into a desirable recreation feature depends upon an accurate analysis of the potential for recreation, recognizing the physical features that would affect the type of facility it can be and the ability to implement ideas and proposals into physical realities on the site.

Following are some pertinent factors that strongly suggest sanitary landfill sites can be successful recreation areas. The realization and appreciation of these factors are prerequisite to any significant recreation benefit the sanitary landfill operation or the public will enjoy.

Optimum Location — Sanitary landfill operations are generally located in close proximity to urban areas where the greatest demand exists for recreational sites and activities. Also, many landfills are located in areas where urbanization is occurring, which will need recreational and open space facilities in the future.

Desirable Site Features — The nature of sanitary landfill sites and operations are conducive to the production of terminal physical site characteristics considered ideal for recreational purposes; namely topographic relief which is useful for a variety of recreational activities.

Alternative Use Sequence — In accordance with wise land management and progressive rehabilitation practices, recreational uses can occur on sanitary landfill sites prior to, concurrent with, or subsequent to site excavation and filling over the extended period of operation.

Multiple Benefits — In consideration of conforming with typical zoning regulations and requirements, creating a positive public relations image, and realizing mutually advantageous economic returns, the development of sanitary landfill sites for recreational uses should be of significant benefit to both the industry and local public agencies.

Recreational Use Determinants: There are many factors that must be considered in determining what specific recreational uses are appropriate to a sanitary landfill. These include the following.

Location and Access — Since the location of the sanitary landfill site must be determined in respect to suitable environmental conditions and land-use policies, the location of proposed landfills are limited. Therefore recreational uses are determined after site selection of the landfill, and the future use related to those conditions.

Sites located near the periphery of urban growth will generally be developed for intensive uses, such as playfields and community centers. Those sites located further from urban areas will be conducive to less intense forms of recreation, such as camping, hiking, or picnicking. Sites developed for intensive recreational uses might require adequate access or be located on major roads, while those sites that have more difficult access would be desirable for less intensive forms of recreation.

Size and Configuration — Specific recreational uses have site size requirements. Length and width configuration dimensions of the site or certain portions of the site will determine the siting and suitability of a particular use. For instance, many active use facilities (court and field games) are rectangular in design. Size may directly affect the type of recreational activities suitable for the site. For instance, an eighteen hole golf course requires at least 150 acres.

Vegetation — Many types of recreational activities are dependent upon existing stands of vegetation, such as camping or hiking. Whereas, intensive forms of recreation, such as ballfields and court areas, may be suitable on sites with less vegetation. Of course, the site could be planted with trees as areas are filled, providing suitable masses of vegetation upon completion of the landfill.

Topography — Topographic features are probably the most functional aspect of a recreational landscape. Not only do they have strong esthetic qualities, but the type of feature can have a direct affect upon the type of recreational uses incorporated onto a site. Hills suggest hiking, climbing, and winter activities. Northeast and north slopes provide shelter from sun and wind, while flat areas may be easily utilized for camping or game fields.

By relating the requirements for a specific recreational use and the conditions of the site, a feasible recreational plan can be developed for the site.

With regard to alternative approaches and uses, two factors determine the approach a landfill operator may take in programming a site for recreation. These are progressive development and sequence of recreation use. Each factor plays an important role in the site development program for recreation on the site.

Progressive Development: Progressive development is the process whereby a pre-development plan becomes an integral part of the various stages of the landfill operations. The desired objective is to ready the site for recreational use by performing development procedures concurrent with the landfill process. In order for progressive development to accomplish its desired objective, all phases of the landfill operation must be geared to the ultimate use, a successful and desirable recreational area.

In instances where more active facilities have been provided for development, cost has been a major consideration due to the amount of earth work involved. Since most recreation plans have to appeal to a diversified population, the necessity for multiple-use recreation becomes a significant factor.

Progressive development is a very logical process in which to approach developing landfills for recreation. Rather than having to commit extra man-hours and capital to subsequent development, the same basic operations can be accomplished concurrent with the basic phases of excavating, filling and covering. General site planning would indicate areas for the planting of trees and vegetation, the supporting elements, such as parking, service areas, access routes, and pedestrian circulation. In reality, progressive development minimizes safety hazards, permits ease of circulation, assures that site factors conform to the proposed recreational intent of the site, and permits recreational utilization of the site sooner than could be realized otherwise.

FIGURE 10.22: PROGRESSIVE DEVELOPMENT – SITE REHABILITATED CONCURRENTLY FOR RECREATIONAL USE

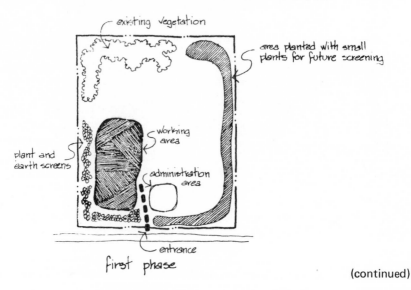

(continued)

FIGURE 10.22: (continued)

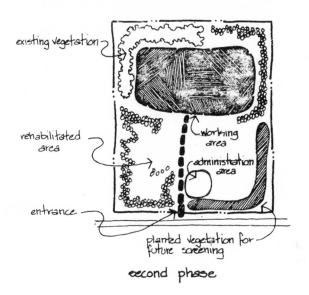

existing vegetation

rehabilitated area

Working area

administration area

entrance

planted vegetation for future screening

second phase

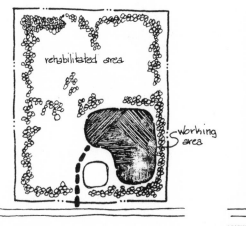

rehabilitated area

Working area

third phase

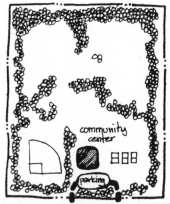

community center

parking

completed landfill rehabilitated for recreational use
fourth phase

Sequence of Activities: There are three conditions whereby recreation can function on land proposed for a sanitary landfill: (1) prior to clearing, (2) concurrent with excavation and filling, and (3) subsequent to operations. In order to facilitate all three, a site will have to be of sufficient size to warrant both filling and recreational uses. Following is an evaluation of each sequence and how it might affect the overall recreational potential of a site.

Previous Use — Considering proposed structures, operational sequence, transportation routes, and size of site, any previous recreational uses on the site should not interfere with later operations. The actual on-site location of a highly desirable and successful recreational area that exists prior to filling could dictate the initial starting point of fill. Of major significance would be the size and shape of such an area which might serve as a guide in determining how the total site will be developed. It may be that the existing use is of such value that it should be retained as long as possible. This would have the effect of postponing all filling phases in the area, allowing fill to proceed in such a manner as not to interfere with this area until the remainder of the site has been filled.

A few examples of the type of recreational uses that could be made available to the public on sanitary landfill sites prior to filling are the following:

Nature trails	Open space	Field games
Bicycle paths	Camping	Picknicking
Hiking and riding trails	Archery range	Garden plots
Hunting	Rifle range	Model airplane flying
Golf driving range		

Concurrent Uses — Both filling operations and recreational uses can coexist adjacent to each other with proper screening and good operational practices as discussed in the previous section. Since a major portion of any site may remain untouched by excavation for a period of time, its continuous use can be appropriately programmed. The site would always be open to public or private recreational use, assuming that as each section is filled it would become available for recreational use by progressive development. This would give neighboring communities a current account of filling and reclamation progress, and would assure local interests that recreational development would be the terminal result of the landfill site.

In the situation where a site is divided into sections based upon duration of operation, there can always be concurrent and subsequent recreational activities if progressive development is practiced. Uses prior to excavation are applicable for concurrent usage. Following is a list of uses that can coexist on a site concurrent with excavation and filling, and because of progressive development, can also be developed subsequent to filling.

Court games	Putting greens	Go-kart track
Creative play areas	Miniature golf course	Motorcycle scramble course

Final Use — In a sanitary landfill operation that does not practice progressive development or permit any recreational use of the land prior to filling, any recreational use must be developed subsequent to operations. In an operation where prior recreational uses are permitted and progressive development is practiced, concurrent uses could also be considered as final uses. If the operator sees any benefit in allowing prior recreational use of his site and land permits such, then the site could be developed in stages. Each stage should relate to the next, and the terminal recreational feature should function as a complete unit.

Following are some recreational uses that would adapt to a completed sanitary landfill site, but could only be utilized in total, subsequent to all filling.

Zoo	Civic center	Golf course
Amusement park	Botanical garden	

Subsequent to all excavation and filling, the total reclamation of the landfill site could also include the following:

(1)   State or regional park (Usually landfill sites are too small to be considered as a total state or regional park, but if the land was adjacent to an existing park, then it could be incorporated in the total park scheme.)

(2)   Municipal park

(3)   Open space land

(4)   Wildlife preserve

(5)   Hunting area

Agricultural

Like recreational land use, agricultural land involves few or no structures on the land. A completed landfill can be made productive by turning it into pasture or crop land. If cultivated crops are used, the final cover should be thick enough that roots or cultivating do not penetrate the buried waste material. If the landfill is to be cultivated, a one or two foot layer of relatively impermeable soil, such as clay, may be placed on top of the solid waste and an additional layer of organic soil placed above to prevent the clay from drying out. Excessive moisture will also be prevented from entering the fill.

As with recreational uses, agricultural uses are adaptable to progressive rehabilitation practices as well as easily adapted to concurrent use as operations are taking place. Besides crops and pasture, other possible agricultural uses may include:

(1)   Tree Farm — The commercial growth of wood for specialized purposes, pulp and other cellulose base products, could aid in satisfying the rapid consumption of and projected future demand for wood and wood fibers. Therefore, a completed site, or one still in operation, that has soil capable of sustaining tree growth has potential for

development as a tree farm, where desired species of trees are
planted, marketed, and replaced on a continuing crop basis.
Even sites of rough topography have potential as tree farm sites.
As filled areas become available, they can be planted, thereby
providing a means of quickly concealing the scars of excavation
and filling, and initiating a source of production for the future.

(2)   Nursery — The demand for plant materials such as trees, shrubs,
and evergreens is quite high in urban and suburban areas, and
with the correct type of soil and topography, and an abundant
supply of water to mature the young plant material, a landfill
site can have great possibilities as a nursery. Again, concurrent
use as a nursery would be possible during fill operation.

(3)   Truck Farm and Orchard — As with a nursery, good topsoil and
an abundance of water is essential for the large scale growth of
vegetables and fruits.

Institutional

Implied in the development of suburbs are needs for institutional development,
such as churches, schools, colleges, hospitals, universities, cultural centers, and
related public service facilities, which require areas of open space for parking
or athletic facilities.

Again, it must be pointed out that where structural footings and foundations
are involved, severe limitations are imposed by settlement and compaction
problems of fill areas. But, if specified areas of the site can be left unfilled,
many of these uses are possible, with the filled areas serving as open space areas.

Many new schools are using the campus, playground, or school park concept
for better integration into the community and natural conditions on the site.
Outdoor activities are increasing in both elementary and secondary levels, thus
imposing new demands for large extensive school grounds.

A landfill operator considering possible use of his site, in part or wholly for
school purposes, should understand that acceptance of a site by the school
board will depend on several factors: first, adequate size for buildings and activities, and a location advantage to education activities; second, the function
the school is to serve, such as grade levels and relation to community activities;
and third, the physical site requirements to meet building and other school site
functions.

ZONING

Due to the prevalence of the substandard dump, zoning ordinances have tra-
ditionally ignored land disposal sites entirely. Even an examination of current
zoning ordinances in the state will reveal that in most cases there is no mention

of sanitary landfill disposal, except as it might be covered as an incinerator.

Those zoning ordinances which do mention sanitary landfills, usually specify it as a conditional use in agricultural or industrial zones, or both. This requires special approval by the planning commission or governmental body, and places the burden of proof upon the applicant. Even with these restrictions, practically all the ordinances do not have specific standards or site planning regulations, almost leaving this up to the operator. The only standards which would apply, would be those of the state environmental agency.

If land disposal sites will be operated as sanitary landfills under the best conditions, then local jurisdictions, particularly the cities and counties, will be obliged to accommodate the sanitary landfill as a permitted or conditional use. This, of course, does not mean that every jurisdiction must, in fact, permit the use, but every jurisdiction should examine the situation and at least consider doing so.

If it is determined that sanitary landfill sites are appropriate uses within a particular jurisdiction, then the problem becomes one of writing an ordinance that substantially locates the use and requires adequate standards for the planning and operation of the landfill, as well as guaranteeing that it be compatible within the appropriate zoning district.

Theoretically, a sanitary landfill should be allowed when it meets conditions and criteria which will guarantee that its operation will not be harmful to surrounding properties or incompatible with them in the ways generally considered under zoning.

Despite the public opposition to waste disposal sites, a place must be made for a sanitary landfill and other approved types of solid waste processing systems that will be developed in the future. Planning agencies have a particular responsibility to find ways to fit these necessary uses into the land-use scheme. The problem should be studied in its local and regional setting, taking into account the operational requirements of the facility as well as the general community and environmental considerations.

Pollution of Subsurface Water

In an attempt to minimize health and pollution hazards, due to the disposal of solid waste by landfilling, sanitary landfill design criteria have evolved which are primarily empirical in nature and which may or may not have a relationship to environmental conditions. Several studies of sanitary landfill behavior have been undertaken in recent years to better understand them and to delineate and define significant design criteria. Unfortunately, many of the results obtained from these studies, most of which were limited in scope, reflect only local conditions and cannot be easily extrapolated outside the specific region.

The study described in this chapter was undertaken by Drexel University in cooperation with the Pennsylvania Department of Health and published by the EPA in 1971. Interest on the part of the Pennsylvania Department of Health was stimulated by its concern with the decreasing availability of suitable landfill sites within the state and the increasing frequency of pollution and health problems resulting from solid waste disposal.

The study, as conceived, was to provide quantitative information as to the behavior of sanitary landfills in an environment common to southeastern Pennsylvania, and in fact, to a large portion of the region extending between Washington, D. C. and Boston, Massachusetts. To suppress local environmental influences, the study was developed so as to generalize results, except those specifically related to the southeastern Pennsylvania region.

SUMMARY

Attainment of project objectives required the evaluation of a substantial amount of quantitative data for a sanitary landfill in a temperate-humid climate; however, available information at the time of project initiation was not adequate. Two experimental facilities, a laboratory sanitary landfill and a field sanitary landfill, were developed. The laboratory facility was operated under controlled environmental conditions, while the field facility was operated under natural (no control) environmental conditions.

The laboratory sanitary landfill facility was the first placed into operation, and as a result, it generated the maximum amount of experimental data. A major portion of this chapter is devoted to a discussion of this facility and related experimental data. The field sanitary landfill was made operational approximately six months after the initiation of the laboratory study. A description of this facility and the experimental data which was available at the time of report preparation is presented.

The laboratory sanitary landfill was contained in a lysimeter, which consisted of a fiberglass-lined steel tank, thirteen feet high and six feet by six feet in cross-section. A bottom collection trough was used to collect the landfill-generated leachate. The top of the lysimeter was closed and temperatures and water input were adjusted on a pre-determined schedule. The lysimeter's vertical sidewalls were insulated to minimize heat exchange with the laboratory proper, while the bottom of the lysimeter was controlled at a constant temperature. Essentially, the lysimeter functioned as a closed system which permitted the contained landfill to be representative of the center of a large sanitary landfill, the depth of which was small in comparison to its areal extent.

Lysimeter leachate and gas samples were analyzed, and temperatures were monitored on a routine basis. While information on gases and temperatures was not essential to attainment of project objectives, the collection was necessary in order to obtain a complete picture of the behavior of sanitary landfills.

The field facility consisted of a fifty foot by fifty foot site with eight feet of refuse and a two foot soil cover. Temperatures, gases and leachate quality within the landfill, as well as temperatures, gases and leachate quality outside the landfill, were collected on a routine basis. Also monitored were precipitation and ground water quality, both under and away from the landfill site.

The laboratory landfill behavior pattern is representative of a young low-compaction density refuse. Within ten days of its initiation, refuse temperatures reached 150°F. at the refuse center. Temperatures at adjacent levels were lower, however, with time there was a general spreading of temperatures from the refuse center to the top and bottom temperature-controlled boundaries. Temperatures at levels other than the center did not exceed 134°F. The temperature pattern is probably unique to the particular system; that is, a young low-density rapidly placed landfill; however, the pattern is representative of a refuse which undergoes initial high aerobic activity; it is probable that with other placement conditions, temperature peaks would occur at different refuse levels, at different times and at different maximums. Maximums greatly in excess of the 150°F. range experienced in this study should not be expected.

Lysimeter temperatures stabilized at approximately $80°F$., approximately sixty days after refuse placement. The general temperature pattern obtained indicated that the refuse was initially in a general aerobic state, and that after sixty days, an anaerobic condition became dominant.

After the refuse temperatures became virtually steady state, that is when the refuse became anaerobic, changes in top boundary temperatures had little influence on internal temperature levels or distribution. The behavior implies that alteration of internal temperatures, due to changes in environmental temperatures, are minimized by soil and refuse insulating properties, as well as by changes in biological activity. The net result of all temperature influences is a virtually constant internal temperature state.

The lysimeter temperature and gas behavior patterns indicated the simultaneous existence of aerobic and anaerobic regions in a refuse. During its early life, aerobic conditions dominated, while during its later life, anaerobic conditions dominated. The percentages and distribution of aerobic and anaerobic states in each region varied with time, because any flushing of the landfill by water infiltration introduced fresh air.

The lysimeter began to produce leachate almost immediately, even though the refuse was placed at a very low moisture content. The quantities of leachate produced were small; nevertheless, the pollution levels, as measured by chemical parameters, were extremely high. The low quantity of initial leachate production is due to the low initial moisture content of the lysimeter components and most of the initial water introduced into the lysimeter functioned to bring each system component to field capacity. At field capacity, net infiltration and leachate quantities were approximately equal.

Results of the leachate quantity studies indicate the phase relationship between water input and leachate production. During periods of low leachate production, any additional decrease further reduced or eliminated leachate production. Conversely, as water input increased, leachate production also increased. The phase relationship existed even when the system was not at field capacity. Leachate production can be attributed to one or all of the following sources: the refuse, channeling, an advanced wetting front, and the main wetting front.

From the results of this study, it is concluded that the first two sources would be responsible for leachate collected from a landfill during the early time period when the landfill had been placed at a relatively low initial moisture content. Once the system reached field capacity, leachate contributed by these sources would be primarily due to the third source. Finally, when the system reached field capacity, leachate production would be due to movement of the main wetting front, the fourth source.

A landfill system whose components were placed at field capacity would produce leachate immediately, and the source would be primarily the main wetting front. One effect of these various leachate generation patterns is to alter the leachate composition. Leachate produced during the slow attainment of the system field capacity will probably exhibit initial pollutant concentrations different than a landfill in which substantial quantities of leachate are produced immediately. Once the system transients have been eliminated, both landfills should produce similar, but not necessarily identical, leachates.

The results of the significant parameters monitored in the lysimeter are summarized as follows:

(1) pH — generally, solutions were acidic with a mean pH of 5.5. It is believed that flow rate through the refuse is a major controlling factor in establishing leachate pH and that with maximum flow rates, pH will be acidic. The general acidic nature of the leachate compounds the potential pollution problem because low pH values tend to reduce exchange capacities of renovating soils at the time when quantities are high.

(2) Iron — iron concentrations tended to be higher when leachate production was high, reaching their maximums at times of maximum leachate production. Leachate iron concentrations were in excess of 1,600 mg./l. during high quantity periods.

(3) Zinc — zinc concentrations were as high as 120 to 135 mg./l. More usual concentrations levels were between 15 and 30 mg./l. Significant quantities of zinc did not appear in the leachate until about 430 days into the test. However, after its first appearance, its presence was continuous. This pattern suggests the delayed release of zinc ions due to the breakdown of some refuse component which had previously resisted leaching action.

(4) Phosphate — high phosphate concentrations occurred shortly after initiation of the test. At that time they reached concentration levels of approximately 130 mg./l. There also were long spans of time when no detectable phosphate concentrations were present.

(5) Sulfate — sulfates were present during the entire period of the test. Concentrations generally increased as time elapsed. Toward the end of the test period, sulfate concentrations peaked between 400 and 500 mg./l. In general, sulfate concentration levels increased with increased leachate production, and as the system approached field capacity.

(6) Chloride — chloride was present during the entire test period. Concentrations were approximately 200 to 300 mg./l. Localized peaks occurred soon after initiation of the test where a peak of 700 mg./l. was attained and approximately one year into the test when approximately 2,400 mg./l. were attained.

(7) Sodium — sodium was present during the entire test period. While sodium concentrations reached 3,800 mg./l. between 200 and 250 days into the test, this peak was not sustained and was much greater than the usual values. More frequent concentration levels were in the 200 to 300 mg./l. range. Toward the

end of the test period, concentration levels tended to increase.

(8) Nitrogen — ignoring an initial peak of 482 mg./l., initial nitrogen levels were approximately 8 mg./l. After initiation of the test, there was a general increase in nitrogen levels to between 100 and 200 mg./l. At the time of project termination, nitrogen levels had reached as high as 200 mg./l. and showed an increasing trend.

(9) Hardness (as $CaCO_3$) — the most frequently recorded hardness values ranged between 2,250 and 2,750 mg./l. A local peak of approximately 5,500 mg./l. occurred about 450 days into the test.

(10) COD — the most frequent concentration levels for COD were between 20,000 and 22,000 mg./l. An initial localized peak of 50,000 mg./l. was recorded within one month of the initiation of the test. It is believed that this initial peak was caused by the release of some organic components due to compaction and placement of the refuse.

(11) Suspended Solids — initial concentrations ranged from 1,000 to 2,000 mg./l. but quickly dropped to average approximately 200 mg./l. for the first 400 days of the test. At that time, they increased with increasing volumes of leachate, to average 750 mg./l.

(12) Total Solids — total solids ranged between 10,000 and 28,000 mg./l. with an initial peak of 40,000 mg./l.

(13) Nickel — no nickel was detected in the leachate until 150 days into the test; after that time, concentration levels did not exceed 0.9 mg./l. Most frequently concentration levels fell between 0.2 and 0.3 mg./l. Like zinc, once nickel was detected in the leachate, it was present on a continuous basis. This again indicates the initiation of some release mechanism which was not active prior to that time.

(14) Copper — copper concentrations were erratic. In general, copper concentrations were less than 0.1 mg./l. although peaks occurred between 100 and 200 days into the test at a level of approximately 5 mg./l., and again a peak at approximately 600 days into the test occurred at a level of about 7 mg./l.

Gas samples taken from various depths within the refuse were analyzed on a routine basis for carbon monoxide, hydrogen sulfide, nitrogen, oxygen, carbon dioxide and total hydrocarbons reported as methane. No carbon monoxide or hydrogen sulfide was detected. Oxygen, carbon dioxide, methane and nitrogen were found to exist in refuse void gases. In general, the percentage of oxygen decreased with depth and increasing time, and the percentage of carbon dioxide and methane increased with depth and increasing time.

While the hydrocarbon gas is reported as methane, the accumulation of increasing percentages with depth indicates that it is possibly a denser, higher molecular weight gas than methane. The lack of significant methane in the top part indicates little migration of the gas occurred. The gas results were a clear indicator of the point of transition from aerobic to anaerobic conditions. As an indicator of the degree of activity, it is believed that gas constituents are more indicative of the landfill age than temperatures.

While the field facility experimental data were incomplete at the time of this report, there are some data which are worthy of consideration. Temperatures at the various levels indicated that the high level of biological activity within the lysimeter refuse did not occur within the field refuse. There are two reasons for this; first, due to ease of compaction, higher field refuse densities were attained, and secondly, field temperatures during refuse placement were lower on an average daily basis than those in the laboratory.

These two conditions, higher density and lower temperatures, combined to moderate the initial biological activity. The overall temperature behavior of the landfill is similar to that of the laboratory lysimeter. Internal temperatures tend to moderate and not be influenced by environmental conditions once a substantial period has elapsed after test initiation.

The gas data for the field landfill indicate that a high percentage of carbon dioxide was present from the start of the test. Oxygen and methane levels were relatively low. Because the field landfill was not under very stable conditions, curves were erratic and no definite conclusions could be reached about the landfill characteristics.

The character of the ground water which underlies the landfill was recorded. In general, the ground water quality met drinking water standards. Between the time of the initiation of the field landfill and the preparation of this report, no significant contamination was detected within the groundwater wells.

A portion of the project was concerned with a moisture routing model for predicting the leachate production pattern of a sanitary landfill. The model was developed for a one-dimensional, downward vertical flow system and was based upon the equation of continuity. Water input was due only to surface infiltration.

Use of the model requires knowledge of the hydraulic characteristics of the cover soil and refuse. The model was used to study the experimental laboratory and field sanitary landfills used in this project, as well as several hypothetical landfills.

The study of the laboratory sanitary landfill provided a test of model reliability. It was concluded that the model is reasonably valid; differences between computed and actual times are attributed to:

(1) The fact that the experimental landfill did not behave exactly like the theoretical field capacity model; that is, i.e., no downward movement of moisture

until field capacity is attained in a particular layer.

(2) The refuse field capacity probably changes during its life cycle, and,

(3) The refuse field capacity and its initial moisture content data are only reasonable approximations of actual values.

The results of the study of several hypothetical sanitary landfill sites across the country indicate that landfills in over half the nation will produce leachate if there is a net water infiltration. First appearance of leachate is dependent on site conditions, including surface grading, vegetation and soil parameters. Parameters include type, thickness, density, permeability, field capacity and initial moisture content. Refuse parameters which control leachate appearance include type, thickness, original moisture content, field capacity and initial density. Based on field and laboratory studies of ground and underground refuse, it was shown that grinding significantly increased field capacity as refuse size decreased; however, for a given ground size the field capacity tended to approach an asymptote which is unique for that size.

It is concluded that most landfills will eventually produce leachate, as well as gases. Whether or not the leachate is visible depends on the landfill's discharge pattern. If the site development encourages leaching to surface areas, then its appearance will be obvious; on the other hand, when leaching occurs directly to ground water bodies, its effect can only be detected by monitoring wells which must be carefully installed and developed.

The leachate produced by a sanitary landfill developed with current refuse composition during its early life is highly polluted. The leachate is acidic (pH of 5.5) and carries many dissolved and suspended solids which place a burden, both as to quantity and quality, on the capability of underlying soils to provide renovation prior to contact with the ground water system.

LABORATORY SANITARY LANDFILL LYSIMETER

Several designs for the laboratory lysimeter were evaluated during the initial stages of the project. The final design, which is presented herein, represents the results of that effort. The lysimeter simulated the center of a sanitary landfill with an 8 foot thick (at time of placement) refuse layer covered with a 2 foot soil layer. These dimensions were chosen since they were representative of current practice, and it was believed that by using these values, an initial quantitative understanding of the behavior of many existing landfills would result. A major design criteria was that the lysimeter environmental conditions should represent climate conditions common to southeastern Pennsylvania for a landfill located above micaceous granite gneiss bedrock in soils derived therefrom. All design criteria were based on a requirement that the laboratory landfill data could be correlated with the field facility data.

Design Criteria

In order to simulate an in-situ sanitary landfill, several site and physical conditions were incorporated in the design of the lysimeter and the preparation of the refuse. These conditions were:

(1) The lysimeter simulated the center portion of a large sanitary landfill. usually, a landfill covers a large areal extent relative to its thickness; therefore, transverse heat losses would be minimal in comparison to heat losses at its atmospheric and soil contact boundaries.

(2) The atmospheric boundary simulated southeastern Pennsylvania conditions. Temperature levels and added water were equivalent to the average monthly atmospheric conditions for the locality.

(3) The refuse-subsurface soil contact boundary temperature was equivalent to in-situ soil temperatures at the same depth for the area.

(4) The lysimeter size was such as to insure the validity of collected data.

(5) The size of the refuse components was such as to insure validation of any data collected.

(6) The composition of the refuse represented a "typical" sanitary landfill.

Tank Characteristics

The lysimeter (Fig. 11.1) was constructed of 1/4 inch low carbon steel plate. Interior walls were covered with 1/8 inch thick fiberglass to protect the steel against corrosion due to the products of decomposition. The tank was thirteen feet high with a six foot square cross-section and was supported by six 6I12 beams equally spaced along its bottom. These beams, in turn, were supported by two 10I35 steel beams which rested on the laboratory floor.

Leachate collection was facilitated by using an inverted pyramid-shaped trough (Fig. 11.2) which was located in the bottom of the tank and was constructed of low carbon steel covered with fiberglass. The side slopes of the trough were 1 on 1, and positioned at its apex was a 1/4 inch stainless steel pipe for leachate removal. The interior of the trough was filled with Ottawa sand and glass beads sized and arranged as shown in Figure 11.3. The sizes of the sand and beads were selected to permit free passage of leachate. The total height of the trough was three feet, which reduced the effective interior tank height to ten feet.

Environmental System

Bottom Air Temperature Control: The air space beneath the trough was maintained at a temperature of 57.2°F. This temperature was equivalent to the average yearly soil temperature at a depth of ten feet below the ground surface in

FIGURE 11.1: LYSIMETER CROSS-SECTION—SIMULATED SANITARY LANDFILL

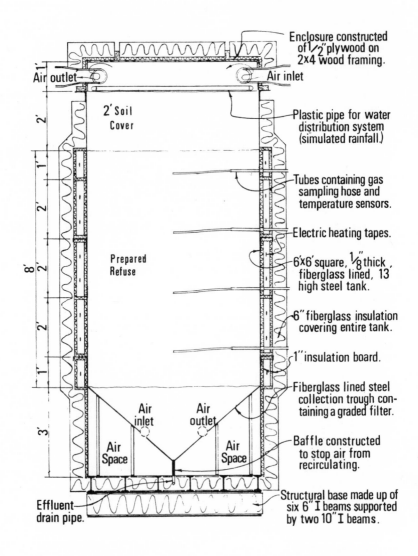

Source: Pollution of Subsurface Water by Sanitary Landfills, EPA, 1971

FIGURE 11.2: DETAIL OF LOWER TEMPERATURE CONTROLLING COMPARTMENT

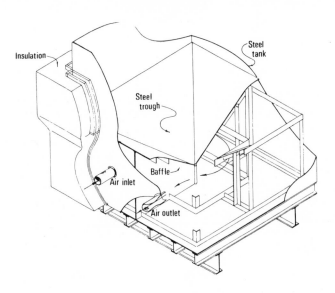

FIGURE 11.3: LYSIMETER EFFLUENT COLLECTION TROUGH

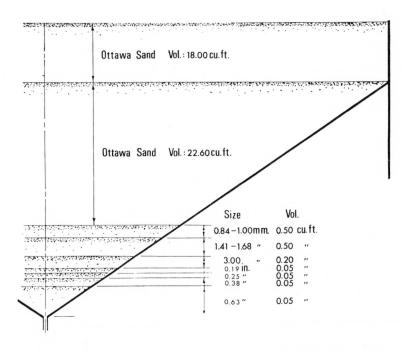

Source: Pollution of Subsurface Water by Sanitary Landfills, EPA, 1971

southeastern Pennsylvania. A schematic of the cooling system is shown in Figure 11.4, in section B—B. A section through the air space is shown in Figure 11.1.

Top Air Temperature Control: Air temperature above the landfill was changed monthly to conform with the average monthly air temperatures in southeastern Pennsylvania. Two systems were used to control this temperature.

The first system consisted of a controlled temperature air sweep which passed directly over the free surface of the cover soil. This system is shown in schematic in Figure 11.4, section A—A in the cross-section through the tank (Fig - ure 11.1). Early in the operation of the lysimeter, it was found that the air sweep across the soil introduced a small (a difference of less than one inch of water) positive pressure in the voids of the refuse. While the presence of this pressure presented no serious system function problem, it was believed that it might affect gas movement within and out of the refuse. To eliminate the problem of positive air pressure, a system using cooling water was developed. This system is shown in cross-section in Figure 11.5 and in schematic in Fig - ure 11.6. Cooling water was pumped through the tubing and its temperature was controlled by an immersible cooling coil placed in a 55 gallon tank. It was possible to place this system directly on the top of the free soil surface due to refuse settlement (see section on compaction). This system and the original air system which was separated from the soil surface by a sealed steel plate interacted effectively in maintaining air temperatures above the soil surface.

Water Application System: Distilled water was added to the top of the soil cover, when needed, on a weekly basis. The water added represented the excess of precipitation over evapotranspiration for southeastern Pennsylvania. The water was distributed over the soil surface by means of rigid plastic pipe with holes drilled in the top. The pipe system was gravity fed from outside the tank. Using this system, the water "rained" lightly on the soil surface.

Insulation

Minimizing of heat exchange through the lysimeter's vertical walls was most essential to its use as a simulator of the center of a landfill. To control heat exchange, the vertical walls of the lysimeter were completely insulated (Figure 11.1). Two inches of urethane insulation board, six inches of fiberglass insula- tion board, six inches of fiberglass insulation, stagnant air pockets and heating tapes were used.

Heat Flow into the Lysimeter: Movement of heat into the lysimeter, when internal temperatures were less than laboratory temperatures, was minimized by the combination of urethane insulation board, fiberglass insulation and stagnant air pockets.

Heat Flow out of the Lysimeter: Flow of heat out of the lysimeter was con- trolled by the same insulation system mentioned in the previous section, and

FIGURE 11.4: DETAILS OF AIR CIRCULATION SYSTEM

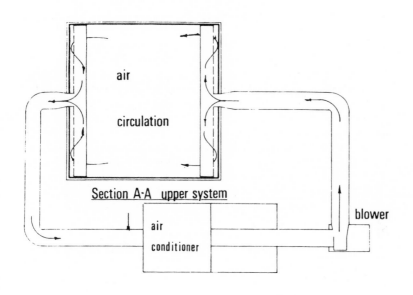

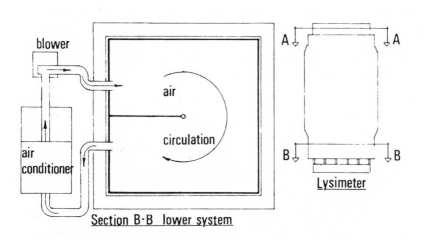

Source: Pollution of Subsurface Water by Sanitary Landfills, EPA, 1971

FIGURE 11.5: LYSIMETER COOLING SYSTEM (MODIFIED)

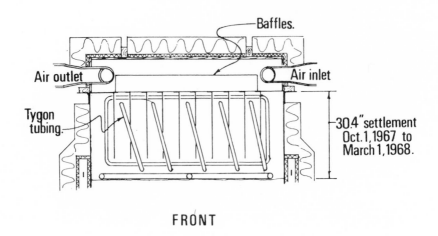

FRONT

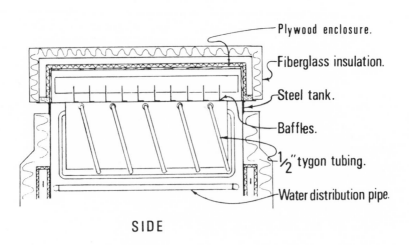

SIDE

Source: Pollution of Subsurface Water by Sanitary Landfills, EPA, 1971

FIGURE 11.6: SCHEMATIC – WATER COOLING SYSTEM

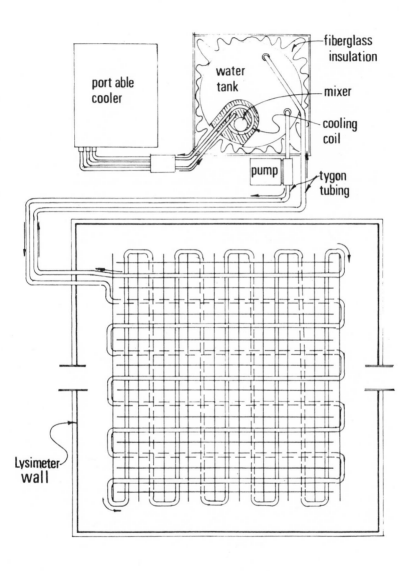

Source: Pollution of Subsurface Water by Sanitary Landfills, EPA, 1971

heating tapes located in the stagnant air pockets (Fig. 11.1). The heating tapes were energized by thermistor-activated controllers which supplied power. These bands of "active" insulation covered one foot segments at the top and bottom of the refuse zone and three two foot intermediate zones. Each zone had its own controller and functioned independently of the others. The use of zoning permitted control of heat outflow at each level. Local control was necessary when temperatures inside the lysimeter were not constant vertically.

When the laboratory temperatures were higher than the interior temperatures, at any level, the tapes did not heat the stagnant air pockets. However, when the temperature at a particular level in the lysimeter was greater than the laboratory temperatures by at least $1°F.$, the corresponding tape was turned on by the controller. Power to heat the tapes was supplied in an amount proportional to the temperature difference, but at a rate so as to minimize overshooting of the desired temperature. The tapes were turned on until the difference between the internal temperature, at any level, and the corresponding stagnant air space temperature was less than $1°F.$ When a difference of $1°F.$ or less was reached, the tapes were inactivated.

In addition to the controlling thermistors, an auxiliary set of thermistors was used to monitor the behavior of the heating tapes. Location of a typical set of thermistors and a schematic of the controller are shown in Figure 11.7.

Instrumentation and Sampling

Three major parameters were monitored: temperatures, gases, and quantity and composition of the leachate.

Temperatures: An automatic scanning-printing system using thermistors and a digital thermometer was used to monitor temperatures. Temperatures were measured at seven locations inside the lysimeter and at two exterior locations. Thermistor locations, at the time of fill placement, are shown in Fig. 11.8 The thermistors monitored temperatures in the air space above the soil cover, at the air-soil cover interface, at the soil cover-refuse interface, at 1, 3, 5 and 7 feet below the top of the refuse, at the refuse-Ottawa sand interface, in the bottom air sweep and at two locations outside the tank.

Initially, temperatures were recorded every hour, but the system was changed over to a four hour record time after the temperature changes ceased being highly transient.

Gas Samples: Gases were sampled at five different locations in the tank. The sampling positions, which are shown in Figure 11.1, were the sampling ports on the side of the tank at depths of 3, 5, 7 and 9 feet below the top soil surface (as initially placed) and in the air space above the cover soil surface, but below the steel coverplate. Side samples were taken through ports on the side of the tank. To sample the air above the soil cover, a 1/8 inch diameter tube

FIGURE 11.7: HEATING CONTROL SYSTEM

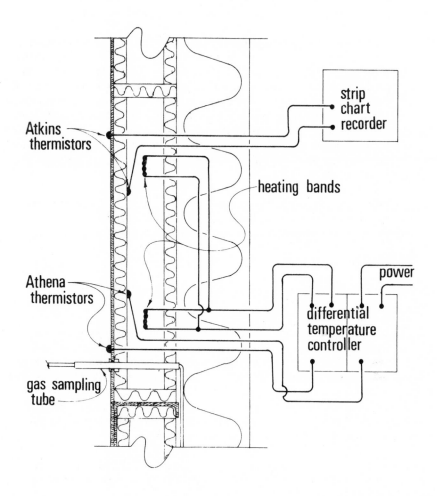

Source: Pollution of Subsurface Water by Sanitary Landfills, EPA, 1971

FIGURE 11.8: THERMISTOR LOCATION

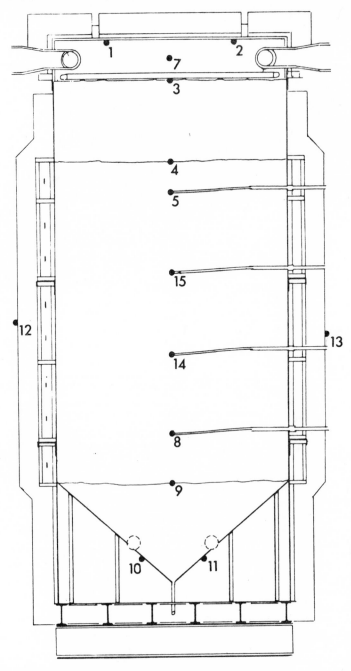

Source: Pollution of Subsurface Water by Sanitary Landfills, EPA, 1971

was temporarily disconnected from a wet gas meter (the wet gas meter was used to maintain atmospheric pressure). After sampling, the air space was purged to maintain "atmospheric" conditions.

Gas samples were taken three times a week and analyzed for the gases listed below:

Carbon dioxide	Methane (total hydrocarbons)
Oxygen	Hydrogen sulfide
Nitrogen	Carbon monoxide

Leachate: Leachate, when available, was collected in the bottom trough and removed through the drain once a week. The analyses performed on the leachate are listed below:

pH	Nitrogen (ammonia, organic)
Hardness	Dissolved oxygen
Phosphate	Chloride
Sodium	Suspended solids
Total residue (total dissolved solids)	Nitrate
	Chemical oxygen demand
Biological oxygen demand	Iron
Zinc	Copper
Nickel	Sulfate

Refuse Placement

Materials: The refuse at placement had the composition listed in Table 1. The refuse was sized so as to minimize size influence. Cardboard pieces were not larger than one foot square. Small pieces of metal and unrolled cans were used to eliminate compaction and placement problems due to arching and large voids. Other paper products, glass, plastics, etc. were also sized to prevent their having an unrealistic influence on lysimeter functioning.

Compaction: A procedure was developed for external compaction, since it was not possible to compact the refuse within the lysimeter. The general scheme consisted of filling (with a mixture of prepared refuse) six foot by three foot by two foot wooden boxes which had a trap door bottom (Fig. 11.9). The refuse components were premixed by hand prior to placement. The refuse was then compressed in the box in the steel frame, shown in Figure 11.10, by using a steel coverplate loaded by the hydraulic jack. The frame was designed to facilitate insertion and removal of the refuse boxes.

The refuse was compacted until the original height of two feet had decreased to one foot for a compaction ratio of 2:1. The 2:1 compaction ratio occurred when the unit pressure on the refuse was approximately six pounds per square inch. Use of the 2:1 compaction ratio criteria did not prove entirely satisfactory. Upon release of the compaction pressure, a rebound of approximately

TABLE 1: REFUSE PLACEMENT

Percent Composition of Refuse

Percent	
23.38	Corrugated paper boxes
9.40	Newspapers
6.80	Magazine paper
5.57	Brown paper
2.75	Mail
2.06	Paper food cartons
1.98	Tissue paper
0.76	Plastic coated paper
0.76	Wax cartons
2.29	Vegetable food wastes
1.53	Citrus rinds and seeds
2.29	Meat scraps, cooked
2.29	Fried fats
2.29	Wood
2.29	Ripe tree leaves
1.53	Flower garden plants
1.53	Lawn grass, green
1.53	Evergreens
0.76	Plastics
0.76	Rags
0.38	Leather goods
0.38	Rubber composition
0.76	Paints and oils
0.76	Vacuum cleaner catch
1.53	Dirt
6.86	Metals
7.73	Glass, ceramics, ash
9.05	Adjusted moisture
100.00	

Laboratory Lysimeter

Component	Gms. Pollutant/gm. dry refuse or wt.percent
Crude fiber	38.3%
Moisture content	18.2%
Ash	20.2%
Free carbon	0.57%
Nitrogen	
a) free	.02 mg/gram
b) organic	1.23 "
Water solubles:	
a) sodium	2.33 "
b) chloride	.97 "
c) sulfate	2.19 "
C.O.D.	42.49 "
Phosphate	.15 "
Hardness	10.12 mg/CaCO$_3$/gm.
Major Metals:	
Aluminum, Iron, Silicon	>5.00% (By spectrographic analysis)**
Minor Metals:	
Calcium, Magnesium, Potassium	1.0-5.0% (By spectrographic analysis)**

**Of non-volatile portion.

FIGURE 11.9: LOADING BOX

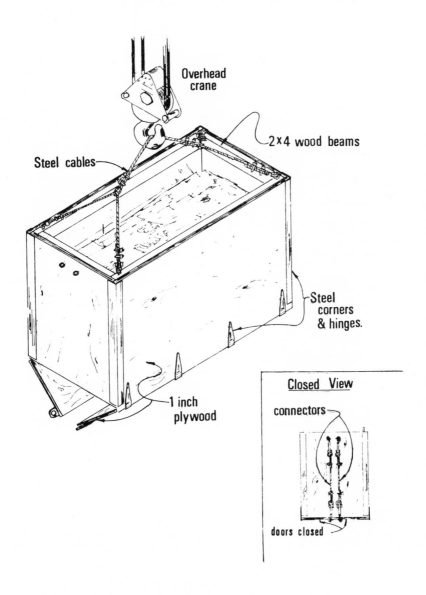

Source: Pollution of Subsurface Water by Sanitary Landfills, EPA, 1971

FIGURE 11.10: REFUSE COMPACTION FRAME

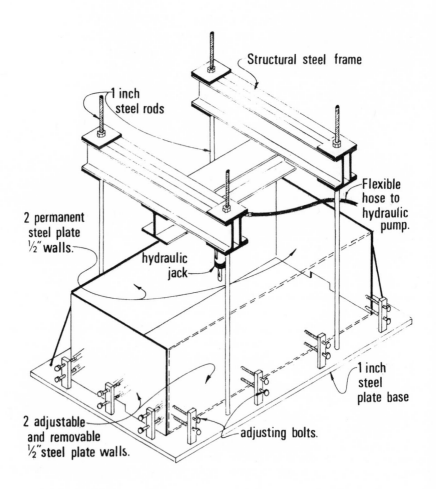

Source: Pollution of Subsurface Water by Sanitary Landfills, EPA, 1971

two inches occurred. At the compaction ratio of 2:1, a dry density at place-ment of approximately 327 lbs./yd.^{3} was obtained.

After compaction in the frame, each load was placed in the tank by means of an overhead crane. Eight one foot layers of compacted material were required to fill the tank to the desired refuse height. Each layer required two loads for a total of sixteen compactions. To place the refuse, the loading box was first positioned so that the bottom trap door rested on previously placed material. Then, the end straps (Fig. 11.10) were removed and the box raised to allow the doors to open. This procedure permitted the compaction material to be depos-ited with minimum disturbance. All voids, corners, etc., were hand filled to insure elimination of any large channels.

After placement, the refuse was covered with two feet of soil taken from the field site. The soil was hand tamped into position, and at placement, had a density of 110 lbs./ft.^{3} . The total weight of the soil cover resulted in approx-imately 1 1/2 lbs./in.^{2} of contact pressure on the refuse. The immediate settle-ment produced a refuse dry density of 378 lbs./yd.^{3}. This refuse surface settle-ment was approximately equal to the sum of the individual rebounds (16 inches) that occurred after each compaction. It was less than the total of the rebounds since during the loading of the tank, each refuse layer caused some recompres-sion of underlying layers.

FIELD SANITARY LANDFILL FACILITY

During the planning stages of this study, several existing landfills were evaluated for their potential use. The primary reason for acceptance of the site utilized was the fact that it was a new landfill, which could be studied from time of initial placement. Other factors which were weighed in the final determination were the quality of the proposed landfilling operation, the natural terrain of the site, the proximity to Drexel, and the site location relative to existing human habitation. Specific reasons for selection of this site, relative to ground water and site geology, are enumerated in the section on location.

Location

The test site was a portion of the southeastern Chester County Sanitary Land-fill located in Kennett Township, Chester County, Pennsylvania at the intersec-tion of North Walnut Street and Route #1 Bypass. It was immediately north of Kennett Square, Pennsylvania and was bordered on the west by the East Branch of the Red Clay Creek.

The test site was selected for the following reasons:

(1) The site was underlain by metamorphic bedrock: the geologic materials were typical of those which extend from Washington, D. C. to Boston, Massa-chusetts.

(2) The test site was located in a new landfill: the use of a virgin site permitted the obtaining of background chemical and physical data for both soil and water, which did not reflect any landfill pollution.

(3) The test site was well above ground water: the soils and saprolite (weathered bedrock) were deep and well drained.

Geology — Soils

Regional Geology: The southeastern Pennsylvania region is largely underlain by the Wissahicken schist formation (Lower Paleozoic Age), granite gneiss and gabbroic gneiss and gabbro (Precambrian Age). These metamorphic rocks underlie the metropolitan region from Washington, D. C. to Boston, Massachusetts. These rocks are extensively faulted and have similar hydrogeologic characteristics. Bedrock is usually deeply weathered and highly decomposed resulting in a thick saprolite zone. The most common soils that develop in material weathered from this rock type belong to the Glenville, Chester, Glenelg and Worsham series.

The Glenelg series consists of moderately deep, well drained soils of uplands. The soils have moderate permeability and are better drained than the Glenville series. The Chester series consists of soils deep and well drained with moderate to moderately rapid permeability.

The Glenville series consists of deep, moderately well drained soils. They are on concave areas in the uplands and around the heads of streams, where the water table is high in the soil for long periods. Their permeability is moderately low.

The Worsham series consists of deep poorly drained soils of uplands. They have low permeability and are water-logged most of the time. They occur around seeps fed by springs at the heads of streams, along small streams, in slight depressions and along areas at the base of slopes.

Ground water is under water table conditions flowing from topographic highs to lows. The source of this ground water is rainfall that has infiltrated locally to recharge the ground water aquifers.

Site Geology: The site consists of a northeast, southwest drained topographic high with a range in elevation from 320 feet to 380 feet above mean sea level. The map location for this site is 11.5 inches west and 3.75 inches south of the northeast corner of the Kennett Square, Pennsylvania — Delaware 7 1/2 minute quadrangle.

Ten soil identification pits were dug during the initial site investigation. Soil in these pits varied from 35 inches to 61 inches in depth overlying saprolite, a highly weathered bedrock. The general soil conditions consist of the Glenville and Worsham soils located below the 350 foot contour line and the Glenelg and Chester soil located above this elevation. The granite gneiss underlying the site is largely deeply weathered, micaceous, friable to compact, fine to medium bedded, has iron staining on joints and bedding planes, and is locally quartz-rich. Depth of bedrock is generally shallower on the crest of the topographic high.

The direction of ground-water movement beneath most of the site is toward the southwest where it discharges into an unnamed tributary of the East Branch of the Red Clay Creek. At the extreme northern edge of the site, groundwater movement is toward the highway cut for U. S. Route No. 1 Bypass. Ground-water movement at the western end of the site is toward the west to the East Branch Red Clay Creek, which flows in a southern direction. Two reservoirs for the Kennett Square water supply are present at the west end of the site between the stream and the landfill site. They are approximately 10 feet above the stream level and are hydrologically isolated from the ground-water flow system. Southwestward drainage is present approximately 1/4 mile south of the site. The confluence of the unnamed tributary and East Branch Red Clay Creek is near the southwest corner of the site in the headwaters region of the creek.

Test Pit Geology: The predominant soil type is a strong brown silt loam which is blocky, friable when moist, non-sticky and non-plastic when dry. It is of the Chester series marginal with Glenelg series. The bulk density of this soil falls within the range of 1.19 to 1.59. The average moisture held at 40 mm. tension is approximately 25% by weight. The permeability of these soils varies between 1.84 and 30×10^{-4} cm./sec. Using an average density of 91.4 lbs./ft.^{3} for undisturbed sub-strata and an average cation exchange data for the "C" horizon for Chester and Glenelg soils, the exchange capacity has been calculated to be 4,440 milligram equivalents per cubic foot of which 2,200 are hydrogen ions and the remainder metallic cations, mostly calcium and magnesium. This cation exchange capacity represents a considerable absorptive and renovating power. The extractible cations consist mainly of calcium.

Air rotary drill borings were made to determine subsurface conditions and to install the various sampling tubes. On the basis of three borings in the immediate vicinity of the test landfill, the following geological conditions were found to exist: three feet of field silt loam soil overlying 33 feet to 37 feet of a soil micaceous gneiss bedrock.

Samples of the saprolite were taken in the base of the test pit. The typical saprolite, which comprises about 75% of the pit floor is micaceous with abundant feldspar and a moderate amount of quartz. Approximately 20% of the area is a predominantly quartz-rich saprolite, and approximately 5% of the area is an iron- and manganese-rich saprolite.

Groundwater was encountered at depths of 20 feet to 22 feet in the 11 borings around the test landfill. The direction of groundwater movement is to the southwest with a gradient of approximately 1/2 foot in 20 feet. The test site is located so that groundwater movement is away from the site and is not affected by adjacent landfilling operations.

Instrumentation

Basic instrumentation of the site was similar to that of the laboratory lysimeter. Instrumentation began in the fall of 1967 after excavation of the test pit. A four foot diameter concrete pipe was located in the center of the test pit. This concrete pipe served as a hub from which all horizontal instrumentation extended into the test pit.

Gas Samples: Gas samples were taken through tubes located within the fill and at various locations in the in-situ earth material above the water table. Locations were chosen so as to monitor gas and temperature changes both horizontally and vertically inside, outside and beneath the test landfill. Lateral sampling tubes extended from the center concrete pipe into the test landfill. Vertical sampling tubes extended from the ground surface to the various sampling depths.

Figure 11.11 is a schematic of a gas sampling tubes and thermistor well. The wells were placed using a four inch rotary drill. Each hole was predrilled and then instrumented using the following sequence:

(1) Six inches of 1/8 inch to 1/2 inch gravel was placed at the bottom of the hole.

(2) Rigid 1 1/4 inch i.d. plastic pipe containing predrilled holes and a neoprene stopper was inserted into and sealed in the stopper. The neoprene stopper was positioned in the tube at the terminal point of the drilled holes. The stopper was sealed in the tube to prevent gas leakage.

(3) After pipe insertion, an additional 12 inches of gravel were placed around the exterior of the pipe.

(4) A coarse to fine sand pack was placed on top of the gravel to a depth of approximately 5 feet.

(5) The distance from the top of the sand to the ground surface was tightly sealed with bentonite clay.

Temperatures: Temperatures were monitored once every four hours by an automatic scanning-printing system using thermistors and a digital thermometer. The thermistors were positioned at 50 locations throughout the test area.

Groundwater Samples: Fourteen groundwater observation wells drilled approximately 10 feet below the groundwater table were located over the site. The groundwater wells were located so as to be in the direction of groundwater movement, which was predetermined by installation of pilot wells prior to excavation of the main test pit.

FIGURE 11.11: DETAILS OF GAS SAMPLING AND THERMISTOR WELLS

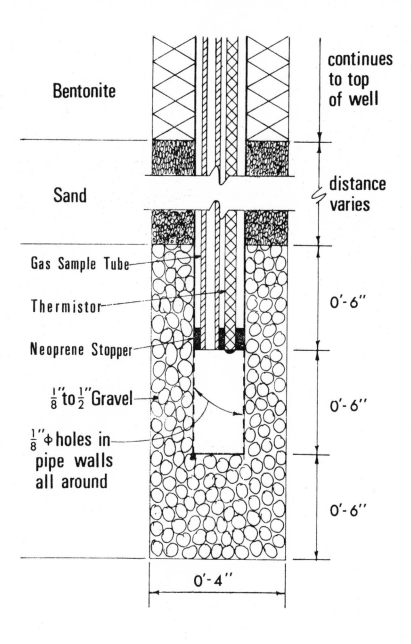

Source: Pollution of Subsurface Water by Sanitary Landfills, EPA, 1971

The wells consisted of 1 1/4 inch i.d. semirigid plastic pipe placed in a 5 1/2 inch diameter drill hole. The pipes were 35 feet long and had 1/8 inch diameter holes drilled along the bottom 9 feet. The volume of the drill hole exterior to the pipe was gravel packed (1/8 inch to 1/4 inch gravel) to a distance of 1 foot above the top of the holes. The remaining volume of the space was filled with bentonite clay to within five feet of the soil surface. From the top of the bentonite to the ground surface, native soil was used to complete the seal. The sealing procedure insured free passage of suspended solids into the wells, but prohibited entrance of surface water.

Unsaturated Soil Water Samples: Water samples were obtained from the soil above the water table and in the refuse by using a soil moisture sampler. Method of placement was the same as for the gas sampling tubes.

Soil Moisture and Density Measurement: Four stainless steel access tubes, 1 5/8 inches i.d. and 0.35 inch wall thickness, were located within the landfill and the adjacent undisturbed soil. Each tube was 18 feet long. These tubes permitted the measurement of in-situ moisture and density.

Sample Analysis

Gas Samples: Samples were obtained weekly and analyzed for carbon dioxide, oxygen, nitrogen, methane, hydrogen sulfide and carbon monoxide using a gas chromatograph.

Groundwater Samples: Samples were obtained weekly. The analyses performed were listed previously. To obtain samples from the shallower wells, a vacuum system was used. A pump, located in the instrument house, was attached to Tygon tubing which was lowered into each well to a depth of 25 feet. The pump was then turned on and the sample was collected in a liter flask and transferred to the sample bottles.

To obtain samples below 28 feet, a Clayton-Mark sand pump with 3/4 inch i.d. Tygon tubing was used. The sand pump operated on the same principle as a bailing bucket with a ball bearing in its housing. As the pump was lowered into the well, the water raised the ball bearing, opening the entrance port. Then, when the pump was pulled from the well, the ball fell back into place and then closed the port. The sampling method insured a representative sample with no filtering.

Unsaturated Soil Moisture Samples: A vacuum was applied to the upper end of each tube for a time sufficient to obtain an adequate amount of sample (determined experimentally). The soil moisture samples accumulated in the bottom of the tube above the porous ceramic cup. They were removed from the tube by a small pump. The samples were analyzed for the same pollutants as the groundwater samples.

Soil Moisture and Density Determination: The testing procedure was as established by Nuclear-Chicago for using their equipment in soils.

Refuse Placement

The filling of the test area began on April 28, 1968 and was completed on May 14, 1968. The trench method of sanitary landfilling with horizontal compaction was used. At the end of each day's operation, the refuse was covered with approximately six inches of soil.

Refuse and daily soil cover were compacted at natural moisture content. The compaction equipment was a Caterpillar Front End Loader, Model No. 955K. This model weighed approximately 16.5 tons and produced a contact pressure of about 7 pounds per square inch.

The refuse used was primarily domestic with a small percentage of industrial, mainly plastics and cardboard. Collection trucks were primarily compacter type with 16 to 20 cubic yard capacities. During the filling operation, gross and net weight of each truck was obtained to compute refuse weights and densities. Incoming densities ranged from a minimum of 150 pounds per cubic yard to a maximum of 700 pounds per cubic yard. Average density was 500 pounds per cubic yard.

Total weight of emplaced refuse was 274 tons. Neglecting the 6 inch daily soil cover, the compacted density of the fill was 740 pounds per cubic yard for a compaction ratio of 1.5 to 1. The estimated total thickness of intermediate soil covers used at the end of each day's filling was 1.4 feet. Using a net height of 6.6 feet for refuse gave an adjusted initial unit weight of 895 pounds per cubic yard.

A random sampling technique was used to obtain representative refuse samples. The chemical composition of the emplaced refuse, based on these composite samples, is given in Table 2.

TABLE 2: FIELD REFUSE CHEMICAL COMPOSITION*

Ash	20.2 percent
Free carbon	0.57 percent
Crude fiber	38.0 percent
Moisture content	26.6 percent
Hardness	2.67 mg./gram
Phosphate	0.01 mg./gram
Sulfate	2.72 mg./gram
Chloride	0.41 mg./gram
Sodium	0.62 mg./gram
Nitrogen	
(a) ammonia	0 mg./gram
(b) organic	0.02 mg./gram
COD	1.32 mg./gram

(continued)

TABLE 2: (continued)

Major Metals:	
Aluminum, calcium,	$>$ 5 percent**
Iron, silicon,	
Sodium	
Minor Metals:	
Magnesium, titanium	1-5 percent**

*Preliminary results (digested 8 hours).
**Emission spectroscopy of nonvolatile portion.

EXPERIMENTAL RESULTS

Lysimeter

Experimental data are reported for the period October 1, 1967 to August 31, 1969.

Leachate Quantity: The generation of substantial quantities of leachate required that each lysimeter component be at its respective field capacity. The soil cover, refuse and Ottawa sand-glass bead bed were placed in the lysimeter in a relatively dry state. As a result, a major portion of the water initially added was adsorbed by each component until it reached its respective field capacity. It is noteworthy that within one week after the initiation of the test, a small amount of leachate was obtained.

As the net quantity of water stored in the lysimeter increased leachate production increased. A significant amount of leachate began to be produced by the lysimeter at approximately 430 days into the test. However, field capacity was not attained until the end of the time period covered by this report.

The phase relationship between water added and leachate production was evident. Even during periods of low leachate production, any decreases in water input further reduced or eliminated leachate. On the other hand, as water input increased, leachate production also increased.

Leachate production can be attributed to one or all of the following sources:

(1) *From the Refuse:* Most of the initial leachate is obtained from the refuse organic components and initial moisture content by the compaction and placement procedure.

(2) *From Channeling:* Some of the water added at the top of the lysimeter finds a direct route through the refuse to the collection trough, due to any refuse inhomogeneities.

(3) *From an Advanced Wetting Front:* The wetting front in the refuse moves

as a broad band rather than as a single-line interface. As a result, substantial increases in leachate occur before the entire system is at field capacity.

(4) *From the Main Wetting Front:* This is the leachate produced when the system reaches field capacity. At this stage, input water and leachate quantities become approximately equal.

From the data obtained it was concluded that sources (1) and (2) were responsible for the leachate collected during the early time period. Their influence on leachate collected during the latter time periods was negligible. Between 175 and 210 days, leachate production increased substantially. However, the amount of leachate produced was significantly less than the input water quantities. This behavior pattern can best be described by the one outlined as source (3). Finally, in the second year, leachate quantity increased to a level almost equal to input water quantities. This behavior indicated that the entire system was at about field capacity, and that a transition between source (3) and source (4) was occurring. Full field capacity, hence, source (4) was attained at the end of the period covered by this report.

pH: Wide variations in pH occurred during the test period. Generally, solutions were acidic with a mean pH value of approximately 5.5. It was also concluded that leachate pH bears a relationship to leachate quantity. It appeared that highly erratic pH values correspond to periods of low leachate production and that pH values between 5 and 6 correspond to periods of high leachate production.

It was believed that flow rate through the refuse is a major controlling factor in establishing leachate pH, and that with high flow rates, the pH will generally be acidic. Generation of large quantities of acidic leachate compound the potential pollution problem, because low pH values reduce exchange capacities of renovating soils at the time when quantities are high.

Iron: The curve for iron concentration on comparison with the leachate volume curve indicates that leachate volumes had a significant influence on iron concentration. During low leachate flow periods, iron concentrations were low, whereas, when leachate quantities were high there was a significant increase in iron concentrations.

This behavior pattern may be explained by the fact that during periods of low leachate volume, solution pH exceeded 5.5 and during periods of high leachate volume, solution pH was less than 5.5. Below a pH of 5.5, many iron salts, both ferric and ferrous, are soluble. Because of their ability to remain in solution, they are more easily removed from the refuse. Above a pH of 5.5, iron salts are less soluble, will precipitate and be filtered from the leachate by either the refuse or underlying materials. Iron concentrations were in excess of 1,600 mg./l. during both periods of high leachate volume.

Zinc: Significant increases in zinc concentrations occurred after one and one third years of testing. Initial concentrations were as high as 120 to 135 mg./l. More usual concentration levels were between 15 and 30 mg./l. After the first appearance of zinc, it was in all leachate samples. This pattern indicated the release of the zinc ion due to the breakdown of some refuse component which previously had resisted the leaching action. Approximately 50 grams had been removed by the end of the test period.

Phosphate: Concentration levels reached 130 mg./l. during the initial period of the test. Thereafter, concentration levels were markedly lower and irregular. While recorded values were usually less than 5 mg./l., 30 mg./l. peaks occurred at 100 and 600 days. A total of 3.8 grams were removed during the test period with most of this removed during the last 60 days.

Sulfate: Initial values of sulfate ion concentrations were 250 mg./l. After a decrease to between 25 and 75 mg./l. at approximately 100 days, they increased to peaks between 325 and 375 mg./l. During a second high period at 600 days, concentrations peaked between 400 and 500 mg./l.

In general, sulfate ion concentration levels increased with increased leachate production, and as the system approached field capacity. It appears as if periods of high sulfate ion concentration lag somewhat behind periods of high leachate production. Sulfate removed during the test totaled 300 grams with most obtained during the latter portion of the test period.

Chloride: Initial chloride ion concentrations peaked at 700 mg./l. shortly after test initiation. Concentrations decreased to relatively low levels during the period between 30 and 210 days and then increased to a maximum of almost 2,400 mg./l. They then decreased to the 1,700 mg./l. concentration level where they remained for a sustained period. Toward the end of the test period they decreased to approximately 200 mg./l. with a trend toward higher values at the end of the period. Approximately 300 grams of chloride were removed during the test period.

Sodium: Sodium ion concentrations reached 3,800 mg./l. in the time period between 200 and 250 days. This peak occurred at the same time as the chloride ion. However, the sodium concentration curve does not have sustained concentration levels as the chloride concentration curve. After the initial peak, concentration levels decreased to as low as 200 mg./l. and then increased with a trend toward significantly higher values at the end of this period. This behavior pattern is similar to that of the chloride ion. A total of 650 grams of sodium were removed during the test period.

Nitrogen: Organic nitrogen concentration decreased from an initial peak of 482 mg./l. to a value of 8 mg./l. at the end of three months. In general, this curve shows that organic nitrogen was increasing during the test period with localized peaks. In the latter portion of the test period, concentration levels ranged between 100 and 200 mg./l. It is believed that the initial peak was due to squeezing of the organic materials during the compaction process. The total nitrogen (organic) removed was 125 grams. The total free nitrogen removed was approximately 90 grams.

Hardness (as CaCO₃): Except for two periods, hardness concentration levels exceeded 1,500 mg./l. and at 420 days peaked at 5,500 mg./l. Most frequent values ranged between 2,250 and 2,750 mg./l. Approximately 2,800 grams were removed during the test period.

Chemical Oxygen Demand: Data taken showed that chemical oxygen demand concentrations were in excess of 50,000 mg./l. within one month of the initiation of the test. It is believed that this initial peak was caused by the release of some of the organic components due to the compaction and placement process. After the initial peak, chemical oxygen demand decreased to a minimum of 1,000 mg./l. after 120 days. Thereafter, it increased with localized peaks and valleys. Most frequent concentration levels fell between 20,000 and 22,000 mg./l. Chemical oxygen demand during the test period totaled approximately 17,000 grams.

Suspended and Total Solids: In general, concentration levels were random with no readily discernible pattern. Initial values for suspended solids were 26,500 mg./l. and for total solids, they were in excess of 40,000 mg./l. Approximately 700 grams of suspended solids were removed by the leachate during the test period.

Nickel: No nickel was detected prior to 150 days of elapsed test time. After that time, nickel was present in concentrations with peaks at 0.8 mg./l. at 300 days, and 0.9 mg./l. at 710 days. The most frequent concentration levels fell between 0.2 and 0.3 mg./l. During the test period, less than 0.2 gram of nickel were removed.

Copper: The concentration of copper ions reached a peak of 4.7 mg./l. at 150 days and a peak of 7.6 mg./l. occurred at 590 days. Concentration levels were less than one mg./l. except for the latter part of the test period when they increased slightly. The copper ion concentration pattern appears to be independent of any of the other parameters measured. Less than one gram of copper was removed during the test period and most removal occurred at the end of the period.

Lysimeter Temperatures: Curves for temperatures at various locations within the lysimeter are presented in Figure 11.12. The dotted curve represents the average monthly air temperatures. The general pattern of initial temperature behavior can be described as a rapid increase in the temperature at the refuse center followed by a slower rate of increase at adjacent levels. The center temperature peaked at 154°F., whereas, temperatures at adjacent levels did not exceed 143°F., and generally were not in excess of 110°F. to 115°F. The temperature distribution pattern indicates that temperatures in the layers of refuse adjacent to the center layer initially increased due to a spreading effect as heat flowed to both the top and bottom temperature controlled boundaries.

FIGURE 11.12: LYSIMETER THERMISTORS' TEMPERATURES

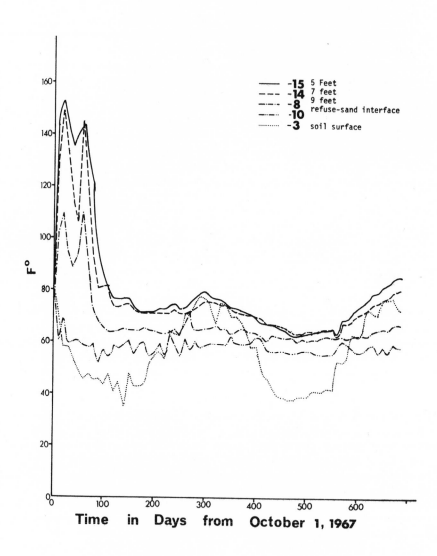

Time in Days from October 1, 1967

Source: Pollution of Subsurface Water by Sanitary Landfills, EPA, 1971

The initial temperature distribution appeared to be controlled by conditions at the refuse center. Once adjacent levels reached their temperature peaks (after approximately 60 days), all temperatures showed a continuous gradual decline until virtually steady state temperatures prevailed. The rapid temperature increase at the refuse center to a peak of $154°F$. is of particular interest in that the rise occurred within 20 days of test initiation. Temperatures then slowly decreased until a 60 day time period had elapsed, and, thereafter, rapidly decreased to a temperature of approximately $80°F$. The initial increase in temperatures at the refuse center was independent of temperature changes at other refuse levels.

The temperature behavior pattern described indicates that the system was initially controlled by general aerobic conditions in the refuse, and that after a 60 day period, anaerobic conditions dominated. Also of interest is that once the internal temperatures became virtually steady state, and the refuse anaerobic, changes in top boundary temperature (bottom boundary temperature was held constant at $57.2°F$.) had little effect on them.

Lysimeter Gases: Gas samples were analyzed on a routine basis for carbon monoxide, hydrogen sulfide, nitrogen, oxygen, carbon dioxide and hydrocarbons (reported as methane). No carbon monoxide or hydrogen sulfide were detected.

Analyses of gases collected from the lysimeter top port indicate a percentage of oxygen approximately equal to that contained in air. It is believed that the concentration level was due to settlement of the refuse in the lysimeter, which positioned the sampling port in or adjacent to the atmospheric air space. This could only be verified upon test completion. In general, gases present at the greater depths in the refuse were not detected (except in minor quantity) in the top gas sampling port.

Gas analyses of samples drawn from the other sampling ports showed relatively similar patterns. Other levels tended to decrease with time and depth, while there was a corresponding increase in carbon dioxide and methane. Significant quantities of methane began to appear 100 days after initiation of the test. However, oxygen, while decreasing in quantity, was detectable over all of the test period. Carbon dioxide was present over the entire test period in amounts which increased slightly with depth.

Methane quantities increased with depth and time. At the second level they were as high as 28% although a more frequently determined maximum was approximately 20%. With increasing depths, maximum values frequently reached 30%.

From the temperature data (Fig. 11.12), it is seen that after the initial transient condition, internal temperatures decreased and were almost nonvarying. This behavior indicates the existence of an anaerobic state within the refuse after the initial high temperature period. However, gas data, particularly the continued existence of oxygen, indicates that an aerobic state also existed in the refuse. From this data, it is concluded that pockets of aerobic and anaerobic activity existed concurrently within the refuse. Temperature and gas curve patterns indicate that the system was becoming more anaerobic with age. That such a behavior pattern existed is not surprising for a young landfill.

While the hydrocarbon gas is reported as methane, the accumulation of increasing percentages with depth indicates that it probably was a denser, higher molecular weight material than methane. No attempt was made to define the exact molecular structure of the gas. The lack of significant methane gas in the top port indicates little migration of the gas occurred, an observation which also supports the contention that the gas was a higher hydrocarbon. It is noteworthy that gas character was more indicative of the internal biological activity and landfill age than internal temperatures.

Field Facility

Background groundwater quality data was collected since the fall of 1967. Concentration ranges for the various ions are tabulated in Table 3.

TABLE 3: GROUNDWATER QUALITY – KENNETT SQUARE FIELD LANDFILL

Ion	Range - mg/1
Iron	0.00 - 0.46
Zinc	0.00 - 1.38
Nickel	0.00 - 0.13
Copper	0.00 - 0.07
Total Dissolved Solids	40.00 - 1.30
Alkalinity	9.00 - 52.00
Hardness	20.00 -112.00
Phosphate	0.00 - 0.50
Sulfate	2.00 - 6.00
Chloride	4.00 - 28.00
Sodium	5.00 - 52.00
Suspended Solids	19.00 -208.00
Ammonia Nitrogen	0.00 - 0.00
Organic Nitrogen	0.00 - 1.50
Chemical Oxygen Demand	21.00 -200.00
Residue	80.00 -330.00
pH	5.30 - 7.00

Refuse was placed in the field test pit in May 1968. After that time, gas, soil-moisture and groundwater samples were collected on a regular basis. Ground-water pollutant levels did not show a significant increase because the entire landfill had not reached field capacity. Reported in this chapter are typical temperature and gas data for various levels within the refuse.

Field Temperatures: The two foot depth sensor data showed maximum response to atmospheric temperatures. The data for the other depths indicated that dur-ing the reported time period, internal temperatures had a highly modulated phase response to atmospheric and ground temperatures. The results indicated very little initial biological activity within the refuse (as compared to the lysi-meter). It is believed that the initial temperature behavior pattern is a result of the relatively high refuse placement density.

Field Gases: Gas samples were analyzed on a routine basis for carbon monoxide, hydrogen sulfide, nitrogen, carbon dioxide and hydrocarbons (reported as methane). No carbon monoxide or hydrogen sulfide was detected. The analyses show an initial high percentage of carbon dioxide at the various depths followed by lower values, with isolated peaks, for the remainder of the test period. Oxy-gen and methane levels were relatively low. The trends of the various gases are very erratic; a pattern which is believed to be due to the dynamic behavior of the landfill because of its young age.

POLLUTANT GENERATION BY UNSATURATED LANDFILL

The generation of liquid pollutants by an unsaturated sanitary landfill is depen-dent upon the content, spacial distribution and time variation of moisture within that landfill. Therefore, knowledge of the factors which control moisture move-ment is basic to a knowledge of the generation and movement of waterborne contaminants. Presented in this chapter are a moisture routing model and a discussion of some of the primary factors which control leachate generation. Included in the discussion are a computer program for evaluating the model, the results of some specific site studies, and a simplified procedure for approx-imating liquid pollutant quantities.

Moisture Routing Model

Theory: The model is for a one dimensional, downward vertical flow system. Water input is due to surface infiltration. The moisture routing procedure is based upon using the equation of continuity for predicting the hydrologic per-formance of any soil layer. For determining water movement, the equation of continuity is of the form: $\Delta\theta = Q_I - Q_O$; where, $\Delta\theta$ = change in water storage in that layer, Q_I = the water flow into the layer, and Q_O = water flow out of the layer.

In the case of a landfill, the uppermost cover soil layer obtains moisture usually by precipitation and loses moisture by evapotranspiration and vertical downward drainage. In underlying layers, moisture is added by drainage from overlying layers. It is removed from underlying layers by drainage to still lower layers or by evapotranspiration, if roots penetrate to, or almost to, the layer. To solve the water-routing problem, knowledge of the landfill's hydraulic characteristics is required. Two quantities must be determined, usually by experimental evaluation: field capacity and permanent wilting percentage.

Field Capacity: This is defined as the maximum moisture content which a soil or refuse can retain in a gravitational field without producing significant leachate. The field capacity of a soil or refuse can be estimated by subjecting it to a capillary suction head of approximately 100 cm. of water. Water applied to a soil at a moisture content greater than field capacity drains rapidly to the lower surface. At this lower surface, it either enters into underlying materials or appears as a leachate. When the moisture content has decreased to field capacity, the soil or refuse remains essentially at that moisture content, unless it loses moisture in other ways.

Permanent Wilting Percentage: This is defined as the moisture content below which moisture is unavailable for withdrawal by plants. The permanent wilting percentage for a soil or refuse can be approximated by subjecting it to the equivalent of a suction of 15 atmospheres. To reach permanent wilting percentage, the soil or refuse must be near the land surface or within the plant-root zone.

When the moisture content of a soil or refuse is below field capacity, a moisture application will not distribute itself uniformly throughout that soil or refuse. Rather, each layer of material must reach field capacity before significant quantities of water drain to underlying material. The mass of percolating water is preceded by a wetting front or region of steep moisture content gradient.

The moisture range between field capacity and the permanent wilting percentage, or initial moisture content (whichever is greater), is referred to as available water. By determining the available water storage capacity of each soil and refuse layer, it is possible to apply the principle of continuity to moisture routing through a sanitary landfill.

The physical system outlined above is an initial and boundary value problem. The solution of such a problem is achieved by solving the equation of continuity taking into consideration the appropriate initial and boundary conditions. To obtain a solution for a particular sanitary landfill system, the continuity equation is solved taking the hydraulic characteristics of the soil and refuse and the environmental conditions of the upper surface as boundary conditions and the initial moisture contents as initial conditions.

Laboratory Simulated Landfill: While there is a variation between predicted time and actual time of appearance of significant leachate, the results indicate a high degree of correlation. The difference between the predicted time and the actual time is due to the following:

(1) The system does not behave exactly like the theoretical field capacity model; that is, there is no downward movement of moisture until field capacity is attained in a particular layer.

(2) The refuse field capacity probably changes during its life cycle.

(3) The refuse field capacity and initial moisture content data are, at best, only reasonable approximations due to the material's heterogeneous nature.

Kennett Square Landfill

Field Conditions: The landfill consisted of eight feet of compacted refuse and a two foot thick soil cover. The soil cover was Glenelg-Channery silt loam. While a prediction of the behavior of the in-situ landfill was performed, at the time of this report the field site had not reached field capacity.

Hypothetical Conditions: Laboratory determinations on undisturbed field samples of the cover soil gave a field capacity moisture content of 0.349 on a volume basis and a permanent wilting percentage moisture content of 0.090 on a volume basis. Therefore, maximum available water was 0.259 on a volume basis, or 6.20 inches of water per unit area for a two foot thick soil cover. Based on asbestos tension table tests at an initial compacted refuse density of 485 pounds per cubic yard, field capacity moisture content was 0.286 on a volume basis, and the initial moisture content was 0.039 on a volume basis.

The rainfall aspect of the system analysis was simplified by the following assumptions:

(1) The fill surface was fully vegetated at all times by plants whose roots drew water directly from all parts of the soil cover, but not from the underlying refuse.

(2) No moisture was removed by diffusing gases.

(3) All rainfall infiltrated the land surface.

(4) The hydraulic characteristics of the soil cover and compacted refuse were uniform in all directions.

(5) The landfill and underlying soil were free draining.

(6) The depth of the landfill was much less than its horizontal extent. Therefore, all water movement was vertically downward.

(7) The refuse and cover were emplaced instantaneously on the first day of the month of the computation initiation.

The results of the analysis of four landfill conditions are summarized below.

Case 1 (Emplacement of all Materials at Field Capacity on January 1) — When the components of the system are initially at their respective field capacities and the materials are emplaced during the wet season, leachate will appear immediately.

Case 2 (Emplacement of all Materials on January 1 with the Soil Cover at Permanent Wilting Percentage and the Refuse at Its Natural Moisture Content) — By emplacing the soil cover at its permanent wilting percentage and the refuse at its initial moisture content during the wet season, leachate appearance can be delayed for thirteen months.

Case 3 (Emplacement of all Materials at Field Capacity on July 1) — When the components of the system are initially at their respective field capacities and the materials are emplaced during the dry season, leachate appearance can be delayed only until the beginning of the next wet season.

Case 4 (Same as Case 2 but with Emplacement on July 1) — By emplacing the soil cover at its permanent wilting percentage and the refuse at its initial moisture content during the dry season, leachate appearance can be delayed twenty months.

Landfill Performance for Various Environmental Conditions: Landfill behavior was evaluated at eight different sites. The results of this evaluation are presented in Table 4. These results are based on 30 year average rainfall and temperature data for the particular region. The landfills consist of 8 feet of refuse and a 2 foot soil cover, with the physical parameters listed in the table.

TABLE 4: COMPUTED ELAPSED TIME TO FIRST APPEARANCE OF LEACHATE

City	Elapsed Time in Months
Wilmington, Delaware	24
Philadelphia, Pennsylvania	25
Mobile, Alabama	15
Sacramento, California	50
Los Angeles, California	145
Bismark, North Dakota	∞
Riverside, California	∞
Phoenix, Arizona	∞

NOTES:

1. Based on average 30-year rainfall and temperature data for each area.

2. Refuse and Soil Data:

	Refuse	Soil
Field Capacity (in/ft)	3.49	4.18
Original Moisture Content (in/ft)	0.46	1.08
Depth (feet)	8.00	2.00

3. Placement data: October 1

The results indicate that there is wide variation in the first appearance of leachate, but that as long as there is a net infiltration, leachate will appear. Again, changes in physical structure, such as that due to grinding, will have a marked influence on the time required for first leachate appearance.

Refuse Field Capacity

Results of field capacity tests on ground refuse show:

(1) That as the refuse size decreases, field capacity increases significantly.

(2) That with increasing dry density, the increase of field capacity will approach asymptotically a maximum which is size-dependent.

It is concluded from these studies that the influence of grinding is to greatly increase soil field capacity, hence, retard the first appearance of leachate from a landfill constructed of such material.

U. S. Potential Infiltration

Studies show that there is potential infiltration of water into landfills over the majority of the United States. As long as there is a net infiltration, leachate will eventually begin to be produced by a landfill. The magnitude of the quantity of actual infiltration depends on surface draining characteristics, surface grading, surface treatment and planting of vegetation.

Sanitary Landfill Multipurpose Machine

The material in this chapter was taken from a 1972 EPA report, PB 212,589, prepared by Battelle Memorial Institute. A multifunctional machine, known as the Multi-Mover, was invented and patented by Ike J. Wardle, Boise, Idaho. The machine is a rubber-tired vehicle that performs the function of a crawler tractor dozer, dump truck, compactor, and loader.

In 1956 Mr. Wardle was awarded two basic patents on the design. One was for the hinged-arm claw-apron. The other was for the drive-chain configuration and the machine's frame, which forms a "Y" configuration, with the box in the fork of the Y. The engine is located at the driver's end of the machine on the stem of the Y.

The results of this first venture were mixed. Although the design proved to be basically sound, the machine lacked hydraulic power and had other deficiencies. Wardle redesigned parts of the machine and completed the second Multi-Mover by 1959. The second machine was used for five years in a sand and gravel operation. Subsequently, Enterprises Inc., an Idaho based firm, acquired the rights to the design. Its subsidiary, Nampa Sanitary Service, operated a sanitary landfill for disposal of solid wastes from Nampa and Canyon County, Idaho.

The Multi-Mover is a machine originally designed to perform the functions of a crawler tractor/dozer, dump truck, compactor, and loader. Use of the Multi-Mover in these capacities as an earthmover created interest in using it to perform the operations for proper sanitary landfill management. A properly equipped crawler tractor is the usual machine used on a sanitary landfill, but it was believed the Multi-Mover could perform more efficiently and economically, particularly in maintaining a number of widely scattered landfills in a sparsely populated region.

Proper operation of sanitary landfills, where they are scattered across a sparsely populated area, is a difficult problem mainly because of the costs and inconvenience involved in site-to-site equipment transfer. As a result, open dumps are the usual situation. The Multi-Mover is a rubber-tired vehicle that can be moved on the highway under its own power, (as opposed to the crawler tractor, which requires a prime mover for transportation) and offers the possibility of being more economical to use on scattered sites in a sparsely populated region.

A three-phase demonstration program was carried out to evaluate the Multi-Mover in sanitary landfill operations and study the solid waste disposal problem in Canyon County, Idaho. The first phase consisted of modification and renovation of the ten-year-old Multi-Mover; the second phase provided for field evaluation and data collection and the third phase consisted of five parts as follows:

(a)   Systems analysis of solid waste disposal in a sparsely populated area.

(b)   An economic and industrial growth study of Canyon County, Idaho, to define present and expected future solid waste generation.

(c)   A market survey to determine the demand for multifunctional machines in sanitary landfill operations throughout the country.

(d)   An operations and cost effectiveness analysis to determine the best way to use multifinctional equipment of this type.

(e)   Transportation problems connected with moving equipment from one site to another.

SUMMARY

An engineering review of the Multi-Mover was performed to assess the repair work required to make the subject machine operable, and determine the modifications required to make it reasonably suited to perform subsequent landfill work. Every major assembly was inspected, and excessively worn parts were either replaced or rebuilt. Major modifications were made to all hydraulic systems and a dual hydraulic brake system was installed. Also, many minor modifications were made to the engine and other major mechanical assemblies.

Performance of the Multi-Mover in accomplishing sanitary landfill and earth-moving operations was evaluated at several sites in the states of Idaho and Oregon. The purpose of the field tests was to determine the effectiveness of the Multi-Mover both absolutely and in comparison with crawler tractors in compacting waste and soil cover material, excavating and spreading soil cover, distributing refuse for compaction, and transportation from site-to-site. A special trip was made to evaluate long distance highway travel and operations under winter conditions.

The basic concept of the Multi-Mover — that of a multifunctional machine — results in a unit which has certain disadvantages when compared to a single purpose machine, such as a dozer, carryall, and blade. These disadvantages include such things as limited carrying capacity, longer turning radius, low ground clearance, and inadequate power or speed for some operations. However, these disadvantages are less significant when considering applications such as a small sanitary landfill, where the multiple capabilities of the Multi-Mover would permit it to replace several single purpose machines.

Some of the disadvantages could feasibly be reduced in impact or eliminated in subsequent models. These include too large a turning radius and inadequate power and minimum speed. Other disadvantages, such as the limited carrying capacity, are inherent in a design that yields a machine small enough for general highway travel. Even so, the machine still carries more load than front loaders of similar size.

From the results of the field tests, it was concluded that the Multi-Mover is approximately equivalent in compaction effectiveness to a heavier crawler tractor and markedly superior to a lighter crawler tractor. In spite of mechanical deficiencies of the machine in its present design, it is capable of performing satisfactorily at a lower cost, all of the functions of a crawler tractor in sanitary landfill operations. In addition, it can function as a snow removal vehicle and it can be driven from site-to-site economically at distances up to 12 or 15 miles to service landfills in sparsely populated counties.

The results indicate that the Multi-Mover in its present configuration would be an economical general purpose landfill machine for operation in sparsely populated counties, and that certain modifications would improve its compaction capabilities and overall reliability. The machine is judged worthy of additional demonstration after its ground clearance is increased and miscellaneous mechanical features are improved.

The cost effectiveness of the Multi-Mover was also compared to that of the crawler tractor. Questionnaires were mailed to sparsely populated counties and to towns and cities in sparsely populated areas to determine the type of equipment currently in use. Data obtained from time and motion studies were used to develop time/unit work effectiveness parameters for each machine in performance of the tasks required for landfill operations.

Cost estimates, which included both the capital and operating costs, were developed on a per operating hour basis. The cost and effectiveness parameters were combined to obtain a cost/unit work measure of cost effectiveness. Both the cost and effectiveness estimates were analyzed to determine the sensitivity of the final estimate to estimates of the various input data.

A computer model was developed to study the economics of operating several remote solid waste disposal sites. The model optimizes the assignment of equipment to service each site, including both transportation of equipment and performance of the tasks required in sanitary landfill operation. The model user must provide parameters describing both capabilities and operating costs of the equipment and parameters describing the operation of his disposal sites.

The model was used in this study to compare the effectiveness of the Multi-Mover with the effectiveness of a bucket-equipped crawler tractor. The parameters for this study were obtained from other sections of the program. With the parameters provided, the Multi-Mover demonstrated a definite cost advantage over the crawler tractor.

Potential interest in the Multi-Mover was determined by a mail survey of 15% of the sparsely populated counties in the United States. Forty percent of the counties which operated sanitary landfills expressed an interest in the machine. A similar survey was made of selected towns and cities in sparsely populated areas in the Pacific Northwest and Northern California, and 44% indicated interest in the Multi-Mover.

Comments solicited on the practicability of the Multi-Mover showed a tendency to question the reliability of such a complex machine, the suitability of rubber tires for landfill services, and the expected high purchase price of the machine. Projection of market potential based on these surveys show an initial market for 1,000 machines over the next several years.

The problems of solid waste generation, collection, transportation and disposal in sparsely populated areas were examined with particular emphasis on ways in which a multifunctional earthmoving machine such as the Multi-Mover could contribute to their solution. Canyon County, Idaho, was used as an example of a sparsely populated area.

Sparsely populated areas are not likely to provide collection service for all their residents, and the disposal of wastes by residents can cause health hazards through land and water pollution. The low population density makes all solid waste services more expensive on a per person basis.

Consolidation of services through transfer operations and multisite servicing on a rotating basis appear to be feasible ways of reducing the cost per person. Also, consolidation of solid waste planning and management on a regional basis would encourage consolidation of services to adjacent areas and would allow the cost of improved management and planning to be shared among a larger number of people.

A mail survey was made to determine what the county officials in sparsely populated areas consider their most serious problems, and the Multi-Mover's possible contributions to solution of these stated problems were analyzed. The Multi-Mover's superior cost effectiveness would contribute to the solution of many of these problems by lowering the overall costs of the disposal operations. Its high capital cost is the most serious drawback. Even though its overall cost per unit work would be lower than that of a crawler tractor, the financial

structure of governments in sparsely populated areas tends to favor lower expenditures for capital equipment over lower operating costs in a trade-off.

RECOMMENDATIONS

Multifunctional Machine

The basic concept of the Multi-Mover is sound. A versatile machine with highway mobility is needed to service landfills in sparsely populated areas, and a
well engineered, reliable Multi-Mover would fill this need. It is therefore recommended that the Bureau of Solid Waste management sponsor an incentive program to aid in developing a marketable Multi-Mover. The incentive program
should aid in developing the machine to a point where it is competitive on the
basis of operability and reliability with the usual sanitary landfill equipment
produced by major heavy equipment manufacturers.

Engineering recommendations based on the evaluations described in this report
are offered to guide those who may undertake future engineering of the Multi-
Mover. In this pursuit the following are recommended:

Increase Machine Power — An engine of greater horsepower (225 to 250 hp.)
well matched to the transmission and drive train would greatly improve Multi-
Mover performance. A lower minimum speed (less than 3 mph) without
sacrifice of top speed (at least 30 mph) would improve the machine's earthmoving performance.

Increase Machine Maneuverability — The machine's efficiency could be greatly
improved if the turning radius were shortened. This would require a different
design than that presently used. Consideration should be given to articulating
the machine to increase its maneuverability.

Simplify and Improve Control of Machine — The rotatable drive station turret
should be replaced with two fixed operator seats and with controls easily
accessible from either operator position. This arrangement could simplify
control connections and eliminate the turret and turret drive mechanism.
Positioning the operator where he could see the depth of the cut would improve the grading ability of the machine.

Loading material into the box while the machine is moving is difficult because
four hand controls must be operated. These are the steering wheel, depth of
blade control, and the claw control and claw arm control. The claw and claw
arm control should be operated with a single control lever, and the claw and
claw arm mechanisms should be automatically programmed for loading cover
on a selectable basis. With automatic operation of the claw and claw arm, the
operator would only need to control the depth of cut and steer the machine
when loading cover. An all-weather cab to enclose the operator is desirable
as optional equipment.

Increase Machine Ground Clearance — The Multi-Mover ground clearance is 10 inches and should be increased to at least 18 inches. With the present clearance the box drags when the machine is being used for waste compaction. On occasion the bottom of the box would drag on waste that had been compacted and tear out large pieces.

Improve Machine Loading — When the blading end of the box is lowered on a loading run, it creates a fairly steep angle, and the earth being loaded must be pushed up this inclined plane. This allows only partial loading of the box and with wheel power only. If the back of the box could be lowered along with the front to decrease this angle, loading efficiency would improve greatly. The location of the pivot point, length of claw arms and rotation of the claw need to be optimized in relation to the box to obtain the most efficient design. The most efficient method for design optimization would employ kinematic analysis and provide for modeling.

Redesign Machine Claw and Claw Arm — Power to operate the claw and claw arm should be increased as much as possible and consideration should be given to a "backhoe" design claw and claw arm to facilitate the loading of cover from a stockpile or bank.

Fit Machine with Larger Tires and Chains — Steel belted tires should be tried on machines built in the future. These tires were not available in the required size during the evaluation, but probably could be obtained in the future if a minimum demand is demonstrated or guaranteed. Clearance between the tires and other parts of the machine should be provided to allow the use of tire chains when operating in mud, snow, or on ice.

Solid Waste Management in Sparsely Populated Areas

One of the most serious problems of solid waste management in sparsely populated areas is the lack of adequate planning. Solid waste operations are carried out on a day-to-day basis and there is little effort to develop plans past the current fiscal year. The lack of planning generally arises from a lack of knowledgeability of solid waste management on the part of local governmental management. Frequently the responsibility falls to the county commissioners, who characteristically have little time to devote to the project and little expertise in the field.

From standpoints of cost and specialized knowledge, sparsely populated counties and the small cities and towns in sparsely populated areas cannot individually support the planning necessary for their area. Regional planning for solid waste could help solve this problem both by spreading the cost of a good planning program over the tax base of a larger area, and amalgamating experience and expertise of individual city and county governments to support the planning.

Daily management of solid waste in sparsely populated areas suffers from the same problems as planning. Responsibility for waste operations often falls to an organization such as the county engineer's office (road department). Solid waste operations are often a small part of the agency's responsibilities and do not get the attention they require. It is also unlikely that the manager has adequate training in solid waste operations. These problems could be approached on a regional basis with the same benefits that are expected from a regional planning function.

In addition, regional management would encourage and facilitate consolidation of solid waste operations, which would alleviate present duplication of effort and provide some economies of scale. This approach would also help to free solid waste programs from local politics. A well planned demonstration should be supported to compare the regional solid waste program with the existing situation both in terms of economic cost and the usual level and quality of solid waste services provided.

Another serious problem in sparsely populated areas is the apathy of the citizenry toward the problems of solid waste. Most citizens in this type of area are not aware of the problems of solid waste disposal and the apathy is, of course, reflected in the attitudes of elected representatives who have the responsibility for the solid waste program.

One surveyed County Commissioner's analysis of solid waste problems was, "It doesn't take any brains to dig a hole and bury garbage in it." More emphasis on public information programs to inform the citizens of the problems and to elicit support for their solution is recommended. This appears for two reasons to be a prerequisite to any significant improvement. First, the public's cooperation is essential to a successful operation (particularly in a sparsely populated area where many of the people must dispose of their own solid wastes). Second, the elected officials must see that their constituents desire improvements and are willing to pay the necessary costs.

Additional research into transfer operations in sparsely populated areas appears to be justified and is recommended. It may be less expensive to move the waste of an area to one disposal site rather than maintain several disposal sites. The choice among transfer operations, independently maintained sites and jointly maintained sites (several sites maintained by one crew on a rotating basis), is one which depends on the exigencies in each individual case. However, in general it appears that transfer operations should allow some savings to be realized and should be the most easily adaptable to future changes in disposal methods, (e.g., increased separation for salvage and recycling).

MACHINE MODIFICATION AND RENOVATION

The Multi-Mover was about 10 years old at the start of this project, and required extensive renovation to restore it to a level acceptable for objective evaluation of its capabilities. The modification and renovation process began with a formal engineering review of the machine and its suitability for landfill service.

It culminated in incorporation of the resulting recommended design changes and performance of extensive corrective maintenance. The following description describes the modified machine.

Multi-Mover Description

The Multi-Mover (Figure 12.1) is a multifinctional machine which performs the functions of four pieces of earthmoving equipment (crawler tractor dozer, dump truck, compactor, and loader). It was developed originally for filling, grading and compacting on construction jobs; has selectable four-wheel drive capability; and can travel at speeds sufficient for highway travel. Table 1 lists pertinent Multi-Mover specifications.

A three point suspension system is used on the machine. This assures that all four wheels will maintain contact even when traveling over rough terrain. The wheels on the side frame alongside the box are in a fixed position relative to the frame. The wheels on the steering end of the machine are mounted on an assembly which is free to swivel about the longitudinal axis of the machine, permitting these wheels to tilt as needed to maintain ground contact.

FIGURE 12.1: MULTI-MOVER

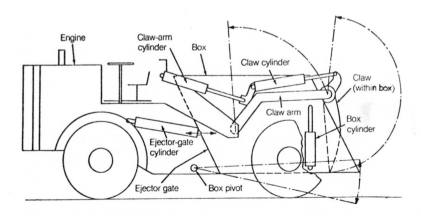

Source: PB 212,589 (1972)

The machine has a hinged box that is lowered for scraping, then raised for transporting material. A claw, supported on movable arms on each side of the box, can be used to scoop material piled ahead of the machine into the box as the machine advances. The wheels on either side of the box are permanently engaged to the engine through a drive system consisting of an Allison transmission, a differential, and chain and sprocket drives which are located in the side frames that support the box. The front wheels are steerable and are driven from the transmission through a manually controlled clutch to a differential on the axle shafts.

The operator's turret is reversible to permit the driver to face forward regardless of the direction of machine travel. It is rotated electrically using a turret-mounted control. The machine is hydraulically controlled except for steering, which is manually operated through a power-assisted system. A pilot control system using "Hydronic" master-slave units is used to position the main hydraulic control valves for the box, ejector gate, claw, and claw arm hydraulic circuits, as well as the transmission controls and engine throttle.

TABLE 1: MULTI-MOVER SPECIFICATIONS

POWER TRAIN

ENGINE

Make	Waukesha
Model	135-DKBS-Turbocharged
Horsepower	167 (max.)
RPM	2400
Torque, lb-ft	400
Fuel Tank Capacity, (gal.)	50

TRANSMISSION

Make	Allison	
Model	CRT-3331-1 (torque converter)	
Ranges	FORWARD	REVERSE
Low	5.27:1	5.11:1
Intermediate	1.91:1	1.85:1
High	0.659:1	0.639:1

AXLES AND HUBS (4WD)

Front Steering Axle and Hub	Timken Detroit PS-150HX-2 (16.65:1)
Jack Shaft Axle	Timken Detroit QT-140-B-2 (4.625:1)
Rear Hubs	Timken Detroit PR-20 (3.6:1)

HYDRAULIC SYSTEM

BLADE, EJECTOR GATE, CLAW AND CLAW-ARM CYLINDERS: Eight (two each) commercial shearing and stamping cylinders.

PUMPS: Zeno dual pump, 32 and 56 gal/min @1000 lb/in.^{2} and 1800 rpm; Vickers variable displacement pump, 45 gal/min @ 1000 lb/in.^{2} and 1800 rpm.

VALVES: Four Hoen pilot-operated hydraulic control valves.

RESERVOIR: 70 gal.

PILOT CONTROL SYSTEM: Eight "Hydronic" master-slave hydraulic units to operate the hydraulic valves, engine throttle and transmission controls.

(continued)

TABLE 1: (continued)

RUNNING GEAR

STEERING
    Type   Power-assisted manual operation
    Turning Radius
        Left   39.5'
        Right   56.5'

TIRES   1600 x 20

BRAKES   Dual vacuum-assisted hydraulic systems with
                         four-wheel hydravac-over-hydraulic 17"
                         x 4" drums

WEIGHT AND DIMENSIONS

WEIGHT, LB   27,225 (unladen)

DIMENSIONS
    Length   22'
    Width   8' 6"
    Height   8'
    Ground Clearance   10" (Box Raised)

OPERATING DATA

TRAVEL SPEEDS

| Engine RPM | Forward (MPH) | | Reverse (MPH) |
	Max	Min	Min
2000	30	3.4	3.5
2400	35	-	-

HYDRAULIC CYCLE SPEEDS
    Claw Arm   6.8 sec up and 2.0 sec down
    Claw   5.0 sec out and 6.0 sec in
    Box (empty)   2.8 sec up and 1.0 sec down
    Gate (w/empty box)
        Box raised   11.0 sec out and 17.0 sec in
        Box down   9.5 sec out and 24.0 sec in

BOX CAPACITY   5.5 yd^3 (Level -- Box raised)

The primary hydraulic system (Figure 12.2) consists of a Zeno dual pump, mounted on the transmission, a Vickers variable displacement pump driven from the engine power takeoff, four Hoen pilot operated hydraulic control valves, and eight Commercial Shearing and Stamping hydraulic cylinders used to operate the ejector gate, claw, claw arm, and box. The hydraulic fluid is continuously filtered in the reservoir tank. These filters, which are equipped with plugging indicators and incorporate magnets for trapping ferrous materials have a built-in bypass that functions only if the filter clogs. The Multi-Mover has a dual braking system. Separate reservoirs, hydraulic lines, and vacuum boosters are provided for the front and rear brakes.

Engineering Review

The engineering review was performed before renovation began. This consisted of a visual inspection of the machine; discussions with the inventor; and analysis of the drive train, hydraulic power systems, and brake system.

FIGURE 12.2: REVISED HYDRAULIC SYSTEM

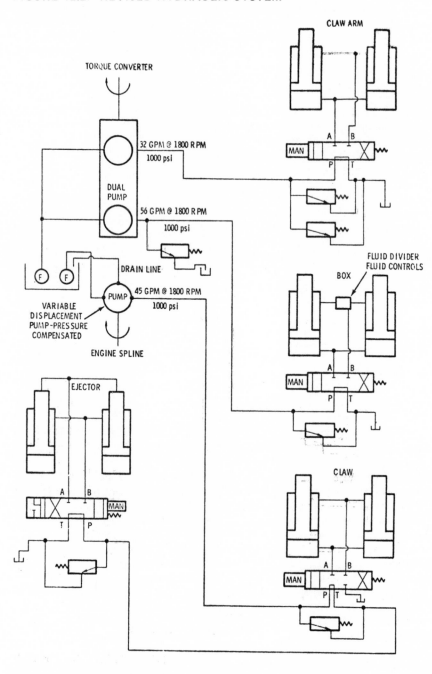

Source: PB 212,589 (1972)

The visual inspection showed that the box, claw, and claw arm were badly worn. Numerous hydraulic system leaks were noted, as well as the use of uncoded pressure fittings. While the motor would run, hydraulic pressure was inadequate indicating that the pumps would require service. Major components were missing from the pilot control system and the operator's turret was inoperable. The tires were badly worn. The main frame was cracked near the motor mounts.

Based on the visual inspection, the decision was made to replace the box, claw, claw arm, tires, and all hydraulic tubing and electrical wiring. In addition, all other components, with the exception of the motor, transmission and differentials, would be removed for inspection and replaced or repaired as needed. Repairs would be made to the main frame with these components removed.

Since the motor and transmission appeared to be operable, the recommendations of the manufacturer's representative were sought to determine what course of maintenance to follow with these components. The transmission pressure was checked with the machine operating and found to be within acceptable limits; this constituted the manufacturer's suggested serviceability test. Since the unit functioned normally, transmission maintenance consisted only of draining the old fluid, flushing the unit, and replenishing it with new fluid. Tests on the engine showed that it was generally in good condition requiring only a major tuneup and overhaul of the turbocharger.

During discussions with the inventor, his drawings were found to contain a design change for relocation of the claw arm pivot points, which had not been incorporated in the subject machine. This change would modify the action of the claw, and though it had not been proven in service, it appeared to be desirable. Since the original design had already been field tested, the decision was made to try the modified design to permit a comparison of the two.

The drive train was analyzed to determine the expected maximum and minimum speeds of the machine and verify that the transmission was sized for the power output of the engine. The drive train consists of a Waukesha 135 DKU supercharged diesel engine; an Allison transmission; and Timken Detroit front steering axle and hubs, rear jack shaft axle, and rear hubs. (The gear ratios for these units are shown in the previous table.) The expected maximum and minimum speeds for the vehicle were determined using engine speeds of 2,000 and 2,400 revolutions per minute.

The specifications for the Allison transmission torque gave a multiplication ratio of 3.5:1 at "stall." This gave a stall speed, or speed at which transmission slippage would occur, of $\frac{1}{3.5}$ x the minimum normal speed, or approximately 1 mph. The minimum speed for continuous operation, based on a converter efficiency of 70%, is 2.4 mph. Continuous operation slower than this could be expected to overheat the converter, according to information obtained from the transmission manufacturer.

The transmission and diesel were found to be well matched. The diesel has a maximum torque output of 350 lb.-ft. at 2,400 rpm; however, a significant proportion of this torque is required to operate the auxiliaries — primarily the hydraulic pumps. Therefore, the net torque input to the transmission does not exceed the transmission torque rating of 300 lb.-ft. This conclusion was verified by the transmission manufacturers, who had made a similar investigation at the time the transmission was sold.

The expected cycle times were calculated at approximately 10 seconds each for the claw arm, claw, and box. These times would increase when the engine slowed. The inventor felt that the desired rate for the claw and claw arm should be about one half of the calculated rate. Although the reduced times could be obtained by using larger pumps, the hydraulic system was already using up to 87 horsepower, a large percentage of engine output, and a larger engine would be required for installation of larger pumps. This would have resulted in a schedule delay as well as unduly increasing the cost of renovation. Since the original engine was in usable condition and would permit evaluation of machine capabilities, engine replacement was decided against.

The braking system was reviewed and found to be generally adequate except that it used a single hydraulic system. For safety the hydraulic booster units and the hydraulic lines would be replaced to provide a dual hydraulic brake system. The brake shoes, drums, and cylinders were adequate and could be used after inspection and overhaul.

Modifications and Restoration

Restoration was completed as required to put the machine in a condition sufficient to permit an adequate comparison with competitive landfill machinery. The basic design of the machine was not changed. The restoration effort in this task comprised both preventive and corrective maintenance as follows:

Major Tuneup of Engine and Accessories — This included setting the injectors, overhauling the turbocharger, overhauling or replacing engine and transmission gauges as needed, adding a motor safety circuit (high temperature and low oil pressure cutouts), disconnecting the "glow" plugs (used originally for starting, but considered dangerous if used in conjunction with the current practice of injecting ether for startup), rewiring the engine, setting the governor, overhauling the starter motor and generator, rebuilding the radiator, and replacing all hoses, fan belts and filters.

Inspection and Repair of Drive-Train Components — The four planetary hubs for the wheels were disassembled, the bearings and gears were inspected and the units were reassembled with new seals. A worn inboard bearing on the left rear wheel was replaced. The universal joints between the engine and transmission were worn and were rebuilt. The drive lines from the transmission to the front and rear axles were removed, cleaned, inspected and reinstalled. The transmission was pressure tested and found to be in satisfactory operating condition. The transmission fluid was replaced. The oil from both differentials was drained into clean containers and inspected for metallic particles. The oil was replaced along with a leaking housing seal on the front differential.

Overhaul and Modification of Braking System — The vacuum assisted single hydraulic brake system was replaced with a dual system with separate reservoirs, hydraulic lines and vacuum boosters for the front and rear brakes. In addition, a low pressure safety switch with indicator on the control turret was installed to monitor both systems. The brake shoes were relined, the brake cylinders were rebuilt and all brake hoses were replaced. The brake drums were inspected and found in satisfactory condition.

The Bendix vacuum pump had a broken housing. A new unit was obtained and installed. The vacuum tank used with the pump was cleaned, inspected and reinstalled. A defective check valve on the pump suction line was replaced.

Replacement of Tires — Before placing the order for tires, four tire companies (Goodyear, B.F. Goodrich, Firestone, and Michelin) were contacted for their recommendation of the most suitable type of tire available for the expected service conditions. Steel reinforced tires, which are believed to be the most suitable, were not available in the size required (1600-20). The available tire most suitable on the basis of load and speed requirements is the same as those which were originally used on the rear of the machine.

The load rating of these tires is less than that required to handle the calculated maximum weight, but they were procured since no tires of greater capacity were available and since this type has been used successfully. The only alternative to this was to replace the existing rims and planetary hubs with units which would accommodate tires of a larger size. This should be considered for future machines to ensure maximum tire life. Since only one type of tire was available, the selection of tires on the basis of desired compaction could not be done as previously planned.

Overhaul and Modification of Hydraulic System — The transmission-mounted dual hydraulic pump was badly worn and replacement parts were installed. The single stage front pump (positive displacement type), also badly worn, was replaced with a variable displacement, compensated pump of larger capacity. The compensated pump was selected to obviate any power loss when its cylinders (claw arm and ejector gate cylinders) were inoperative. The main frame was lengthened to accommodate the new pump.

The hydraulic system valves and valve manifold were removed, disassembled, cleaned and inspected. The valves were satisfactory with the exception of the built-in relief valves, which were worn. Since these valves are no longer manufactured, they were repaired by lapping the seats and plunger. The valves were reassembled and the relief settings adjusted to 1,100 lbs./in^2.

All hydraulic cylinders were removed, disassembled and inspected. After obtaining comparative cost estimates of overhauling and replacing them, the choice was made to overhaul. During the overhaul the low pressure (150 lbs./in.^{2}) galvanized pipe fittings, which were originally welded to the cylinders, were replaced with high pressure (3,000 lbs./in.^{2}) steel fittings. While the galvanized fittings had functioned satisfactorily, they are not coded for the operating pressure of 1,000 lbs./in.^{2} and therefore were not used.

The original hydraulic oil filters in the reservoir tank were replaced with finer mesh filters of larger capacity and equipped with visual plugging indicators. They also have a built-in bypass, which functions if the filter clogs, and magnets for trapping magnetic particles. Neither of these features were on the original filters.

Modification of Vehicle Lighting — Taillights and stoplights were installed. The existing headlights were rewired.

Modification and Repair of Structural Components — Cracks at a weak point in the main frame just above the front axle were repaired and the section strengthened by the addition of ½-inch thick stiffening plates. The frame cross bracing in this area was also reinforced.

Renovation of Load Handling Components — New fabrication drawings were prepared for the box, claw, and claw arm. These components, which were badly worn, were replaced. The original ejector gate was modified to fit the new box.

Modification of Control Components — The operator's control turret was re-built and a new pilot control system, using "Hydronic" master-slave units, was installed. Individual units control the box, claw, and claw arm hydraulic cir-cuits; the transmission controls (Forward-Reverse, Speed Range, Front Drive Clutch); and the engine throttle (through a foot-operated unit). While this system has improved machine performance somewhat by providing more positive positioning of the primary hydraulic system operating valves, mechanical link-ages were preferred, but would have required elimination of the operator's turret.

Evaluation

Speed Ranges — The Multi-Mover speed ranges were selected originally as a compromise between a maximum speed adequate for highway travel and a minimum speed suitable for earthmoving operations. The resulting minimum speed is somewhat higher than that found in competitive equipment and should be reduced in future models. A transmission with more than three speed ranges will be required if the top speed is to be maintained. Such units are available, but are not physically interchangeable with the present transmission without some redesign of the machine.

Turning Radius — The turning radius of the Multi-Mover is greater than the turning radius for front loaders and wheeled dozers. These units obtain the shorter turning radius because of their articulated design, and incorporation of this feature in the Multi-Mover would require a major redesign. The Multi-Mover does have an additional feature that most other types of units do not have which makes a short turning radius less significant at least in landfill service. This is the capability to operate in either direction with the operator facing in the direction of travel.

Vehicle Clearance — The relatively low road clearance increases the possibility of high centering the machine. However, the ability to raise and lower the box, and hence the machine, affords the operator a means of freeing the machine if high centering should occur. The four-wheel drive capability assists in freeing the machine in the event of high centering.

Hydraulic System — The operation of the hydraulic system could be made more reliable by elimination of the rotating turret. This would permit the direct mechanical operation of the control valves, rather than operating them through a hydraulic pilot control system, resulting in more positive operation of the valves. Another change which would improve the overall reliability would be to use gear type pumps. The close clearances of other type pumps render them susceptible to damage from the pumping of fluid containing very small amounts of particulates. Even extremely fine mesh filters do not always provide sufficient protection. A replacement pump with larger clearances is desirable.

Vehicle Code Compliance — A review of state road and highway regulations was made to assure that the Multi-Mover would comply with these regulations when operating in the highway mode. The review showed that the width of the machine exceeds the maximum allowable width of 8 feet by approximately 6 inches. Therefore, the Multi-Mover must have an oversize permit to operate on the highways. A design modification reducing the machine width to 8 feet would be desirable on future models to overcome this limitation.

The machine complies with the requirements concerning weight per axle and minimum speed. The modified braking system complies with the requirements for a dual hydraulic brake system. Installation of taillights and stoplights, in addition to the existing headlights, will provide code lighting.

Operator Protection — Only one state, Michigan, requires an all-weather cab. Since standard cabs will not fit the machine, a specially designed cab would be needed to allow operation in Michigan. This feature is a necessary adjunct to marketing the Multi-Mover as an all-weather machine. A review of options available for competitive machines reveals that the all-weather cab option is widely available.

FIELD EVALUATION

Comparative evaluations of Multi-Mover performance with crawler tractor performance were performed at landfill sites near Nampa, Idaho and Ontario,

Oregon. The purpose of these tests was to determine the effectiveness of the Multi-Mover in compacting waste and soil cover material, performing excavation, depositing soil cover, distributing refuse for compaction, and transporting itself from site to site. The compaction tests were performed at the landfill site near Lake Lowell located five miles north of Nampa, Idaho.

Earthmoving tests were conducted at the Lake Lowell site, the Ontario site, and the Black Canyon site, while highway transportability tests were conducted between the sites at Central Cove, Black Canyon and Lake Lowell. A special trip was made to Cougar Mountain Lodge, Idaho to evaluate long distance highway travel and operation under winter conditions.

Data Collection

Data collection for the field evaluation included measuring and recording the weights or volumes of waste entering a compaction cell, surveying the cells to obtain data on compacted volumes, timing earthmoving operations and weighing the loads, timing machine operations, recording fuel usage and obtaining other data necessary to provide a basis for machine evaluation. Data collection sheets were used to selectively obtain the data on refuse weights (or volumes), compaction, earthmoving, highway travel, and fuel and oil usage.

It was originally planned to perform all compaction tests on a volume basis and evaluate the machine on the compaction ratio achieved (trucked volume/in-place volume). However, it was decided to weigh the refuse and obtain compaction data expressed in pounds per cubic yard, a more meaningful figure which would afford a better comparison. Truck scales were used for weighing refuse for the majority of the cells, but before completion of this phase, the scales were destroyed in a fire. After that time, cells had to be evaluated on a volume basis.

Sites Characterization

Evaluation work was performed at three landfills — Lake Lowell, Black Canyon, and Ontario, Oregon. The Lake Lowell site was operated as an area landfill for the first three cells and later as a ramp type. It serves a population of about 49,000. Regular equipment consists of two medium size crawler tractors with front end bucket loaders. The climate, being dry and temperate, has little effect on landfill operations, i.e., there are little or no problems from mud or extreme winter conditions. The site is located in gently rolling terrain. It was originally a gravel pit, and at the time of compaction tests on cells L-1, L-2, and L-3, it had nearly been filled. Cover material is readily available and ranges from silty loam to a sandy loam with cobble gravel found beneath the cemented hardpan. Table 2 lists data for this site.

The Black Canyon site is operated as a trench-type landfill. It serves a population of less than 5,000 and does not have permanently assigned equipment. It is located in gently sloping terrain, and has the same climatic conditions as the Lake Lowell landfill. The available cover material is sandy loam in ample supply. Site data is listed in Table 3.

TABLE 2: LAKE LOWELL SITE DATA

```
LANDFILL TYPE:              Ramp
POPULATION SERVICE:         49,000
TOPOGRAPHY:                 Gently rolling terrain


CLIMATICS

PRECIPITATION, in./yr       10.6
MEAN TEMPERATURES, °F       50.7 (annual)
                            65.0 (max)
                            36.5 (min)
MEAN WIND VELOCITY, MPH      9.0


SOILS

COVER MATERIAL
      Type:                 Loam
      Texture:              Silty to sandy with 3 in. maximum diameter
                            cobble gravel
      Depth:                20 to 36 in.
      Availability:         Excellent
      Shrink & Swell
        Potential:          Low to moderate


SUBSTRATE
      Type:                 Cemented hardpan
```

TABLE 3: BLACK CANYON SITE DATA

```
LANDFILL TYPE:              Trench
POPULATION SERVICE:         5,000
TOPOGRAPHY:                 Gently sloping terrain


CLIMATICS

PRECIPITATION, in./yr       10.6
MEAN TEMPERATURES, °F       50.7 (Annual)
                            65.0 (max)
                            36.5 (min)
MEAN WIND VELOCITY, MPH      9.0


SOILS

COVER MATERIAL
      Type:                 Loam
      Texture:              Sandy
      Depth:                8 ft
      Availability:         Excellent
      Shrink & Swell
        Potential:          Low to moderate


SUBSTRATE
      Type                  Cemented hardpan
```

The Ontario site is operated as an area-type landfill in a ravine. It serves a population of about 5,000. Regular equipment consists of one small crawler tractor with dozer blade and one medium size crawler tractor with front bucket loader. The site is located in a ravine, and has the same climatic conditions as the Lake Lowell site. The available cover material is a sandy loam with some cobble gravel. Material is in short supply and must be taken from the steep ravine sides. Site data is listed in Table 4.

TABLE 4: ONTARIO SITE DATA

LANDFILL TYPE:	Area
POPULATION SERVICE:	5,000
TOPOGRAPHY:	Ravine
CLIMATICS	
PRECIPITATION, in./yr	10.6
MEAN TEMPERATURES, °F	50.7 (annual)
	65.0 (max)
	36.5 (min)
MEAN WIND VELOCITY, MPH	9.0
SOILS	
COVER MATERIAL	
Type:	Loam
Texture:	Sandy with 3 in. maximum diameter cobble gravel
Depth:	N.A.
Availability:	Poor--must be taken from sides of ravine
Shrink & Swell	
Potential:	N.A.
SUBSTRATE	
Type	Cemented hardpan

Field Testing

Field testing of refuse handling and compaction effectiveness, consisting of constructing refuse cells with the Multi-Mover and crawler tractors, was done entirely at the Lake Lowell landfill. Earthmoving evaluations were conducted at Lake Lowell and at the Black Canyon site near Middleton. Highway travel was evaluated by trips between sites and a trip to Cougar Mountain Lodge, where the Multi-Mover was tested for its ability to plow, load, and unload snow, in addition to its general winter operation capability. Waste characterization was performed at the Lake Lowell landfill. The methods used in these characterizations and evaluations and the results are described in detail in the following paragraphs.

Waste Characterization – Waste characterization studies were performed in November 1969, April 1970, and May 1970, to identify the types of waste being handled and to note seasonal variations therein. Classification of waste was done visually by dumping the compactor truck refuse onto the fill and spreading the loads into layers about 24 inches deep; then the volume percentages were estimated (Table 5).

TABLE 5: WASTE CHARACTERIZATION

Type of Waste	Volume ($\sim$ % of total)		
	Nov	April	May
Paper and Paper Products	55.0	48.0	45.0
Food Wastes	15.0	14.0	14.0
Metal	4.0	5.0	4.0
Glass	2.0	5.0	3.5
Bulk Leaves and Grass	3.0	5.0	6.0
Wood	8.0	15.0	15.0
Plastics	5.0	3.5	3.5
Cloth, Rubber, Leather and Synthetics	6.0	3.0	7.0
Dirt, Ashes, Rocks	2.0	1.5	2.0

Commercial, residential and industrial wastes were used which are typical of those regularly entering the landfill. The November classification was made on two separate waste cell lifts totalling 138,000 lbs.; the April classification on 8 compactor truck loads; and the May classification on 24 compactor truck loads.

Inasmuch as the characterizations were visual estimates, they can be considered only approximate. Seasonal variations apparent in Table 5 are also approximate. The most significant seasonal variation which affected the compaction operation in April and May were the larger amounts of bulk leaves, grass, and wood, which compact less than the other wastes. This was particularly noticeable with discarded plywood panel trimmings from a local mobile home manufacturer.

Landfill Performance — Tests were conducted to evaluate Multi-Mover performance compared to that of a crawler tractor in compacting waste and soil cover, spreading refuse, excavating and hauling earth, spreading earth cover, and highway travel.

Compaction Comparisons — Compaction comparisons were made by constructing refuse cells of varying sizes at the Lake Lowell landfill separately with the Multi-Mover (27,225 lbs. unladen) and two crawler tractors (33,757 lbs. unladen). Crawler tractor No. 1 was equipped with a 1 ¼ yd. front loader bucket. Crawler tractor No. 2 (21,000 lbs. unladen) was also equipped with a 1 ¼ yd. front loader bucket. A total of eight compaction cells were constructed. Observations made in the field indicated that the compactive effort of the Multi-Mover was markedly better than either of the crawler tractors used. The Multi-Mover tires would compact up to one-third the original depth of a loose waste lift in one pass with little springback, whereas the crawler tractor would compact to about one-half the depth with springback of the upper loose materials to nearly the original level.

Distributing Refuse for Compaction — The Multi-Mover was able to move large amounts of light, loose wastes better than crawler tractor No. 1, moving 15 to 30 yd.^{3} of waste at one time compared to 6 to 8 yd.^{3} for the crawler tractor. However, in soil moving, as a dozer, they were about equal. When large heavy loads were encountered under poor traction conditions, the crawler tractor was clearly superior.

In spreading and compacting the wastes, the Multi-Mover did not perform as uniformly as either crawler tractor. Because of the 10 inch clearance above the fill, the machine caught refuse already spread and rolled it ahead. The operator was often unaware of this since the box and ejection gate obstructed his view of the area directly in front of the machine. On the crawler tractor, the front end loader could be lifted several feet to clear and spread the wastes and visibility was better. This tendency to catch refuse contributed to the Multi-Mover achieving lower actual compaction than it was capable of achieving, and left the fill surface uneven. This was judged to be the most serious short-coming of the Multi-Mover in compacting refuse. The Multi-Mover did spread wastes faster than the crawler tractor, achieving a spreading rate of about 6 yd.^{3}/min. compared to 4.2 yd.^{3}/min. for crawler tractor No. 1. The higher rate of the Multi-Mover is due to its ability to move a larger amount of waste at one time and its higher speed in the low gear range used in spreading.

Depositing Soil Cover — In depositing soil cover the Multi-Mover achieved approximately the same spreading rate as crawler tractor No. 1 with front bucket loader. This rate was about 0.05 yd.^{3}/sec. The Multi-Mover spread 2 ¼ to 3 yd.^{3} in 45 to 50 seconds and the crawler tractor spread 1 to 1 ¼ yd.^{3} in 15 to 25 seconds. Uniformity of cover thickness as spread by the Multi-Mover was better.

By controlling forward speed and ejection gate speed, a fairly uniform layer 6 to 8 inches thick and 4 feet wide could be deposited. The crawler tractor spreading was controlled by tractor speed and rate of bucket tipping. Because the soil tended to hang together until the angle of repose was exceeded, it tipped out unevenly and the resulting layer varied from about 2 to 6 inches in thickness and 6 to 8 feet in width.

Excavation and Earthmoving — Tests were performed to compare excavation and earthmoving from a vertical bank at the Lake Lowell site. Multi-Mover loading time from a vertical bank or stockpile is comparatively slow. As the machine moves into a stockpile, the front wheels climb the slope and raise the box and claw above the point where efficient loading can be accomplished. In contrast, the crawler tractor bucket loads very quickly under these conditions because it is well ahead of the tracks.

Machine Performance

Speed, Maneuverability, and Handling — The Multi-Mover speeds on level ground were the same for loaded (3 yd.³, 7,500 lbs.) and unloaded conditions as shown below:

Maximum at 2,400 rpm		Average at 2,200 rpm on Landfill	
1st gear (fwd. and rev.)	3.9 mph	1st gear	3.0 mph
2nd gear (fwd. and rev.)	9.5 mph	2nd gear	6.2 mph
3rd gear (fwd. and rev.)	30 mph	3rd gear	not used

Maneuverability of the Multi-Mover for most landfill operations was good because its direction could be reversed immediately and it could travel at the same speeds in forward and reverse for spreading and compacting operations. For right angle turns during highway travel or for instances where the machine was turned around on the landfill, maneuverability was poor. The turning radius is 39.5 feet to the left and 56.5 feet to the right. This requires a large clear space to complete a turn on a landfill and a wide swing to complete right angle turns during highway travel without backing up.

Generally the Multi-Mover has the good low speed control needed for landfill service. Speeds over about 8 miles per hour on an uneven surface gave an uncomfortable ride and bouncing action because of the heavy, stiff springs; otherwise, the machine gave an acceptable ride.

Maneuverability of the crawler tractors for landfill service was very good since they were able to both reverse and turn in their own length by stopping one track and powering the other. Regulations prohibit highway travel with the crawler tractors under their own power; however, their low speed makes this an uneconomical long distance travel mode. Any speed over about 3 miles per hour on an uneven surface produced a rough, uncomfortable ride. The crawler tractors were easily started and responded well to the controls.

Highway Travel — In highway travel the Multi-Mover was driven from Nampa to Cougar Mountain Lodge, Idaho and back. On that trip the following data were obtained on highway travel:

Total distance traveled (hill & mountains, dry highway)	164 miles
Maximum speed attained	30 mph
Average speed	18 mph
Actual travel time, 164 miles	9 hr
Average fuel consumption	3.36 gal/hr
Mileage (includes fuel used for snow work and idling during stops)	3.5 miles/gal
Tire wear	1/16 in. on **front** tires. None on rear tires.

While the maximum speed attainable is 30 mph, slow steering response while traveling downhill and stiff, undamped springing dictated a safe maximum speed of about 20 mph. The large turning radius required extra care while maneuvering sharp corners. In general, the machine performs well in highway travel; braking is good and steering is smooth at the recommended safe maximum speed. On short trips of 5 to 30 miles, fuel consumption was 3.0 miles per gallon.

Snow Removal — While at Cougar Mountain Lodge, during April 1970, the Multi-Mover was used to plow, load, and unload snow. Operations were good even though heavy spring snow conditions prevailed. The machine easily loaded, unloaded, and plowed snow. Plowing was hindered by lack of traction where snow over slick ice was encountered. When traction was lost, the machine regained mobility by using the claw to back out and resume plowing. Sufficient wheel clearance for the mounting of chains to improve traction under these conditions would have been beneficial.

Miscellaneous Observations — During the field evaluation of the Multi-Mover the following general observations on the machine performance were noted:

(a) Until protected with guards, the universal joints would readily pick up discarded wire on a landfill, which would foul the drive shaft. After guards were installed, no further problems were experienced with wire.

(b) The tires were considerably abraded by glass and sharp metal in the refuse. Cuts in the tread up to ½ inch deep were observed, but they did not cause flat tires or noticeably impair tire function or traction. One flat tire was experienced from puncture by a large nail.

(c) Several hydraulic leaks developed in difficult-to-reach areas. These leaks were never completely stopped. Similar leaks occurred in hydraulic equipment on the crawler tractors but were generally more accessible for repair.

(d) The Multi-Mover was able to move and compact large amounts of waste rapidly. During a period when the crawler tractors were undergoing repair, the Multi-Mover was used to move approximately 1,475 yards^3 of refuse and compact it in a 10,000 ft.^{2} area in 1 ½ hours. During this operation the Multi-Mover routinely moved several loads of refuse up to 30 yd.^{3} each approximately 300 feet across loose refuse that was 6 to 7 feet deep. In contrast, the crawler tractors were able to move only about 6 to 8 yd.^{3} under these conditions.

(e) The Multi-Mover had good traction on loose refuse. Although it could no doubt be stuck under some conditions (as can a crawler tractor), it did not get stuck during the performance evaluations.

(f) The position of the operator is such that he cannot see the cutting depth of the blade on the box. This made it difficult to do good grading work.

(g)   The Multi-Mover loaded most efficiently on level runs. The design of the machine favors this operation over loading from a stockpile.

(h)   The exhaust stack temperature limitation (1350°F. max.) prevented steady use of the engine at the rated 2,400 rpm. Operation for over a few minutes generally had to be done at 1,900 rpm. This prevented use of full engine power.

(i)   The transmission had a tendency to overheat when subjected to more than about ½ hour of heavy work. The transmission is an older model with a small oil cooler, using the engine radiator fluid for cooling by convection flow. Later models of this transmission are equipped with separate oil cooling radiators.

It should be pointed out that data obtained on the repair costs of both the Multi-Mover and the crawler tractors were higher than would be normally incurred for equipment of these types. Both crawler tractors involved in the majority of the comparison testing were older models in poor condition and consequently required maintenance at a higher than normal rate. They were under repair or awaiting parts for repair approximately 50% of the time. Use of this costing data would not provide realistic cost projections typical of crawler tractor operations. Instead, typical maintenance costs of crawler tractors obtained from equipment maintenance were utilized as discussed in the section on systems analysis.

The Multi-Mover, though overhauled at the start of the project, was not restored to completely new condition. The original transmission and engine, for example, though worn, were indicated to be capable of performing satisfactorily during the test period. The total repair costs on the Multi-Mover from October 1969 to October 1970 were $7,522. The major items of repair were:

(1)   Overhaul of the transmission (required removing the box from the frame of the machine.
(2)   Replacing front hydraulic pump.
(3)   Replacing cracked engine head including new firing cups.
(4)   Repairing fuel injector line leaks.
(5)   Cleaning plugged fuel injector lines.
(6)   Replacing transmission oil seal.
(7)   Adjusting ejection gate and hydraulic divider valve to gate cylinders.
(8)   Repairing broken hydraulic hose.
(9)   Repairing broken weld on claw arm.
(10) Repairing flat tire.
(11) Rewiring and repairing battery charging circuit.
(12) Repairing miscellaneous hydraulic leaks.

Many of these Multi-Mover maintenance costs were unusual, not representative — particularly the complete transmission overhaul, replacement of the front hydraulic pump, replacement of the cracked engine head, and repairs and cleaning of the fuel injection lines. Again, maintenance costs typical of similar equipment were used in the systems analysis to enable comparison on a more representative basis.

SYSTEMS ANALYSIS

Cost Effectiveness

The primary purpose of this analysis is to compare the cost effectiveness of a multifunctional earthmoving machine (Multi-Mover) with a crawler tractor. The operating rates and costs developed in the course of this analysis were employed as input parameters for a computerized transportation model used to evaluate the economics of servicing several landfill sites in a sparsely populated area.

A total of 473 questionnaires were mailed to sparsely populated counties and small towns and cities in the Pacific Northwest and Northern California to determine the type of equipment used in landfill operations. The results of the survey indicate the use of a wide variety of equipment, ranging in size from a small agricultural tractor to 20 yd.^{3} capacity scrapers. The most frequently used equipment is a medium size (25,000 to 40,000 lbs.) crawler tractor equipped with either a bulldozer blade or a bucket loader.

Several of those responding reported the use of equipment larger than usually recommended for landfills of the size they operate. This is attributable to the fact that many landfills are operated by county and municipal governments that minimize equipment inventory by sharing equipment between landfill operations and road work; road construction and maintenance requires the larger capacity equipment.

Method of Analysis — The first step in the analysis was to develop an operations flow diagram to establish the various operations required in a sanitary landfill and their relationships. The operations were chosen to provide a reasonable balance between the detail required for validity and ease of data collection and manipulation. To facilitate comparisons of productivity under normal landfill conditions, some of the operations were combined into groups, or tasks. A task consists of the operations required to perform a common landfill function, such as excavating a cell.

Certain operations may exist as alternative tasks. For example, in a trench-type operation, after a load of material is excavated from the trench it may be transported to either a stockpile for dumping or to a partially completed cell for spreading to a controlled depth. The flow will depend on the specific requirements and operating policies of the particular site.

Data obtained from test site time and motion studies were used to develop average time coefficients for each task. The Multi-Mover is faster than the crawler tractor in performing every task. The performance parameters were developed from time and motion data collected under controlled conditions.

The Multi-Mover is more than twice as fast as the crawler tractor in spreading waste. This is due to the large blade area of the Multi-Mover compared to the small bucket on the crawler tractor. Had the crawler tractor been equipped with a bulldozer or trash blade the comparison would have been more equal. Both machines tended to catch and tear loose waste that had already been spread. The operator of the crawler tractor could see this happen and correct it by lifting the bucket to drop the offending object(s). The operator of the Multi-Mover frequently could not see the blade area, and even if he did, the Multi-Mover's box could not be lifted high enough to drop a large object.

The crawler tractor was frequently able to produce smoother waste cells, particularly when the waste included bulky objects such as tires. The difficulties caused by the Multi-Mover's maximum blade height were compounded by a tendency for the wheels to sink into soft areas of the cell, effectively lowering the blade and digging up already compacted waste.

The Multi-Mover was operated by several different people in the course of making the time and motion studies, and no one operated the machine long enough to become really proficient in its operation. On the other hand, the operators of the crawler tractors were well experienced in operation of their machines in landfills. Although efforts were made to discount data taken when the Multi-Mover operators were unfamiliar with the machine's operation, it is expected that the data are somewhat biased in favor of the crawler tractor.

The task time data which depend on haul distance were handled in the following manner: Observed times were recorded for several different haul distances and then a least-squares linear regression analysis was used to determine the equation of the regression line. This approach was used to simplify later modeling of the tasks for various haul distances and the determination of breakeven points.

Cost Estimation for the Multi-Mover — Table 6 summarizes the derivation of the hourly operating costs for the Multi-Mover. The selling price of $45,000 is based on estimates of production costs made in 1967. The estimated 1970 manufacturing cost is $30,000. The total cost of promotion, distribution, service under warranty, profit, and related selling costs is estimated at 50% of the total manufacturing cost, bringing the total selling price to $45,000.

The cost of capital was assumed to be 8% annually and the insurance rate was assumed to be 1% of the new value of the machine per year. The salvage value of the machine after 10,000 hours was estimated at 25% of the original selling price.

Operating expenses were estimated by applying the current costs of fuel and lubricating oils in the Richland, Washington area to consumption rates based on equipment manufacturer's estimates for similar sized equipment. This approach was chosen in preference to relying on actual operating data since numerous minor problems with various systems were encountered, which resulted in abnormally high consumption of transmission fluid, hydraulic oil and diesel fuel. The present design of the machine does not offer reliability equal to competitive equipment now on the market. Redesign to make reliability and longevity comparable to that of currently available equipment is considered a prerequisite to successful marketing of the machine. This would also result in lubricant and hydraulic fluid use rates similar to currently marketed machinery.

TABLE 6: SUMMARY OF MULTI-MOVER HOURLY OPERATING COSTS

10,000 hour   useful lifetime over 5 years

	5-Year Total	$/Hr
Initial cost (excluding sales tax)	$ 45,000	
Interest @ 8% annual rate	10,035	
Insurance	2,250	
Total	$ 57,285	
Less salvage value	11,250	
Net capital cost (owning expense)	$ 46,035	4.60
Fuel @ 4.5 gal/hr and $0.188/gal		0.85
Tires @ $500 each and 2000 hr life		1.00
8000-hr major overhaul	1,500	0.15
Repairs and labor @ 20% of initial cost		0.90
Lubricants, etc.		0.32
Total hourly operating expense		3.22
Total hourly owning and operating expense		7.82

Actual maintenance costs observed during the test program were not considered reasonable estimates of those which could be expected for a production version of the Multi-Mover. The maintenance cost estimate was derived from those suggested by the manufacturers of currently available equipment. Since the estimate is expressed as a percentage of the owning expense, the complexity of the Multi-Mover is reflected in the owning expense and the absolute maintenance cost is proportionately higher than that for the wheeled loaders on which the percentages were based. The overhaul cost and time period were similarly derived.

Tire life was particularly difficult to estimate because of the expected multiple use of the Multi-Mover.

For example, the Multi-Mover is expected to operate on landfill haul roads and waste cells as well as on highways between landfill sites. If the Multi-Mover were used to haul maximum loads of cover material over moderate distances at highway speeds, the tire life would be only a small fraction of that which would be expected if the same time was spent at lower speeds and short hauls on landfill haul roads. An estimate of 2,000 hours average tire life was chosen after discussions with several dealers of tires for heavy equipment.

No estimate of taxes was included in the cost estimates because this will, of course, vary from state to state. If the Multi-Mover is to be used on the public highways, it will require some type of vehicle license.

The fee and licensing structure will vary from state to state, and for this reason, it is not included in the analysis. State and federal highway taxes, which would have to be paid on the fuel used for highway travel, are not included for the same reason.

Fuel taxes are included in the cost of operating the tractor-trailer for transporting the crawler tractor, because those taxes are included in the sale price of the gasoline; however, no other taxes or license fees are included.

Cost Estimation for the Crawler Tractor — Table 7 summarizes the hourly operating costs for a crawler tractor with a front end loader. The initial cost of $24,000 was the estimate obtained from the manufacturer's representative. Interest, insurance, and salvage value were estimated in the same manner as those for the Multi-Mover.

The fuel, lubrication, and hydraulic fluid use rates were obtained from the manufacturer's representative and costs are based on current prices for the Richland, Washington area. These costs will vary with location and supplier. The manufacturer's estimates were used in preference to observed values for two reasons: first, to make the estimating procedure for the crawler tractor and Multi-Mover as similar as possible, and second, because the crawler tractor was in a poor state of repair during the testing, the use rates and maintenance costs encountered were not expected to be typical of those which would be experienced over the entire lifetime of the machine.

The literature received from the manufacturer estimated repairs and maintenance expense at 90% of the owning expense and did not include separate estimates for major overhaul of the machine. Cost of a 5,000 hour major overhaul was estimated at $7,500 and the 90% figure was adjusted downward to reflect this change. After this change the repair and maintenance expenses estimate was found to be reasonably consistent with the rates suggested by other manufacturers of crawler tractors.

TABLE 7: SUMMARY OF CRAWLER TRACTOR OPERATING COSTS

10,000 hour lifetime over 5 years

	5-Year Total	$/hr
Initial cost (excluding sales tax)	$24,000	
Interest @ 8% annual rate	5,350	
Insurance	1,200	
Total	$30,550	
Less salvage value	7,500	
Net capital cost (owning expense)	$23,050	$2.30
Fuel @ 4.0 gal/hr and $0.188/gal		0.75
5,000 hour major overhaul	7,500	0.75
Repairs and labor @ 55% of initial cost		1.32
Lubricants, etc.		0.22
Total hourly operating expense		3.04
Total hourly owning and operating expense		$5.34

Comparison of Cost Effectiveness

The estimates of the costs associated with the operation of each machine and the times required to perform typical landfill operations were combined into one set of cost effectiveness parameters. There are several different cost parameters as well as different performance parameters which may provide relevant comparisons between the two machines. The most important of these is the total cost/unit work performed. Others which might be of interest include the fixed expense/unit work or fixed expense/yr., operating cost/unit work and labor cost/unit work. The Multi-Mover's cost/unit work is lower than that of the crawler tractor for waste spreading, waste compacting and cover compacting (Table 8). The cost/unit work for the other operations depends on the distances involved.

The crawler tractor is more economical at short haul distances because of its faster loading and dumping times. Multi-Mover's greater speed and payload make it the more economical of the two machines at longer haul distances. These breakeven distances are all within the range that would be encountered in many landfill operations. If several landfills were being considered for service by the same machine, the crawler might be slightly more economical at some sites and the Multi-Mover at others.

In general, it is not possible to say that either machine should prove superior consistently in normal landfill operations for these tasks; the economics would depend on the circumstances at the particular landfill. Systems of landfills for sparsely populated areas are usually planned with a goal for providing a disposal site within 8 to 15 miles of each resident in the area.

TABLE 8: COST/UNIT WORK FOR MULTI-MOVER AND CRAWLER TRACTOR

Task	Multi-Mover	Crawler Tractor
Excavate trench	$\dfrac{(0.144\ d^{(1)} + 173)\ \text{dollars}}{1000\ \text{yd}^3\ \text{excavated}}$	$(0.96\ d + 98)\ \dfrac{\text{dollars}}{1000\ \text{yd}^3\ \text{excavated}}$
Spread waste	\$32.10/1000 yd^3 loose$^{(2)}$	\$58.30/1000 yd^3 loose
Compact waste	\$26.00/1000 yd^3 loose/pass $^{(3)}$	\$36.10/1000 yd^3 loose/pass
Spread cover from stockpile	$(0.192\ d + 141)\ \dfrac{\text{dollars}}{1000\ \text{yd}^3}$	$(0.96\ d + 98)\dfrac{\text{dollars}}{1000\ \text{yd}^3}$
Spread cover from excavation	$(0.144\ d + 173)\ \dfrac{\text{dollars}}{1000\ \text{yd}^3}$	$(0.96\ d + 119)\dfrac{\text{dollars}}{1000\ \text{yd}^3}$
Compact cover	\$0.37/1000 ft^2/pass $^{(3)}$	\$0.43/1000 ft^2/pass
Travel between sites	\$0.83/mile	\$0.52/mile + \$3.64

(1) d = one-way haul distance from trench or cell to stockpile or other cell.

(2) Waste spreading and compaction figures are based on as-delivered volumes of waste. This was delivered primarily by compactor-type collection vehicles, and yardages are based on as-delivered volume and not on volumes loaded into the trucks.

(3) A pass is defined as a series of trips across the area to be compacted so that the entire area receives one tire or track mark.

Transportation Model

A way of reducing the cost of maintaining disposal sites in sparsely populated areas would be to service several remote, small waste disposal sites with multi-functional equipment of highway mobility, such as the Multi-Mover.

A computer based model has been developed to study the economics of such an operation. The model compares two types of equipment, which must be described by the model user in terms of capabilities and operating costs. In this context, an equipment type may describe a single machine, or a group of machines working together.

In computer runs made for this study, the Multi-Mover was compared with a single crawler tractor equipped with a 1¼ yd.^{3} bucket in the operation of several sanitary landfill sites in Canyon County, Idaho. In these computer runs, the Multi-Mover has exhibited a definite economic advantage.

Solid Waste Disposal in Sparsely Populated Areas

The problems of solid waste generation, collection, transportation and disposal in a sparsely populated area are not fundamentally different from those of a densely populated metropolitan area. In both cases, the primary objective of a solid waste program is to provide the maximum solid waste disposal service within the limitations of law, funding, and public demand for services. The tasks which must be completed to meet this objective are basically the same in either a sparsely or densely populated area. The citizens must be educated to store their waste in such a way as to minimize health hazards and aesthetic blight, and the waste must be collected and transported from its point of generation to some central location for reclamation or disposal.

These three major steps reduce to many different tasks and the proper execution of each of these tasks becomes a problem for the agency(s) charged with the responsibility of administering the solid waste program in a given area. Although the problems encountered are similar for densely and sparsely populated areas, the relative importance of the various problem areas depends on the population density. This section defines some of the problem areas that are likely to be particularly important in a sparsely populated area and examines solutions to these problems. Particular emphasis is placed on ways that a multifunctional machine (such as the Multi-Mover) might contribute to the solution of these problems.

The average population density for the entire county which was the subject of this study was approximately 120 people per square mile. Areas considered as sparsely populated may differ considerably. However, in the context of this report the primary criterion for a sparsely populated area is that its solid waste collection and disposal operations are hampered by low population density. Although no two sparsely populated areas are exactly similar in terms of population distribution and solid waste disposal problems, use of a typical example facilitates the discussion of some of these problems.

Description of a Typical Solid Waste Disposal System — The solid waste disposal system in a sparsely populated area includes all the steps of handling solid waste from the time it leaves the point of generation (the housewife's kitchen garbage pail, or the merchant's trash barrel) to the time of its disposal or recycle. Common practice in sparsely populated areas at the present time is to dispose of the wastes in some type of open dump or landfill.

Figure 12.3 shows the most common possibilities of solid waste generation, transportation, and disposal in a sparsely populated area. This flow chart shows only the solid waste bound for disposal in a solid waste disposal operation. It does not include solid waste which is reused, or recycled. For example, a significant amount of solid waste from food processing operations is used by nearby feedlots and does not enter the county solid waste system.

A sparsely populated area is not likely to provide collection service to all the producers of solid waste. There is no organized collection service available to approximately 40% of the residents of the county. Many of the residents in areas where collection service is available do not take advantage of the service, but prefer to handle the disposal of their household refuse themselves. In addition, many of the processors of commercial and industrial solid waste also handle their own disposal operations.

FIGURE 12.3: SOLID WASTE DISPOSAL SYSTEM IN SPARSELY POPULATED AREAS

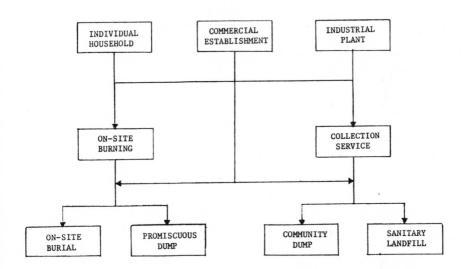

Source: PB 212,589 (1972)

There are several possibilities open to those residents and industries who either must handle their own solid waste disposal or elect to do so rather than availing themselves of a collection service. Many residents simply collect their household refuse and periodically transport it to a county operated disposal site. Other residents elect to burn the combustible portion of their refuse, collecting the ashes and noncombustibles for a later trip to a disposal site. Some rural residents dispose of their refuse by burying it on their own property, or by burning it and burying the ashes. Some residents simply dump their refuse wherever it is convenient, and in spite of "no dumping" signs and ordinances, promiscuous dumps are common in sparsely populated areas.

Major Problem Areas — Whether any part of a solid waste disposal system is described as a problem area often depends on the observer's point of view. For example, a person familiar with solid waste disposal in a large, densely populated metropolitan area would not be likely to consider site acquisition in a sparsely populated area a very serious problem. To the County Commissioner faced with finding a suitable disposal site in a convenient location at a reasonable price, this may be a very serious problem.

This example, then, emphasizes that the term "problem area" is subjective. The situations to be discussed are defined as problem areas only because they are most likely to be major stumbling blocks to either efficient or cost effective operation of a solid waste program in a sparsely populated area.

Before discussing how the Multi-Mover may contribute to the solution of specific problems, it is necessary to discuss the general characteristics of the multifunctional machine and to compare it to other equipment currently in general use. The most commonly used equipment for small landfill operations (such as those usually found in sparsely populated areas) is the crawler tractor equipped with either a bulldozer blade or a bucket loader. In some operations other equipment such as scrapers (either drawn by a crawler or self-powered), wheeled loaders and dump trucks are also used.

In most cases the use of this additional equipment indicates the disposal operation is large enough to take advantage of this specialized equipment to achieve lower unit costs. Landfill operations which must use the minimum amount of equipment most often use a crawler tractor equipped with a loader attachment. This one piece of equipment is capable of performing all of the functions required for landfill operation such as digging trenches; moving and compacting waste; transporting, spreading, and compacting cover material; and maintaining haul roads.

The crawler tractor with a bucket loader is reasonably efficient at excavating trenches and handling the wastes. It is less efficient in spreading cover material, and its efficiency decreases greatly with longer haul distances for cover material. When additional equipment is added to an operation, it is frequently a dump truck, scraper, or perhaps a wheeled loader to increase the efficiency of the hauling part of the operation. When this equipment is available to expedite hauling and excavation, a crawler tractor with a bulldozer or "trash blade" (a large bulldozer blade fitted with extensions to allow more waste to be pushed at one time) is often used instead of the front loader.

In the detailed cost effectiveness comparison of the Multi-Mover and a typical crawler tractor included in this report, the Multi-Mover was found to be somewhat more expensive to own and operate, but its productivity is great enough to more than offset its higher cost, particularly where longer haul distances are involved. The Multi-Mover was quicker in transport from site-to-site for distances less than 21 miles, and less expensive to transport for distances less than 12 miles. Each of the major problem areas is analyzed in light of the results of the cost effectiveness analysis to determine whether the Multi-Mover would help to solve the problem.

Sanitary and modified landfill operations will continue to be a popular and suitable means of solid waste disposal for some time in sparsely populated areas where suitable landfill sites are available and the tax base does not favor large capital outlays. Therefore, it is appropriate to determine ways in which a multifunctional machine such as the Multi-Mover might help to improve service or lower costs, or both.

Disposal Site Availability — Disposal site availability appears to be the most widely felt problem, since it was mentioned by 58% of the respondents to the questionnaire. The problems related to the acquisition of disposal sites include:

(1) the lack of area (more precisely, usable volume) sufficient to handle the projected waste input for a reasonable length of time,

(2) zoning ordinances prohibiting landfill operations,

(3) unreasonable haul distances from the population center(s) served,

(4) lack of accessibility from population centers without creating heavy truck traffic through residential areas,

(5) nonavailability of suitable on-site or nearby cover material,

(6) potential of ground and surface water pollution,

(7) need for suitable separation from existing residential and commercial developments,

(8) prohibitive real estate prices,

(9) public acceptability of the site.

One of the most straightforward approaches to the problem of disposal site availability is to make more efficient use of each available site. If more waste can be disposed in a site, it will have a longer useful lifetime. Smaller sites are generally easier to find and less expensive than larger sites. This may mean an available parcel of land suitable for landfill service may be used in spite of its small size. In addition, higher refuse densities usually result in more rapid stabilization of the fill, thereby making it available for other uses sooner after completion of the landfill operations.

Studies indicate the Multi-Mover is capable of higher compaction ratios than the crawler tractor under similar conditions, with observed compaction ratios of approximately 4.2:1 and 2.1:1, respectively. Thus, under these test conditions, about 100% more waste may be disposed in a given site by using the Multi-Mover for compacting.

Maximum use of available land is one reason for operating a disposal site as a sanitary landfill. An open dump operates at essentially a one-to-one compaction ratio (trucked volume/in-place volume). In sanitary landfills, which are compacted and covered daily, average compaction ratios from 2:1 to 3:1 are achievable with conventional crawler tractors, and with the Multi-Mover, ratios as high as 4:1 are possible at a reasonable cost.

A dump that is covered periodically might typically consist of one part earth cover for each ten parts waste, while a sanitary landfill typically consists of one part cover for each four parts waste. Even though more cover is included, a landfill operating at a 3:1 compaction ratio can store approximately 2.6 times as much waste per acre-foot as a covered dump.

Landfill Composition from Ore Processing Wastes

Since valuable ore deposits often occur in nature intimately mixed with a variety of less valuable or desirable constituents, it is a primary function of the ore processing industry to remove or separate as much of these extraneous constituents from the desired ore as possible. The flotation process developed in the early 1930's has proven to be a valuable tool for assisting in the removal of unwanted waste products from ores and is in wide usage in a variety of ore processing operations. However, since the development and utilization of the flotation process by the ore processing industry, disposal of the waste products resulting therefrom has presented a monumental problem. Basically these waste materials fall into two categories identified by the terms "slimes" and "tailings."

The slimes are aqueous suspensions or dispersions of the ultrafine solid wastes most of which are ordinarily separated from the ore feed stream to the flotation step prior to carrying out the flotation step. Slimes may be more precisely defined as comprising an aqueous suspension of ultrafine soil solids associated with the ore such as, for example, clays, quartz, and mineral values, the solid particles of which are of sufficiently small particle size so that at least about 99% by weight of the solids (dry basis) passes through 150 mesh screen.

The tailings are the solid waste from the flotation step itself and are essentially water-insoluble granular particles of soil which are associated with the ore which have a substantially larger particle size than the slime solids. Tailings typically comprise a mixture of from about 90 to 95% by weight (dry basis) of quartz and from about 5 to 10% by weight (dry basis) mineral values wherein at least 95% by weight (dry basis) of the solids possess an average particle size within the range –16 to +150 mesh. Accordingly, at least 95% by weight average between about 105 and 1,000 microns and a major portion of the tailings are generally larger than about 65 mesh.

Slimes and tailings are produced as waste products in a lot of widely varying ore processing operations such as, for example, in copper mining, in the mining of heavy minerals such as titanium and rutile, and in virtually all nonmetallic mining such as the mining of phosphate, potash, feldspar, clays, and fluorspar. A principal generator of copious amounts of slimes and tailings is the phosphate rock processing industry, a substantial portion of which is located in the state of Florida.

It is disposal of the tremendous amounts of slimes generated by ore processing plants which present the waste disposal problem. Slimes present a problem because they retain substantial amounts of water and consequently their fluidity even after years of settling and, as a result, possess substantially no bearing strength whatever. Even after settling for many years, the slimes settle to only about 25 to 30% by weight solids and still possess a jelly-like consistency. As such, the disposal site in which they are deposited becomes virtually useless and is an obvious hazard to passers-by.

The slimes are typically disposed of by discharging them into excavations or, as is perhaps more common, into reservoirs or ponds which are formed by a constructed earthen dam-work. The slimes are allowed to settle by gravity; the water which separates from the slimes during settling is usually recovered from the slimes settling pond for reuse in the ore processing plant.

Where dammed sites are utilized, the dams must be continuously maintained for when a dam fails, as they may occasionally do, the countryside and rivers surrounding the site are inundated with vast quantities of the jelly-like slimes resulting in pollution of the land and surrounding waterways. Moreover, when the slimes disposal area is filled, the site is nothing more than a liability. A crust may form on the surface of the site but a few inches below the surface the slimes are a jelly-like mass, and obviously a serious hazard to anyone crossing the site. Backfilling over the surface may permit use of the filled up disposal site for limited agricultural use but use of heavy equipment and building on the site is not possible.

Disposal of tailings, while not as serious a problem as the disposal of slimes, is still a problem. The tailings have acceptable bearing strength when deposited in a firmly confined area but are essentially barren of plant nutrient, have practically no capacity for holding water, and are easily carried aloft by wind and eroded by storms. These properties present an obvious disadvantage to useful reclamation of these tailings disposal sites.

C.C. Cook and E.M. Haynsworth; U.S. Patent 3,761,239; September 25, 1973 have developed a means for eliminating the substantial waste disposal problems attendant with presently used procedures for disposing of slimes and tailings and, in particular, for eliminating the safety hazards and land and water pollution hazards associated with such waste disposal procedures.

It was found that when slimes are admixed with tailings, the slimes dewater at a substantially greater rate than is achievable using gravity settling and, moreover, that the reconstituted slimes-tailings mixtures produced thereby are sufficiently fertile to support plant life and possess acceptable bearing strength. By acceptable bearing strength is meant that the bearing strength of the reconstituted mixture will approach that of normal soil in the region from which the ore being processed originates. In general, an acceptable bearing strength means that the land will support animals and human beings, heavy equipment such as tractors and the like, and can be used for the construction of buildings and dwellings.

Where the slimes have a solid concentration below about 10% prior to admixture with the tailings, tailings trickle through the mixture, with most of the tailings forming as a layer in the bottom of the disposal area. The slimes are simply displaced and rest on top of the tailings. Where the slimes have a solids content which exceeds 25%, the tails bridge across the slimes surface and a jelly-like mass remains trapped below the tails, resulting in nothing more than capping the slimes. In both instances, the resulting slimes-tailings mixture is unsuitable for use in land reclamation.

If the resulting mixture contains more than about 99% tailings, the landfill composition lacks the requisite fertility and moreover would provide for only minimal utilization of the waste slimes. If the resulting mixtures contain less than about 60% tails, the landfill composition lacks sufficient bearing strength for effective land reclamation.

It has been found that within a few hours after the slimes-tailings mixture is produced and deposited in the disposal site that it possesses sufficient bearing strength to support a man's weight. With a few (2 to 3) weeks, the mixture has sufficient bearing strength to support heavy equipment such as D-8 tractors. A somewhat longer time period is required to achieve a bearing strength within the mixture which is sufficient to support construction of buildings and dwellings.

The preferred landfill composition contains about 30 to about 40 parts slimes, about 60 to 70 parts tailings, a moisture content of about 15 to 25%, and at least 97% of the solids having a particle size of minus 16 mesh. This composition may also contain from about 1 to about 50 parts by weight on a dry basis of hydrated calcium sulfate.

Figure 13.1 is a schematic flowsheet of the process. The waste primary slimes 10 from the flotation pretreatment process steps in a phosphate ore processing plant and the waste secondary slimes 11 from the flotation step itself are admixed to form a dilute aqueous suspension of slime solids 12 which typically contains 1 to 2% solids. Usually about 90% of the total slimes produced are primary slimes with the remaining 10% being secondary slimes. All or a portion of the primary or secondary slimes may be used to produce stream 12. It is, of course possible to use only the primary or only the secondary slimes to make up stream 12 if desired. Slimes stream 12 is fed to thickener 13 where it is typically thickened for 20 to 50 hours, and preferably 22 to 26 hours, to produce a solids content in the slimes of about 3 to 6%.

FIGURE 13.1: FLOWSHEET FOR PRODUCING LANDFILL COMPOSITION FROM ORE PROCESSING WASTES

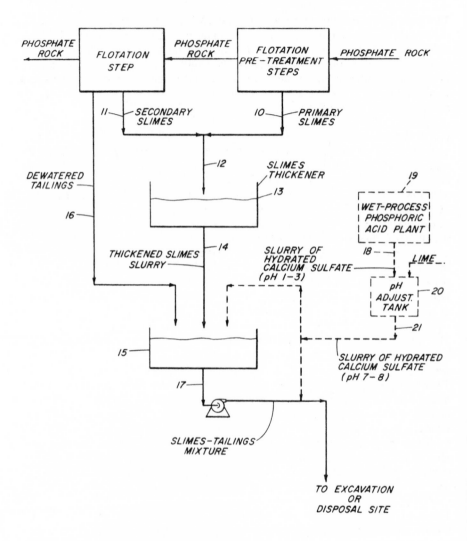

Source: C.C. Cook and E.M. Haynsworth; U.S. Patent 3,761,239; September 25, 1973

The thickener underflow **14** containing 3 to 6% solids and typically 3 to 4% solids, is then fed to tank **15** whereupon it is admixed with waste tailings **16** from the flotation step. Tailings **16** are dewatered and typically contain about 20% water. The thickened slimes stream **14** is used to repulp tailings **16** in tank **15** to produce an aqueous slurry of a mixture of slimes and tailings **17** which is then pumped out of tank **15** to the waste disposal excavation or other suitable land reclamation site.

The respective quantities of streams **14** and **16** fed to tank **15** will, of course, depend on several factors such as, for example, the ratio of tailings to slimes solids desired in the landfill composition and provision of sufficient water to render stream **17** pumpable to the excavation site. The required proportions of tailings to slimes in the landfill compositions have been discussed hereinabove. Generally, stream **17** will contain a solids content of from about 15 to 45%, and preferably, 40 to 45%.

If it is desired to add hydrated calcium sulfate to the landfill composition, an aqueous slurry of hydrated calcium sulfate **18** from the wet process phosphoric acid plant **19** or from the calcium sulfate ponds of such a plant is fed to a suitable vessel **20** where the acid pH of stream **18** is rendered alkaline by treatment with lime. The alkaline calcium sulfate slurry **21** is thereupon added to tank **15** where, along with the slimes stream **14** , it serves to repulp tailings **16**. Optionally stream **21** can be injected directly into the pipeline which conducts the slimes-tailings mixture **17** to the excavation site where, due to the continuous churning and mixing which occurs in the stream flowing in the pipeline, the calcium sulfate admixes with the slimes-tailings mixture. The quantity of stream **21** required will, of course, depend on how much hydrated calcium sulfate is desired in the landfill composition. Stream **21** can contain a wide range of solids content, usually up to about 20%.

The slimes-tailings mixture is then pumped to an excavation which is typically a ditch one-half to one mile or longer in length, 40 to 60 ft. deep, 30 to 50 ft. wide at the base and from 100 to 150 to 200 feet wide at the top. Mixture **17** is introduced at one end of the ditch. Once the mixture is deposited in the ditch, a substantial portion of the slimes tend to physically separate from the tailings and flow away from the tailings. These slimes roll on ahead of the tailings accumulating ahead of the tailings where they are then given the opportunity to concentrate to the required solids content of 10 to 25%. Almost as soon as mixture **17** is deposited in the ditch, water is rapidly released from the mixture and proceeds by gravity down the ditch until it eventually reaches a dam at one end of the ditch.

This dam will typically have an overflow weir which directs the overflow from the accumulated water into the fresh water return canal of the phosphate rock processing plant. After those discharged slimes which have accumulated ahead of the tailings have become concentrated to the required 10 to 25% solids levels, the discharge pipe for mixture **17** is advanced to discharge mixture **17** onto these concentrated slimes. As the mixture is discharged, most of the slimes discharged again separate from the tailings in the mixture and flow on ahead of the tailings. The discharged tailings, however, settle by gravity into the concentrated slimes and mix with these slimes to form a fertile landfill composition of acceptable bearing strength. In effect, these concentrated slimes remix with the slimes-tailings mixture as the deposited mixture advances along the ditch.

The discharged slimes-tailings mixture is gradually advanced along the length of the ditch until the ditch is substantially filled with the landfill composition. Where desired, low check dams can be placed at intervals across the ditch to impede slimes flow and assist in concentrating the slimes solids to the 10 to 25% level where the tailings will mix with the slimes instead of merely displacing them or capping them.

It should also be noted that despite the fact that substantial portions of the slimes flow away from the tailings when the slimes-tailings mixture is deposited in the ditch, the tailings will retain as much as 1 to 3% by weight on a dry basis of the slimes even at the surface of the deposited tailings. This clay provides nutrients for plant growth and also acts as a sponge to retain the moisture necessary for plant growth and erosion inhibition.

In the following land reclamation test, a cut or ditch, approximately 8,500 ft. long and averaging 38 ft. in depth and 136 ft. in width at the top, was filled with approximately 1,219,038 tons of plant tailings and 87,382 tons of plant slimes in accordance with this process. Across the exit end of the cut there was erected a dam and an overflow weir leading to the fresh water return canal of the phosphate rock processing plant. Tailings from the phosphate processing plant were pulped with return water and pumped to the cut where they were deposited as landfill. Approximately 3,400 ft. of the cut was filled in this manner before this process was put into use. The waste disposal area at this time has good bearing strength but is not fertile.

At this point, the plant slimes thickener was run to produce maximum underflow density. The thickened slimes underflow containing about 3.5 to 4.0% solids and typically 3 to 6% solids was used to repulp the dewatered plant tailings and the resulting mixture was then pumped to the disposal cut. The mixture contained a solids content of about 15 to 18% by weight at this time. Due to the nature of the mixture, the slimes tended to separate and run ahead of the tailings after the mixture was discharged into the cut. However, analysis of the soil samples showed that at least about 1 to 3% of slimes (dry weight) are trapped within the tailings despite separation of most of the slimes. This improved fertility and compaction as the clay contained in the slimes retains a substantial amount of moisture.

Since some initial separation of the slimes was evident small check dams were placed across the cut at intervals along its length. The dams impeded the advance of the densifying slimes permitting the clear water to proceed down the cut. When the separated slimes thickened to about 10 to 15% solids, mixing of these thickened slimes with the now advancing slimes-tailings mixture occurred. Such mixing improved the release of water from the slimes.

After the cut was completely filled to ground level, six borings were made.

The results indicate that the landfill possesses good bearing strength. The entire site has been seeded with Bermuda grass and good growth is evident. The landfill has good bearing strength and supported a variety of heavy pieces of equipment such as, for example, D-8 tractors, within very short periods after the filling of the cut was completed.

Sanitary Landfill Accounting System

The material in this chapter is taken from PB 215,907 published in 1969.

SYSTEM BENEFITS

Implementation of a system such as the one described herein has several important advantages, as follows:

(1) It facilitates the orderly and efficient collection and transmission of all relevant data. In fact, much of the recommended data is probably already being collected, although haphazardly and inefficiently. Hence, the added cost of implementing the system is minimal.

(2) Reports are clear and concise, presenting only data required for effective control and analysis. Because they can be completed and understood by landfill personnel, operation of the system can be made almost foolproof.

(3) The data is grouped in standard accounting classifications. This simplifies interpretation of results and comparison with data from previous years or other operations. In turn, this allows analysis of relative performance and operational changes.

(4) The system accounts for all relevant costs of operations.

(5) Accumulated data from the system can over a period of time lead to standards of performance and efficiency. These standards are used to control costs. They indicate what costs are high and what is causing them. The landfill supervisor may then take corrective action.

244

(6)   The system includes automatic provisions for accountability. Cost control becomes more effective when the individual responsible for cost increases can be pinpointed.

(7)   The collected data aids in short-range and long-range forecasting of operating and capital budgets. This facilitates estimation of future requirements for equipment, manpower, land, cash, etc., which, in turn, aids planning at all levels of management. The data is also available for later evaluation and analysis, using operations research techniques.

(8)   With only minor modifications, the system is flexible enough to meet the varying requirements of landfills of different size and scope.

REPORTS AND INFORMATION FLOW

The cost system is designed for medium-size sanitary landfills. It assumes that the community or private firm has an accounting section or department to aid in preparation of the summary reports. The system also assumes that a scale is on-site. Actual measurement of solid waste quantities is possible only with scaled weights. Due to the system's flexibility, however, neither of these assumptions is critical. Only minor modifications are required to adapt the system to significantly larger or smaller operations. Due to the diversity of disposal operations no attempt will be made to suggest all of the possible variations.

FIGURE 14.1: INFORMATION FLOW DIAGRAM

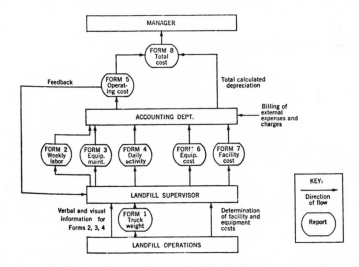

Source: PB 215,907 (1969)

The flow of information through the cost system is by means of reports (Figure 14.1). The eight reports transmit information from the field where data is recorded to the point of data use, various levels of supervision and management.

The reports are most easily classified as those that are prepared daily and those that are prepared at less frequent intervals. Cost control, responsibility accounting, and the preparation of periodic summary statements cannot be accomplished without the daily recording of all pertinent activity and cost information. Data not recorded daily is not retrievable at some later date.

Daily Truck Weight Record

This form (Form 1) records the quantities, sources, and types of solid wastes delivered to the site. Cover material, if it is delivered from off-site, may be recorded on this form. If the cover material is acquired on the site, the cover material column may be deleted or a daily estimate of cubic yards may be recorded. The information is recorded manually on this form for the entire day.

If the landfill has a scale that automatically records the weight data, that part of the form would be replaced by the weight ticket. Each delivery is recorded separately by the weigh-master. A second weighing of the empty truck may be taken, or the vehicle's tare weight (as determined by a licensing agency, etc.) may be substituted.

Truck identification, load weight, and solid waste type are useful in billing private concerns and others for the privilege of using the landfill. The record of truck delivery times and frequency, along with truck identification, load weight, and waste type, are an important aid to operation and control of a municipal collection system.

Weekly Labor Ticket

This record of labor activity (Form 2) is recorded in duplicate at the landfill. One copy is forwarded to the payroll department for determining weekly wages. The other copy is used by the landfill supervisor for computing total labor hours and the assignment of these hours to the landfill's various activities.

Monthly Equipment Maintenance Record

This form (Form 3) facilitates the detailed collection of equipment operation and associated cost data. A separate sheet is used for each piece of equipment at the site. Daily entries are made as appropriate. The form is used for an entire month.

Daily Activity Summary

This form (Form 4) summarizes the truck deliveries, solid waste quantity disposed of, man-hours worked, machine hours utilized, cover material used (if measured or estimated), and miscellaneous expenses incurred. Since this provides a continuous cover material inventory, it is useful in keeping the landfill supervisor advised as to his present status and when more cover material will be required. The form is used for an entire month. It is completed at the end of each day by the landfill supervisor. At the end of the month, it is forwarded to the accounting department.

Less Frequently Prepared Reports

These reports may be prepared as often as desired. The Operating Cost Report is used for control purposes. Hence, the more frequently it is prepared (perhaps even weekly), the more useful it would be. The remaining reports are summary reports (preparation quarterly would be sufficient).

Landfill Operating Cost Report: This report (Form 5) summarizes the landfill's operations. It is compiled from all the daily tickets. As a summary of the landfill's total operating costs, it may be used to hold the supervisor responsible for any adverse trends in costs. In addition, the calculated unit cost and efficiency factors are helpful to the supervisor in analyzing these adverse cost trends and controlling them.

If most of the expenses incurred in operating the facility are billed directly to the municipality, the necessary cost data required for preparation of this form would not normally be available to the supervisor. Under these circumstances, the supervisor should forward the information he has collected (the daily tickets) to the accounting department. This department will then compile the Operating Cost Report and send a copy back to the landfill supervisor.

Equipment and Facility Cost Reports: These two reports (Forms 6 and 7) are compiled at the landfill site or wherever the data is available. They are then updated only when additional equipment or facilities are acquired. The periodic depreciation charges are then computed and posted by the accounting department.

Landfill Total Cost Summary: This report (Form 8) summarizes all the activities and costs incurred by the landfill during the period. It is compiled from data available in present and past Operating Cost Reports and the depreciation data available on the Facility and Equipment Cost Reports.

REPORT FLOW SUMMARY

A brief summary may help to put the system in perspective. Operating reports are generated daily at the landfill site and transmitted periodically to the accounting department. The accounting department combines these reports with additional information it accumulates to produce total operating costs.

SYSTEM UTILIZATION

Now that the actual system has been described utilization must be discussed. Only with efficient and intensive utilization of the information generated, can the additional time, effort, and money required to implement and maintain the system be justified.

All the factors which affect the quality and effectiveness of sanitary landfill operations can be translated into costs. Extent of cover material use, the size of the face, degree of compaction, litter control and dust control, among others, determine how good a job of sanitary landfilling is performed, and they are more costly than simple operation of an unattended open dump. Cost control at a landfill does not call for economizing at the expense of quality. To the contrary, once a level of acceptable operation has been determined along with the attendant costs, the cost control system can help the supervisor maintain that level of operation.

The routine control of costs is slightly more complicated. Effective cost control has two prerequisites: recognition of excessive costs and identification of responsibility for the increased costs. By comparing present unit costs with the currently budgeted unit costs and the actual unit costs of the previous period and the same period last year, some determination can be made of whether present costs are excessive. The determination of responsibility is facilitated by the efficiency factors. The system described allows both of these critical factors to be determined. Corrective action may then be effectively initiated.

At the highest level of management, the Total Cost Report indicates whether costs are excessive, in which case the supervisor of the particular sanitary landfill can be held responsible. The supervisor, in turn can use the cost system to determine the cause of increased costs. He may trace the increased costs to the particular cost element, and possibly to the employee, piece of equipment, or method of operation responsible. All of the needed data is in Form 5 (the Operating Cost Report). To aid the supervisor in the analysis of Form 5, a decision tree may be used (Figure 14.2). It illustrates the methodology required to analyze the cause of increased costs. For clarity, a hypothetical situation will be examined.

Let us assume that the landfill supervisor receives his copy of the Operating Cost Report from the accounting department. His analysis of the data starts at the extreme left of Figure 14.2. Quite obviously, the first question to be answered is whether any analysis is required. If total operating cost per ton is less than or equal to the budget, the answer is no.

However, if total cost per ton is greater than the budget, additional analysis is indicated. Next, it is desirable to isolate the cost element which is abnormally high. It may be one or more of the four shown (labor, cover material, equipment, or overhead). Let us assume that only labor cost per ton is higher than its budgeted amount. (We are now on the uppermost branch.)

FIGURE 14.2: DECISION TREE FOR SANITARY LANDFILL COST VARIANCE ANALYSIS

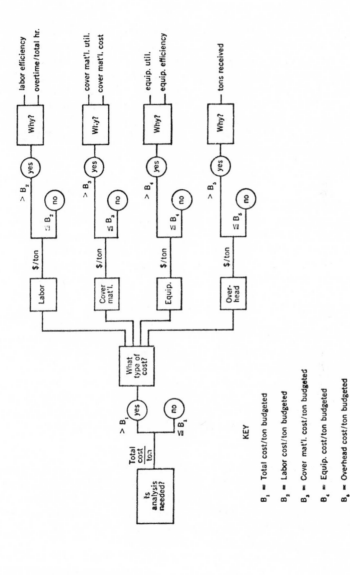

KEY

B_1 = Total cost/ton budgeted

B_2 = Labor cost/ton budgeted

B_3 = Cover mat'l. cost/ton budgeted

B_4 = Equip. cost/ton budgeted

B_5 = Overhead cost/ton budgeted

Source: PB 215,907 (1969)

We must determine why labor cost per ton increased, so that corrective action can be taken. Several factors are listed which may be relevant. Assume "overtime hours per total labor hours" is excessive. This implies that either scheduling is poor, there is a temporary peak load, the employees are working overtime when not required, or perhaps more regular employees are required. Under any of these circumstances, corrective action could be initiated by the supervisor.

This example is an over-simplification of actual operations. Nevertheless, it does illustrate the use of the decision tree (Figure 14.2) and more importantly, the methodology needed to pinpoint and correct factors which might have caused increased costs.

In addition to routine cost control, the data collected is useful in doing special analyses of trends in composition and quantity of wastes, peak load hours, on-site waiting times, and equipment evaluations. These and other quantitative evaluations can improve performance and reduce the costs of operation.

PART III

REGIONAL STUDIES

Los Angeles County Study

BACKGROUND

The County of Los Angeles, State of California, in order to formulate construction criteria for sanitary landfills and improvements which would lead to optimum land development and use, has conducted a three-year program of investigation and demonstration into the problems associated with solid waste disposal by sanitary landfilling. A report of the study was published by the EPA in 1973. Landfilling of municipal refuse is expected to continue for many years to be the principal means of disposal in many areas of the United States.

Community development over the years has surrounded and encroached upon many completed landfills resulting in unattractive, potentially hazardous areas within some populated areas. During the study, Los Angeles County, Department of County Engineer, and Engineering-Science, Inc. have been engaged in the study of the subjects of gas movement, groundwater pollution, fire hazard, construction of landfills, maintenance of completed landfills, and construction on and adjacent to completed landfills.

Landfill control within highly populated areas has two facets: (1) existing and completed landfills built without close regard for gas and leachate movements; and (2) prospective landfills for which control devices and procedures can become part of the process of operating and constructing a sanitary landfill. Major factors affecting the integrity of improvements on top of, within, and adjacent to sanitary landfills are gas movement and settlement of the fill. These factors are interrelated because both are influenced by the amount of the decomposition of the refuse. The objectives of the study were to:

(1)   Alleviate or eliminate existing problems of adjacent property owners because of proximity to existing sanitary landfills.

252

(2)   Establish a basis for regulating the various facets related to sanitary landfilling.

The objectives were met through the performance of the following tasks:

(1)   The study of the existing state-of-the-art in sanitary landfill construction and operation;
(2)   An evaluation of gas movement in certain existing sites;
(3)   Review of literature regarding possible effects of sanitary landfills on groundwater quality;
(4)   Laboratory experiments for testing flow rate of gas through various soils;
(5)   Development of solutions for controlling gases generated in sanitary landfills;
(6)   In situ gas sampling and settlement surveying;
(7)   Collection of pertinent information on subsidence, odors, and nuisances in existing sanitary landfills;
(8)   Evaluation of the uses of completed sanitary landfills in terms of the conditions of surface and subsurface structures, vegetative growth, and prevalence of odors and nuisance;
(9)   Correlation of subsidence to the method of construction and composition of sanitary landfills and the stage of decomposition of refuse materials;
(10)   Development of solutions to odor and nuisance problems in completed sanitary landfills;
(11)   Evaluation of materials and methods of safe construction of —
       (a) Surface structures on or near sanitary landfills, and
       (b) Subsurface structures in sanitary landfills;
(12)   Review and evaluate the scope of existing ordinances, codes, and regulations throughout the United States for control of sanitary landfills;
(13)   Formulate criteria for the design and construction of sanitary landfills;
(14)   Formulate criteria for inspection, control, and maintenance of sanitary landfills;
(15)   Formulate criteria for the uses of lands on and adjacent to sanitary landfills;
(16)   Formulate criteria for the design and construction of structures on, and substructures in, sanitary landfills; and
(17)   Prepare "Sanitary Landfill Standard Specifications for Good Practice."

During the first year of this study, 1967, local sanitary landfills were inventoried, examined and evaluated. The extent of migration of refuse-produced gases in local sanitary landfills was measured; the geometry of existing sanitary landfills was investigated; the properties of the soil affecting gas movements were identified; gas control devices at existing landfills were designed; and gas and subsidence monitoring controls were installed at strategic locations on existing landfills.

Various types of gas barriers and control devices to retard subsurface gas migration were evaluated. The excavation of a cutoff trench backfilled with highly permeable gravel and rock proved to be an effective method for control of gas movement. Two other gas control systems were developed. One of these systems consisted of five wells located about 100 feet from the completed landfill. Each well was excavated to the equivalent depth of the refuse and operated on the basis of combined gas suction and air flushing.

Another control system consisted of an asphalt-type membrane installed under a greenhouse constructed directly upon a fill. This barrier was designed to prevent gases from moving through the fill cover into the confinement of the greenhouse. Gas monitoring indicated all systems were effective.

Subsidence of monuments and survey points that were established at six selected sites during the first year of the project study was measured throughout the study period. The resulting data were examined for correlation between subsidence and other construction parameters. A laboratory experiment for investigating subsidence characteristics was correlated with the field data. Formulas were developed for predicting ultimate subsidence of completed sanitary landfill surfaces under a range of specific material and moisture controls.

Groundwater quality degradation was studied and analyzed. A detailed study of leachate production characteristics as a function of the stage of decomposition of typical refuse materials was conducted in the laboratory. A leachate pollution index was developed based on total dissolved solids to determine the quantity of solutes leachable from refuse fills.

Available information on landfills throughout the United States, was obtained by mailed questionnaires, visits to completed sanitary landfills, and interviews with selected experts. All data were collated for the development of criteria for materials and methods for safe construction of surface structures, surface improvements, and subsurface improvements on, in, or adjacent to the sanitary landfills. Previous recommendations were reviewed and reevaluated on the basis of latest information and analyzed for means of implementation.

"Standard Specifications for Good Practice" were developed into two sections providing for administration and regulation of planning, design, construction, and maintenance of: (1) sanitary landfills; and (2) improvements on, in, and adjacent to sanitary landfills.

MONITORING AND PREDICTING SUBSIDENCE

Surface subsidence, differential settlement and lateral surface displacement were monitored at certain completed landfills. Settlement records were maintained, plotted, and selectively analyzed. Cumulative settlement appears to be independent of fill depth in this case, but apparently it is a function of the water content.

The number of landfills observed did not represent an adequate statistical sampling, but the program was useful in determining the reliability of future correlations. Lack of material control will hinder accuracy of any predictive methodology except in unusual cases.

To date, the technology available for predicting subsidence and compaction of landfills is comprised almost totally of empirical procedures. The fundamental mechanisms active in sanitary landfill subsidence predictor equations require observation of the effects of varying generic factors such as initial compaction, compaction due to overburden, and biodegradation of organic fill components.

The general components of landfills include garbage, fibrous organics, metal, old tires, glass, objects of varying biodegradability and density, demolition wastes, and ashes. Biodegradation may be generally defined as the process whereby organic material is metabolized by microorganisms. In a landfill essential nutrients for biodegradation are usually present.

The primary premise of this study was that the mechanisms explaining the action of consolidating soils and of organic matter undergoing biological decomposition provide a basis for developing relationships to describe the behavior of landfills under controlled conditions and for deriving rational relationships describing these phenomena.

The laboratory program was divided into successive efforts dealing with compaction and with decomposition as separate and sequential unit processes. Stock mixtures of nine varied compositions were subjected to initial compaction analogous to conditions at a landfill.

The composition of the components was classified and documented. Two sets of refuse compaction experiments were conducted, one set to establish maximum densities and minimum porosities and one set to simulate the compaction by earthmoving equipment at a landfill. The compacted cells were allowed to decompose and subside in a constant temperature room for 193 days. Records were kept of weight, temperature, and subsidence. At seven months time, confined compression tests were made. The refuse compaction tests were then conducted.

Observations were made on the time variation of weight loss and subsidence. Unit weight changes were then calculated and analyzed as a function of its parameters for selected paper contents, water contents, and refuse texture. Average annual subsidence rates for all cells were established and analyzed.

GAS MOVEMENT AND CONTROL

Inside sanitary landfills, biological decomposition of organic matter takes place resulting in the production of gases. These gases, primarily methane and carbon dioxide, may create problems which restrict beneficial use for completed landfills by contributing to potential fire hazards, and causing impairment of ground-water quality.

The basic objectives of the study included: (1) the analysis and evaluation of the directions and extent of the gas movement; (2) the correlation between the direction and extent of gas movement and the surrounding soil characteristics; (3) the performance of laboratory experiments for testing the effectiveness of various natural soils in reducing movement of gases from sanitary landfills; and (4) the development of practical methods for controlling the movement of gases.

Ten completed sanitary landfill sites were considered for conducting detailed gas movement studies. A soil sampling program was executed to obtain a know-ledge of the nature of the soil material adjacent to the fills. Indigenous soils were analyzed for determination of grain size distribution, soil classification, specific gravity, dry density, and moisture content. In-place density of the soils was measured.

A monitoring program of gas concentrations adjacent to selected landfills was instituted. Gas probes were installed and samples were collected and analyzed in percent by volume for carbon dioxide, oxygen, nitrogen, methane, and in some cases hydrogen sulfide. The extent of the gas movement, primarily meth-ane, from each landfill was demonstrated where possible by plotting contours of equal concentration.

Laboratory experiments were conducted on various natural soils to determine the gas permeability characteristics under a range of moisture content and the gas pressure conditions. The objective was to study the suitability of various soils for gas barrier membranes. Coefficients were calculated based on an analy-tical solution of a fundamental differential equation governing the flow of gases through porous media and utilizing methane concentration history curves de-rived from each experiment. The results of these experiments indicate that the rate of movement of methane by diffusion-dispersion is slower through soils with fine particles than those with coarser particles, for both air-dry and opti-mum moisture conditions and under all conditions of in-flow gas pressure. Molecular and dispersive components of the calculated coefficients were not distinguished.

However, the high convective movement of gases in coarse grained soils is un-doubtedly responsible for the high diffusion-dispersion coefficients of methane in these soils. The convective flow component of gas migration may be signi-ficant for the case of highly permeable media such as the sand and gravel, whereas it will be rather insignificant for fine soils and when subject to small pressure gradients. The coefficient of gas permeability of the various media was not de-termined; however, when a fine soil is compacted under optimum moisture con-ditions to 90% or more of the maximum density, the gas permeability of the medium will be so small that the flow by pressure gradient will be reduced to inappreciable amounts. The results substantiated the presumption that fine tex-tured soils, such as sandy clay, silty clay, or clay, form an effective barrier to gas movement even at low moisture content. When compacted at optimum moisture content these soils prevent any appreciable flow of methane or other gases under differential pressures of one or more atmospheres.

Fires and explosions have resulted from the accumulation of methane gas in confined spaces on or adjacent to landfills after the gas became trapped and concentrations reached flammable levels. Measures which have been taken to prevent the movement of gases into adjacent soils include barrier and ventilation devices.

Part of a training course conducted by Pacific Telephone Company is a demonstration of the characteristics of toxic and flammable gases. The Training Division uses a model manhole, consisting of a forced ventilation blower, a control box, and appurtenances to supply, regulate, and explode prepared gases simulating natural gas.

A similar apparatus was designed and built to investigate the explosive characteristics of gases on selected research sites. The unit consisted of two separate boxes: one simulating a confined space such as a substructure or under-floor area of a building; the other, a control unit containing a source of power, connected to the box in which the explosions occur.

Methane concentrations were tested near the bottom, the center, and top of the explosion box and recorded. Detonation may be induced at any selected level at tested concentrations. The explosion unit was field tested on landfill gas. Methane concentrations were sampled. Concentrations ranging between 5 and 7% were read prior to explosions. Concentrations of less than 5% did not explode.

In some instances explosive concentrations were rapidly reached within minutes after previous explosions had resulted in complete evacuation of gases from the explosion box. A log, consisting of two sheets, was kept to provide the necessary information regarding sites and site characteristics, soil characteristics, weather, insulation data, detonation data, etc. Other pertinent and necessary information was then developed and used for further testing. The use of this apparatus demonstrates a transition between the theory of landfill gas flammability and potential enforcement of any future Sanitary Landfill Ordinance.

GROUNDWATER POLLUTION

Analyses of waters which have been in contact with solid wastes have shown that both chemical and biological pollutants may be present. The liquids that result when water comes into contact with refuse either by percolation or immersion are generally termed leachates. A fill may be in contact with groundwater or surface water resulting in direct leaching through the fill material; or water originating in another location may drain through the fill. Groundwater in the immediate vicinity of a disposal site may become polluted and unsuitable for domestic and/or irrigation use if the solid wastes intercept the zone of saturation and come into contact with the groundwater or if the leachate reaches the groundwater. The velocity of water through the material is dependent upon the permeability.

Indices of groundwater pollution were determined in laboratory experiments during this study. Leachates were analyzed for total dissolved solids, chemical oxygen demand, hardness, alkalinity, pH, organic and ammonia nitrogen, fluorides, sulfates and nitrates.

The major gases normally produced within a sanitary landfill are carbon dioxide and methane. Since methane is relatively insoluble in water and lighter than air, it is not expected to contribute materially to groundwater pollution. Carbon dioxide gas is heavier than air and highly soluble in water and may contribute to increased mineralization in groundwater. However, water that has been impaired by carbon dioxide will be diluted within the groundwater body.

CRITERIA FOR THE LOCATION, DESIGN AND CONSTRUCTION OF SANITARY LANDFILLS

The selection of a location for a sanitary landfill should be based on benefit to the community while assuring maximum personal safety and security of property of its neighbors, and a function of the local topography and geology. Under certain circumstances existing depressions in lands, such as old gravel quarries, normally useless gullies, and abandoned strip mines may be suitable for landfill sites. The prime physical considerations of a potential location are the practicality of preventing water pollution and gas migration. To minimize water pollution, sanitary landfills would be most ideally located above native soils of low permeability if over a usable water supply.

Decomposable solid wastes should not be placed in seawater, salt water, or waters with high sulfate content since they may react to form hydrogen sulfide gas. Hydrogen sulfide gas is exceedingly toxic and dangerous to animal life.

General planning should provide for a horizontal separation distance between sanitary landfills and adjacent incompatible land uses to allow for the possibility of explosive gas migration. Engineering and geologic data may not be available at this stage of community planning. A horizontal separation distance of 1,000 feet is recommended for this purpose.

The means for accomplishing the separation of water and pollutants requires planning for the construction of the landfill. Original construction plans should show the proposed means of controlling the basic types of water intrusion. Periodic maintenance and monitoring may affect the success or failure of pollution defenses. A groundwater monitoring program should be developed at the planning stage and implemented during construction of the landfill.

One means of separating water and pollutants is by requiring a vertical separation distance between the bottom of the landfill and of the high water surface of underlying groundwaters. In soils of low permeability the required vertical separation distance varies from state to state. Until results of testing under controlled conditions yield satisfactory distances, landfills located in permeable soils less than 30 feet above groundwater should be underlain with barriers to lessen the chance of pollution.

Drainage galleries may be required to keep underground waters from flowing across the interface between the landfill and natural soils, where several aquifers separated by impervious soil would be intersected by a proposed landfill. In addition to subsurface controls and setbacks, ditches, piping and dikes should be used to keep surface waters from flowing across the interface of the landfill and natural soil.

Gases originating within a sanitary landfill which escape directly through the soil cover into the atmosphere are quickly diffused. Gases migrating to confined spaces produce explosion hazards in addition to water pollution. Controls should be a matter of properly directing the gases to harmless points of disposal. The major factors affecting gas production and control are the percentage of organic material, the permeability and thickness of soil cover, temperature variation, and moisture content. Control efforts will also be affected by factors such as the permeability of the soils underlying and adjacent to the landfill and subsidence.

The selection and arrangements of systems of materials and methods for gas control have been classified as: (1) peripheral; (2) central; (3) natural; (4) mechanical; (5) internal; (6) external; and (7) combination. A variety of materials are available for use as barriers but most have not been tested for impermeability, inertness, and endurance. In addition to natural soils these materials include polyvinyl chloride sheeting, neoprene, butyl or synthetic rubber, laminated hot-asphalt-mopped building paper, and others. A gas monitoring program is essential to the proper evaluation of gas production, gas movement, and gas control systems.

Subsidence is a function of consolidation resulting from initial compaction of refuse materials, compaction of refuse materials due to overburden, volume reduction caused by decomposition of the refuse, volume reduction caused by saturation with water, and volume reduction resulting from removal of leachable materials.

Differential settlement may be defined as nonuniform settlement in the area adjacent to a structure or surface improvement due to consolidation of underlying strata caused by dead and live loads and other phenomena. It differs from subsidence in that it is less uniform and is caused by applied forces in addition to overburden of the fill. A major factor which will affect the economic life of a development on a completed sanitary landfill surface is the effectiveness with which a sanitary landfill supports its improvements. This will be a function of the magnitude and timing of its ultimate consolidation and the reliability of predictions which affect cash flow funding for maintenance. Engineering control is, therefore, imperative during the construction of the landfill if a usable and dependable surface is to result.

The condition of the finished surface of the landfill is also dependent upon conditions at each finished surface at the top of each lift within the landfill. If compaction of the intermediate lifts is not maximized, this will have an effect on the ultimate use of the landfill. Where adequate material is available, one foot is recommended as the compacted thickness for the daily cover. The minimum final cover for the entire landfill is recommended to be three feet. In no case should any permanent excavation be made to reduce the cover to less than three feet.

The major purposes of the daily earth cover are to control noxious odors, inhibit access of pests and vectors, and improve the appearance of the landfill. The cover should be free from putrescible matter or large objects, be well compacted, and not subject to excessive cracking or erosion. The cells also provide a degree of fire protection.

Maximized initial compaction coupled with minimized heterogeneity should result in the earliest ultimate consolidation. Surcharge loading applied to sanitary landfills will accelerate earlier consolidation. Volume reduction caused by biological decomposition may be expected to result from wetting of the refuse. The addition of water, to an appropriate moisture content, for refuse material and cover material may be expected to provide the earliest ultimate consolidation. However, the addition of water to a sanitary landfill should be carefully controlled. Excess water in the interstices may be avoided by providing for drainage over finished cells and installation of surface and subsurface drainage facilities.

Side slopes should be designed to minimize potential sloughing. A desirable average side slope should be 3 (horizontal) to 1 (vertical). This average side slope includes required benching and interceptors. Under certain conditions sloughing should be anticipated and slough protection should be required. Slough protection may be provided by the placement of inert embankment or cutoff walls.

Monitoring of the vertical movement of the individual level of daily cover could be of benefit to eventual determination of the utility of the site. Topographic control within a few tenths of a foot, after each lift operation, would facilitate monitoring; or, risers could be installed during construction of the landfill and extended to the completed surface for subsidence monitoring surveys. Close vertical survey controls should be provided for the subsidence monument system.

Materials should be selectively classified and placed in predefined sanitary landfill site locations. Each site should receive two classifications, a location classification and a materials classification. The location classification is based on the unmodified and unprotected geology and configuration of the site. A site having received its location classification may, with the installation of suitable protection, receive a materials classification of greater groundwater hazard than the unmodified location classification and consequently would accept all materials of greater or lesser hazard than the materials classification.

Uniformity of settlement requires a limit on the size of acceptable materials. However, exceptions should be provided for portions of landfills planned to be utilized only as green space or in deep canyon landfills. Bulky, heavy materials, such as concrete or bricks or large diameter logs should be placed at the bottom of the fill and not in the top or sides where they may provide an unwanted surcharge effect, create increased heterogeneity, and provide rodent harborage.

In deeper landfills the overburden will contribute to consolidation of the materials placed near the bottom. Although the extent of this consolidation is variable, some adjustment of the active material lift heights would be appropriate. Therefore, the following table was developed on this premise using maximum lift height as a function of the remaining fill depth or height. For depths of 0 to 20 feet to the bottom of the final cover, a lift height of more than three feet would create an inordinately large proportion of active material to inert material.

From the following table, for a maximum lift height (h), for each remaining fill depth or height (H), it may be observed that the ratio of active material to inert material (based on one foot intermediate cover between lifts) varies from 3 to 1 in the shallowest landfill to 20 to 1 in the deepest landfill. The least percentage of lift height to remaining fill height varies uniformly from 15% in the shallowest landfill to 5% in the deeper landfills. The following maximum allowable lift depths should be considered:

H (feet)	h (feet)	Minimum % (h/H)
0 - 20.0	3	15
20.1 - 50.0	4	8
50.1 - 75.0	6	8
75.1 - 100.0	8	8
100.1 - 200.0	10	5
200.1 - 300.0	15	5
deeper than 300.0	20	5 (if H = 400)

Daily cover should be in place and compacted by the end of each working day. The daily cover should be placed to form a completely enclosed cell. The final cover should be in place and compacted within not more than 120 days after the final daily cover and prior to a rainy period. During periods of precipitation, cover should be applied as rapidly as possible. Two percent should be the minimum final slope. Four percent is recommended as a maximum, where possible.

Finished landfill surfaces require drainage protection. Terrace drainage should be provided with slopes adequate to drain as subsidence occurs. The slopes should be designed for the tributary drainage area and a flow of not less than 4 ft./sec. nor more than 8 ft./sec. All finished slopes should be planted and irrigated to promote the growth of ground cover. Planting requirements vary for differences in side slope. The most dependable water system is considered to be the sprinkler system, but this is not always practical. In some cases hand watering may be adequate.

A responsible representative of the landfill operator should be available at all times. A daily log of all operations should be maintained and include the quantities and types of refuse accepted each day, placement and lift heights, unusual occurrences, the numbers and responsibilities of employees on the job, and the type and use of equipment used on the site. Precautions should be instituted to prevent fire. Communication between the employees and site office and the local fire department should be provided in addition to standard safety equipment.

Reclamation and reprocessing operations (away from the sanitary landfill site) should be encouraged to enhance the economic desirability of landfilling. Metals, papers, fiberboards, rags, and glass have variable economic values in different locations. The removal of reclaimable items will tend to diminish heterogeneity.

All-weather, dust-free access roads, turnaround space, clearly marked directional signs, and no smoking signs should be provided. Clean sanitary toilet facilities and a first aid kit should be provided on the premises for all employees. Operations which extend beyond daylight hours should be provided with night lights. Common shelter and heating should be provided as necessary.

CRITERIA FOR INSPECTION, SUPERVISION AND MAINTENANCE OF SANITARY LANDFILLS

Inspection by a qualified deputy of the local governmental agency is necessary to determine the effects of the completed work upon the plan objectives and the likelihood of danger or inconvenience to any person or property. During the course of any construction project, various interpretations may be placed upon the plans and specifications. Appropriate remedy should be available. Sanitary landfill operations should be inspected as often as necessary to accomplish regulatory objectives; however, continuous inspection by a public agency is uneconomical and may be avoided.

Structures on and adjacent to a sanitary landfill should be inspected to assure compliance with legal regulations. Surface improvements on a sanitary landfill and the subsurface improvements in or adjacent to a sanitary landfill should be inspected as often as necessary during and after construction. Access to structures, surface improvements, and subsurface improvements should always be available.

All construction activities on a landfill site should be continuously supervised by a responsible representative of the operator, the constructor, or a subcontractor. If none are available, an inspector certified by an officer of the local governmental agency should be provided.

Special conditions may require that reports be submitted. These should be certified by the supervisor responsible for the particular work item. Structures designed under special provisions of the applicable local building code may require continuous supervision due to special conditions. It is possible that the administrative officer and the chief building official may have bilateral responsibilities for construction on sanitary landfill surfaces. If so, the architect or engineer responsible for such design should provide written certification to the administrative officer that each structure or portion thereof requiring continuous supervision was constructed in conformity with the approved design and applicable regulation. The designer of surface improvements and subsurface improvements may be either a civil engineer, mechanical engineer, or an electrical engineer, who should certify in writing that the construction is in conformity with the approved design and applicable regulations.

The final cover on a landfill may be expected to subside and crack, thus impairing drainage slopes and possibly resulting in ponding. Filling and scraping of the affected surfaces will be necessary to alleviate or prevent ponding and maintain the integrity of the cover. Ground cover vegetation should be required to stabilize the surface. The effects of erosion on ground cover vegetation may be minimized by replanting similar or more stable species. Maintenance of monitoring devices may be facilitated by well kept records. The integrity of each gas control device should be maintained.

Patching of membranes may be required and feasible in some instances. Gas vents may be infiltrated by materials reducing cross-sectional area. Corrective measures may require flushing out with water or blowing out with compressed air. Monitoring and analysis of gas concentrations should be required until gas production declines to a safe level and remains safe over a measured period of time. Control of odors may occasionally be required. Regular periodic inspections should be made for signs of rodents and winged pests and appropriate steps taken as necessary.

CRITERIA FOR USES OF LAND ON OR ADJACENT TO SANITARY LAND-FILLS

The uses of all the lands should remain principally a function of the general plan of each individual community which should recognize that landfilling and its associated phenomena should be considered. The best possible completed landfill surface cannot be expected to provide the stability required for heavy structural and traffic loadings; however, properly planned, completed landfills in the future may be used for heavier loadings if planned and engineered for them.

A general plan may be importantly affected by a correlation between the recreation plan and the solid waste plan. The street and highway plan is a component of the general plan that could remain unaffected by the reuse of the sanitary landfill, if the landfill is planned to comply with the street and highway plan by providing for central rights-of-way as part of the landfill construction.

The surfaces of existing or completed landfills, upon which there is no prospect for successful development requiring extensive improvements, should be controlled by statute law to facilitate compatible uses which may include park and recreational use, open assembly area, temporary heliports, or other uses with minimal or no improvements.

Some existing completed landfills may have been planned and constructed to minimize the problems due to settlement and subsidence. Such landfills may be acceptable for planned use if they can be provided with suitable gas controls. They should be subject to applicable engineering and governmental regulations and should not be used for any purpose not allowed on proposed landfills. Future sanitary landfills may be engineered and constructed to be suitable for a variety of uses. If the landfill is planned to minimize subsidence effects by reserving inert strips and areas and by increasing the ratio of earth to active material, loadings from traffic and building uses will be more acceptable.

A gas monitoring and analysis program is the best practical means of determining the existence and extent of hazards from gases. If gas concentration histories and refuse core sample analyses indicate a long-term decrease in methane production potential, construction of enclosed occupancies without gas control systems may be permissible, unless hydrogen sulfide is present.

Where there is the remotest possibility that gases may migrate to and concentrate in confined areas or rooms, human use should be prohibited. Closed habitable construction on adjoining undeveloped and uninhabited lands should be subject to a minimum separation distance of 1,000 feet, if engineering and geologic data is not available to indicate otherwise.

Under controlled conditions the selection of a location for a landfill may be a function of adjacent existing uses. An indefinite number of uses encroach upon lands adjacent to existing dumps and sanitary landfills. The degree of safety can be determined by monitoring gas concentrations. Residents of land adjoining existing landfills should be made aware of the potential hazards, if any, and of the degree of hazard, if determinable.

CRITERIA FOR THE DEVELOPMENT, CONSTRUCTION AND MAINTENANCE OF IMPROVEMENTS TO SANITARY LANDFILLS

The use of each completed landfill site should be planned on the basis of specific merit. Although construction on sanitary landfilling is not generally advocated, the following construction techniques and precautionary measures are offered. They are not intended to be complete solutions to landfill problems, but are presented to provide a basis upon which further specialized engineering thinking can be applied.

Gases may be prevented from entering improvements by utilizing gas control barriers and vents of proper material. Acceptable alternatives for barrier materials include: vinyls, copolymers, terpolymers, building paper, and water stop materials. Gas vents may be required around the periphery of a structure, in plumbing access spaces, and electrical panels. The gas control system around a building may be comprised of trenches filled with granular material, perforated pipe drains, combination vent stacks, and foundation drains. Utility entries should be protected to prevent gases from following permeable trench bedding and venting into confined spaces. Collars and connectors to seal off gases may be fabricated.

The most pronounced differential settlement generally will occur under buildings founded partially on inert material and partially on sanitary landfills. Under buildings located totally on a sanitary landfill, prediction of the locations at which differential settlement will occur is more complex. It should be anticipated that this might locate anywhere under a foundation wall. The magnitudes, locations, and directions of additional stresses, due to resulting distortions, should be predicted and resisted.

Proper structural design should include the assessment of all potential loading. Safety factors should be conservative and analyses intensified. The primary structural components which will be affected are slabs, piling, raft foundations, walls, and the total structure concept which includes connections. Piling should be designed for all vertical and horizontal loading, the down drag effects of frictional resistance to subsidence and settlement, and any floor loads transmitted directly to the fill adjacent to piling.

Raft foundations upon which the total stability of the structure is dependent are less desirable than piling foundations, but may be permissible. Spread footings and pads should not be permitted to rotate. Rotation can be inhibited by monolithical struts. Under select span and width conditions it would be advantageous to utilize rigid building walls as deep girder foundation elements.

Surface improvements are more likely to be damaged by the effects of differential settlement or subsidence. Surface channels, ditches, and drains that might settle unevenly will have their hydraulic characteristics impaired. Design alternatives include either design for the conditions accruing from subsidence or differential settlement or design to prevent differential settlement.

In the first instance, flow lines may be designed at the steepest subcritical slope. Subsequent flattening of the grade might result in uneven deposition of solids but need not impair the overall function of the drain. It should be recognized in the design that slopes may become supercritical; therefore, freeboard should be provided. Drainage channels which are provided with overlapping sections may be undercut by eddying currents. At the points of overlap, subsurface cutoffs or checks should be provided at right angles to the flow line and also parallel to the flow line.

When possible streets should be founded on inert material. This can be accomplished by means of preplanning if the cost of building a high inner embankment does not render a landfill operation uneconomical. Streets built on a landfill with an optimized ratio of solid wastes to inert material should be of asphalt concrete, thus flexible and able to sustain light automobile traffic loadings.

The design of concrete curbs, gutters, and sidewalks may be modified to provide horizontal spans with maximized resistance to horizontal and vertical loading. During the data survey phase of this study it was discovered that surface improvements such as utility poles, fences, street signs, and simpler improvements lost their plumb due to subsidence. Utility poles may be set in concrete bases with adjustable anchor bolts and some poles may be releveled by the use of adjustable turnbuckles and cables, but individual ingenuity may also be required in specific design situations.

A building not founded on piles probably will settle more than the surface improvements. A building founded on piles will settle less than surface improvements over landfill cells. In both cases flexible connections should be required between the building and the surface improvement. Subsurface improvements in juxtaposition to surface improvements and structure improvements will be subject to the same peculiarities of gas control.

Particular attention should be directed toward the design of pipe bedding. Granular materials convey gases but may be acceptable if vertical barriers are built into the bedding between manholes, in the form of concrete saddles or cradles. Plain or reinforced concrete bedding is effective for gas control but it imposes an additional load on the supporting landfill.

Subsurface improvements are susceptible to the effects of differential settlement under conditions which are usually difficult to detect. Placing utility lines in an openable trench may be one solution to the inspection problem. The design for underground piping should be conservative.

Monitoring subsidence of underground utility lines can be facilitated by providing risers to the ground surface. Prior to placement in a sanitary landfill any subsurface improvement that might come into contact with active materials should be protectively coated. Access manholes in sanitary sewer lines should provide a means for monitoring the line profile. Natural gas mains should be provided with valves near and exterior to the landfill interface if automatic shutoff instrumentation has not been provided. Individual gas services should be provided by shutoff valves next to the mains.

Maintenance requirements on sanitary landfills should be stringent. Gas control devices or safeguards should be maintained at all times in good working order.

Detection of incipient structural deficiency in an architectural or structural component is usually visual. Upon noticing a deficiency, the connections of the structure should be suspected and reference should be made to the original building plans and design calculations, if any. Surface improvements should be maintained in good condition and subsurface improvements installed within a sanitary landfill should be repaired or replaced when the structural factor of safety is less than 1.0.

CONCLUSIONS

(1) Landfill gases may migrate a considerable distance (700 ft. has been recorded) from the fill, depending on the nature of the soil formations around the fill.

(2) Gas movement from sanitary landfills takes place by molecular diffusion and convective gas transport mechanisms. The rate of this transfer is determined by the permeability characteristics of the soil formations around the fill.

(3) Landfill produced gases can and should be controlled and directed to areas of harmless dispersal.

(4) Control systems installed during this study have proven effective in interrupting the flow of migrating gases. Natural and mechanical barriers may be provided, ventilation devices have been demonstrated to be effective, and special design techniques are logically promising.

(5) Landfills are potential sources of pollutants to usable underground waters. Water pollution from landfill sources may be prevented by means other than prohibiting landfills over underground usable water. The Leachate Pollution Index, developed during the study, is a new and effective means of quantifying and predicting the leachate pollution potential from sanitary landfills.

(6) Subsidence of the surfaces of sanitary landfills and dumps is a prime inhibitor in planning for future use of completed sites. Subsidence occurs in three phases: (a) initial subsidence; (b) intermediate subsidence; and (c) ultimate subsidence. The three phases of subsidence are subject to control. Initial subsidence and ultimate subsidence investigations have resulted in delineation of control parameters and formulation of a method of quantification to predict ultimate subsidence under controlled conditions.

Differential settlement may be incurred as a result of loading the landfill surface. Buildings, surface improvements, and subsurface structures can suffer damage or destruction if contructed on sanitary landfills without proper regard for the potential differential settlement.

(7) The most frequently reported use of completed sanitary landfills has been recreational. A significant number of uses as industrial, commercial, and resi-

dential were also reported. Planning, prior to landfilling, for use of the completed landfill surfaces has been reported to vary from nonexistent to almost comprehensive, with corresponding successes. Planning which included gas control was not reported. Planning for water pollution prevention has been effective. Planning as a function of subsidence and subsequent differential settlement generally appears to be inherently cognizant of initial subsidence only, in many instances.

(8) Many existing building codes do not provide for protection of structures, located adjacent to, or on, refuse fills, from the fire and toxic hazards of landfill produced gases. However, some building officials are providing for this protection by enforcing policy memoranda.

RECOMMENDATIONS

(1) Landfill locations should be selected to be compatible with relevant elements of a functional general plan which includes: (a) a land use plan, solid waste plan, and street and highway plan; and (b) community ordinances which include a sanitary landfill code, water pollution laws, building code, plumbing code, electrical code, excavation and grading code, and engineering regulations and standard specifications. A recreational plan could be beneficially included in (a) above for many communities. Many landfills could be designed and constructed as an engineered product with concern for the future property value, manifesting the potential of the completed site.

(2) Gas movement, if any, adjacent to existing sanitary landfills should be detected and traced. Gas monitoring programs should be established. Local govermental agencies should implement staff technical capabilities. Gas control system economics should be quantified to develop optimally costed systems. Improved gas control technology can result from further research. Broader application can result from dissemination of available knowledge to educators, engineers, and public officials.

(3) Leachate pollution prevention studies should be conducted, in cooperation with state water pollution officials, to establish the conditions under which selected manufactured leachate pollution barriers may be utilized over strata bearing usable waters. Leachate characteristics should be examined as a function of permeability through a variety of porous media to establish capacities to prevent pollution of usable underground water.

(4) In order to minimize subsidence and related effects, the ratio of inert cover material to biodegradable material can be increased without detrimental effects on the economics of "landfilling only" as compared to the next cheapest alternative, "incineration and residue landfilling."

The technical benefits of materials control will also diminish subsidence effects but is probably not politically attainable. Materials control should be continuous during collection, transfer, and disposal to minimize heterogeneity. Segregation by organic content and bulk reprocessing and reclamation, and pulverization such as hammermilling and comminuting will also aid to minimize heterogeneity. Any landfill that is in the path of urban development and expected to be used within the next 20 years should be periodically monitored for subsidence.

Santa Clara Landfill Stabilization Study

The material in this chapter is derived from PB 216-754 (1968) prepared for the Department of Health, Education, and Welfare. In June 1966, the City of Santa Clara initiated work on a three-year demonstration of land reclamation by accelerated stabilization. The general objectives of the program were to reduce sanitary landfill health hazards and problems by controlled high rate oxidation of solid wastes; increase landfill disposal capacity; stabilize wastes; minimize or eliminate odors and nuisances; improve waste reclamation technology; and study other effects of accelerated decomposition.

Two aerobic test cells were constructed, including provision for controlled aeration of the solid wastes. One cell demonstrated in situ aerobic treatment and the second demonstrated controlled, high rate oxidation. In addition, settlement/compaction tests were conducted within an area of conventional anaerobic fill, natural ground and aerobic and stabilized fills. Six months of support studies for the full-scale demonstrations were provided by eight separate pilot plants, investigating various operating parameters.

THE SANITARY LANDFILL SITE

General

The full-scale demonstration program was accomplished at the City's 73.2 acre sanitary landfill, about 4½ miles south of the upper reaches of San Francisco Bay. The natural ground elevations ranged from 9 to 16 feet above sea level. The site met the normal criteria for a sanitary landfill; it was centrally located and accessible by paved roads; the soil was easily excavated; a public water supply and electrical power were provided for test service; fencing allowed adequate protection from public intrusion; and the site was in an isolated

270

area with limited residential habitation. The low lying lands were improved by the subsequent filling and grading program. The landfill had been in operation since 1965. The site was located within a six-mile radius of the City Halls of Santa Clara, Sunnyvale and San Jose.

Geology

The Santa Clara Valley is a downdropped block separated from uplifted mountains by complex faulting. The site is underlain by up to 1,000 feet of upper Pleistocene and Recent sands, gravels and clays. Marine fossils in blue clays taken from 300 feet in the Alviso area indicate this was once an arm of San Francisco Bay. More recent alluvial fan and flood plain deposits now constitute the surface cover.

Soils

Proximity of the land reclamation site to Saratoga Creek which flows into San Francisco Bay and to the Guadalupe area indicated the existence of an alluvial fan and flood plain sediment consisting of fine to medium grained permeable soils.

Land Subsidence

Area-wide land subsidence at the average annual rates of 0.27 feet from 1948 to 1960 and 0.33 feet from 1960 to 1965 was attributed to groundwater overpumpage and the resulting compression of the deep clay horizons. The rate of subsidence increased in the last two years. No salt water encroachment was observed. The amount of future subsidence is dependent upon the subsurface recharge and pumping rates; since subsidence is expected to continue until the overpumpage is stopped, it is necessary to fill any areas that are to be used for industrial sites or other higher type land uses.

Groundwater and Water Supply

In December 1965, the groundwater was observed 8 feet below the surface throughout the landfill site. This water was of minimal quality. Two wells were located at the site; however, neither could be developed to provide a dependable water supply for this demonstration.

Climate

The climate of Santa Clara is relatively mild and temperate. Neither freezing temperatures nor temperatures exceeding 100°F. are often experienced. The average annual rainfall is about 20 inches and normally is concentrated in January through April. The rainfall, since initiating this demonstration program, was sporadic from November 1966 through May 1967.

Statutory Landfill Requirements

The California State Water Quality Control Board prescribed requirements for
the landfill site to preclude the occurrence of nuisances and pollution of groundwater and to define the nature of the wastes to be accepted for disposal at the
site.

REFUSE AND SOIL

Refuse Source

Refuse used to fill the demonstration cells originated in the residential areas of
the City of Santa Clara. Collection vehicles containing other materials, such as
construction, demolition wastes, were excluded from the test site. Weekly rubbish collection was provided by the City's nine 26-cubic-yard packers. On a
normal day the amount of refuse collected averaged between 7 and 7 ½ tons
per truck.

Refuse Characteristics

Refuse was being sampled as the demonstration cells were filled. General
records of the seasonal variation in refuse composition, moisture content,
volatile matter and other pertinent characteristics were kept, but the general
composition of refuse delivered to the site did not exhibit major variations
from spring to fall except for moisture content. On a dry weight basis, about
35% of the refuse placed in the aeration cells was garden trimmings, 55% paper,
3% plastics and 7% metals, glass, ceramics and other inerts. The average moisture content has ranged from 71% in the spring to 15% in the fall. Volatile
content averages about 84% on a dry weight basis.

Soil Characteristics

The topsoil was fine, sandy clay overlying a clayey silt subsoil. This material
was normally used to provide 24 inches of final cover on the landfill. As
available, asbestos cement and certain other inert industrial waste and demolition products were used to supplement this cover material to provide a surfac-
ing course for winter access and to exclude surficial drainage from the fill.

CELL CONSTRUCTION

Anaerobic Test Cell

This test consisted of excavating an existing anaerobic cell and then recompact-
ing the excavated refuse into a new cell. A 30 feet wide by 100 feet long section of a cell, completed in November 1965, was excavated to a refuse depth
of seven feet. The D-9 tractor which accomplished this job encountered no

significant difficulty in opening the cell and moving the refuse. The refuse was piled into a conical mound. The old fill material created noxious and characteristically putrid odors which were especially severe when the tractor was moving the freshly exposed refuse. When the tractor construction stopped, the odor level diminished. A special survey indicated that five miles upwind low level characteristic odors could be observed due to a prevailing one to two miles per hour velocity wind and temperature inversion. However, no complaints were received and the test received no special notice.

The freshly excavated refuse was moist; newspapers, tin cans and plastics showed minimum decomposition and could be readily identified; grass cuttings had turned brown; woody vegetation indicated only minor decomposition; and cans and boxes were well compressed, indicating good compaction in the original landfill construction. As soon as the survey crew completed their topographic work, the refuse was placed in a newly prepared cell in normal one to two ft. layers and carefully recompacted. The new cell was then quickly covered to prevent further odors or fly production. No flies were observed within the 56 hour test period.

The volume of refuse excavated from the old cell was determined to be 530 cubic yards. The volume of recompacted refuse in the new cell was 667 cubic yards for a net expansion of 25.6%. This compared favorably with observed settlement compaction for one year measured at the Spadra, Walnut, California landfill. Representative test refuse samples were obtained for analyses.

Preload Test Cell

The purpose of the preload test was to determine the foundation and settlement characteristics of a normal anaerobic landfill when supporting a one kip per sq. ft. load. Technical information of this nature may aid in stabilizing sanitary fills for higher uses. The settlement characteristics of this loaded cell were compared with those of various compaction procedures, a clean earth fill, natural soil and oxidized residue.

Aerobic Test Cells

The demonstration cells were located to minimize interference with the City's normal landfill operation. Essentially, the aerobic test cells were subdivided into two areas: the aeration cell area, into which air was distributed into the refuse, and the residue cell area for disposal of the oxidized waste residue. Two separate aeration cells were constructed. Initially, biological oxidation processes were investigated in these cells. The residue cells were adjacent to the aeration cells.

Excavation

The site was relatively flat and at approximate elevation of 12 feet mean sea level (MSL). Since the finished grade for the landfill was planned for about

17 feet MSL, it was necessary to resort to excavation into natural earth with a buildup of compacted earthen berms around the cells. The end slopes of the cells were no steeper than 2:1 to permit entry and exit of equipment; excavated side slopes were about vertical; embankments were no steeper than 1½:1. To develop maximum volume of aerated refuse per unit cost of aeration system, the side walls of the aerated cells were built up to a height of 17 feet. The bottom and top of the aerated test cells measured about 50 feet by 200 feet, and 85 feet by 270 feet respectively. The residue cells were approximately 450 feet by 300 feet and 350 feet by 250 feet and about 13 feet deep.

Aeration System

The aeration system consisted of two underdrain systems, a blower, valving and appurtenances. The underdrains, which were designed to distribute air throughout the aerated cells, were closed loops of 4 inch diameter perforated, vitrified clay pipe. Each was composed of two parallel 192 ft. lines crossed at right angles by 33 lines on 6 ft. centers. The aeration piping was laid in trenches 12 inches wide by 12 to 15 inches deep and was backfilled with select gravel. An 8 inch steel pipe conveyed the air from the blower to the underdrains.

Water Supply and Irrigation System

The City of Santa Clara constructed a water main to the demonstration site for irrigation and fire protection. A time clock and solenoid valve were designed to start and stop the irrigation automatically at designated times.

Construction Summary

The refuse used to fill the aeration cells was weighed at the gate house. The cells were surveyed periodically and the volumes calculated. As the cells were filled, landfill equipment mixed and compacted the refuse. Definitive compaction densities were calculated, settlement plates and bench marks installed, and subsequent volume reduction and settlement recorded.

PILOT STUDIES

Objectives

Preparatory to initiating the large-scale field demonstration program for the rapid oxidation and stabilization of solid wastes, certain pilot plant facilities were established at the project engineer's laboratory to demonstrate improved volume reduction. The concepts employed included: (1) underground incineration; (2) rapid biological oxidation by controlled aeration, moisture application, heating and natural thermophilic heat generation; (3) improvement of odor and particulate filtration and adsorption by varying the soil cover in terms of depth, type, moisture content and charcoal admixture; and (4) other chemical and physical methods for accelerated degradation.

Operation

Thirteen test runs were made over a five month period. Parameters such as rate of aeration, admixture of petroleum products, heating, drying, and refuse composition and density were studied. The tests evaluated the following factors: underground incineration, predrying, smoke filtration, and odor control.

Results

The total incineration process cycle involved some 8 days: predrying (3 days); rapid burning (3 days); and residual burning (2 days). During the drying phase, the refuse and soil exhibited some settlement, averaging 4% per day; O_2 consumption and CO_2 production were negligible. The principle results of drying were to improve combustion and reduce smoke and odors during rapid burning.

The rapid burning phase began when temperatures reached the ignition point of approximately 450°F. adjacent to the burner element. The burning face then advanced through the refuse at a rate inversely proportional to the density of the refuse and directly proportional to the amount of oxygen (air) supply. Very little odor or smoke occurred when the rate of aeration was adequate, i.e., when there was more than 500% excess air. At lesser rates of aeration, CO_2 production decreased, CO production increased and smoke and odors began to appear, indicating partial combustion.

Most of the refuse was either paper or plant trimmings. When dry, these materials ignited rather easily and burned at a generally uniform rate during the rapid incineration phase. There were, however, some materials such as thick (3 to 4 inches in diameter) wood and plastics which continued to burn for longer durations. This residual burning accounted for small amounts of settlement during the later stages of each test and averaged 2% per day. The consumption of O_2 and production of CO_2 decreased considerably, but these quantities were still detectable.

Several tests achieved almost total volume reduction because of refuse slag and earth fusion. Other tests achieved the less dramatic volume reductions normally associated with partially burned refuse and ashes. As might be expected, moisture content had a pronounced effect on the rate of burning and settlement. Predried refuse burned more rapidly than damp refuse, and excessively wet refuse exhibited incomplete combustion and only partial volume reduction.

Reduction of odors was achieved by adding moisture to the soil filter at the appropriate time. A layer of activated charcoal was also effective for this purpose. The possible use of an enclosure such as a portable building or asbestos blanket for the collection of gases, in conjunction with a stack for their afterburning and dispersion in the atmosphere, is considered as a third alternative for future investigations.

The experimental data derived from this series of tests indicate that underground refuse incineration is technically feasible. Preliminary results of these later studies indicated that predrying and heating the refuse produced more satisfactory oxidation with less obnoxious odors and improved operational control and reliability.　A major advantage of underground incineration is the effective oxidation due to the high temperatures resulting from the insulating effects of the earth blankets and the long burning contact period with low air velocity and soil filtration which minimize air pollution.

Sanitary Landfill
San Francisco Bay Region

The material in this chapter comes from a report prepared by the Department of the Interior, United States Geological Survey, July 25, 1972. Solid-waste disposal is a problem for all communities. Because it is not nearly as pervasive a problem as air or water pollution, it usually suffers from austerity budgeting and low public priority. Historically, solid-waste disposal has been considered in land-use planning only after prior lack of consideration has caused water pollution or public health hazards.

This report was written for use by San Francisco Bay region planners and the public. Present methods of solid-waste disposal in the nation and the bay region are described, and criteria for locating solid-waste disposal sites are presented. These criteria are based on land-use practices, optimum water-quality protection, and sanitary disposal methods. Alternate methods of solid-waste disposal and management are described.

SOLID-WASTE PRODUCTION RATES

Per capita solid-waste production is increasing annually nationwide. For example, between 1959 and 1970, national per capita production rates for residential solid wastes alone (primarily paper, cans, glass, garbage, and other household wastes) increased from 2 to 3 pounds per capita per day to more than 5 pounds per capita per day. These rates correspond to a nationwide per capita annual production of approximately 913 lbs. in 1959 and 1,825 lbs. in 1970.

SOLID-WASTE DISPOSAL METHODS

Many methods of solid-waste disposal are used in the United States. Landfilling is the most commonly used method. Landfills vary from unsightly open dumps to strictly managed sanitary landfills. A sanitary landfill is the most desirable type of landfilling method known when properly designed and managed. Ideally the site is located and designed to minimize chances for surface and ground-water pollution; the wastes are covered and compacted daily. A modified sanitary landfill differs from a sanitary landfill only in that the wastes are not covered with earth as frequently and some burning or salvaging may be allowed. Burning is prohibited at landfills in the bay region.

Incineration is the combustion of solid wastes at high temperatures. This reduces the volume of the wastes, but the ashes and noncombustible materials remain and are not easily disposable. Air-pollution problems may also occur. Incineration is used widely in the eastern United States but, because of strict air-pollution control standards, burning is prohibited in the bay region. Further, a serious nationwide restriction which has developed and is certain to worsen is the high and rising cost of any fuel suitable to operate an incineration system.

Composting is the aerobic (with oxygen) decomposition of organic material to a humus-like end product, which can be used as a soil amendment. This requires that wastes be sorted either at their source or following collection. Little solid-waste composting is done in the bay region because of high costs and a limited market for the final products.

Grinding of garbage in home disposal units with discharge to municipal sewers is widely practiced in the bay region. This reduces solid-waste problems somewhat, but puts a heavier load on municipal sewage-treatment plants.

Salvaging of metals, cardboard, paper, and other materials which have a local market is practiced to a limited extent in the bay region. Salvaging of scrap iron is sometimes part of a landfilling operation. Ocean disposal is not desirable because of debris returning to beaches and the danger of damaging the marine environment. In the bay region, the only solid wastes that can be released to the ocean are cannery wastes and bay dredge materials.

Onsite disposal of solid wastes consists of burning or spreading and plowing in agricultural wastes and incineration of institutional refuse and industrial wastes. Open agricultural burning is no longer practiced in the bay region because of air-pollution control standards. Incineration of institutional refuse is practiced to a limited extent.

In the near future, full sanitary landfill operations will be used to a greater extent for solid-waste disposal in the bay region. This will result from the currently tightening governmental restrictions on solid-waste disposal, and the exhaustion of older and unsatisfactorily operated waste-disposal sites. Most new landfill sites will be large and will be located in rural inland areas owing to the lack of suitable land near population centers.

It will continue to be expensive to handle solid wastes, even with the anticipated technological advances in waste-disposal methods. Source control of wastes will become a necessity in keeping this expense down. The public and industry must be made aware of the need for reducing the quantity of solid waste generated in the home and at work. Separating reclaimable materials and delivering them to municipal recycling centers will help somewhat to reduce per capita generation of solid wastes. Solid-waste management will improve greatly if such cultural changes can be fostered together with the implementation of technological advances and efficient land-use planning in waste disposal.

CLASSIFICATION OF SOLID-WASTE DISPOSAL SITES IN CALIFORNIA

The California Water Resources Control Board classifies solid-waste disposal sites according to the site's potential for water-quality impairment and its danger to public health and wildlife resources.

A Class I waste-disposal site is one where the deposited wastes cannot contaminate usable groundwater or surface water. Such sites require a geologic or manmade barrier between the waste materials and any groundwater or surface water bodies. This barrier must be effective for all time. Further, if manmade barriers are constructed, they must be used only to prevent lateral movement of waste or leachate. All types of municipal, agricultural, and industrial wastes, except radioactive materials, can safely be disposed of at Class I sites.

A Class II-1 waste-disposal site is one having the same characteristics as a Class I site except manmade barriers can be used to prevent both vertical and lateral waste or leachate movement. Class II-1 sites must afford protection from inundation by a 100-year flood and high tides. Some toxic solid and liquid wastes may be permitted at Class II-1 sites.

A Class II-2 waste-disposal site is one which lies over usable groundwater where the lowest elevation of the site can be kept several feet above the highest anticipated groundwater level. The site must afford protection from inundation by 100-year floods and high tides. Any water collected at the site is subject to regional waste-discharge requirements. Nontoxic solid wastes and decomposable materials, such as wood, certain metals, sewage-treatment residue, and food wastes, can be disposed of in Class II-2 sites. This is the most common type of site found in the bay region.

A Class III waste-disposal site is one which can only afford protection to water quality by preventing erosion of deposited wastes. Only nontoxic, nonsoluble, nondecomposable solids such as earth, rock, concrete, glass, and plastics can safely be placed in Class III sites.

SELECTION AND MANAGEMENT OF LANDFILL DISPOSAL SITES

The selection and management of solid-waste disposal sites is a consideration in land-use planning. This section describes some important aspects of site selection and management of landfills, the most widely used disposal method in the bay region.

New sites for landfill disposal must be given careful consideration to reduce potential health hazards, air and water pollution, and the public nuisances of odor, scattered debris, and unsightliness. In the past, sites were often selected solely for convenience or economy where land was cheap and unpopulated. In the bay region this type of land is now scarce. New landfill sites will have to be located in areas remote from urban centers. Moreover, protection of water resources from pollution requires that potential sites be fully evaluated as to topography, soils, geology, hydrology, and suitability for sanitary operation.

Ideally, a sanitary landfill disposal site should be located on nearly impermeable land to prevent percolation of leachate to a groundwater reservoir. The site must not be subject to flooding. Depressions with groundwater at or near their surfaces should be avoided. Steep slopes should be avoided because of their erosion potential. The site should be of sufficient size for the wastes received, be accessible by arterial roads, and have enough earth available for daily covering of the refuse. Few ideal sites are available and therefore site alterations will probably be necessary in most cases.

Operation of a sanitary landfill requires good planning and supervision. Records need to be kept of the weight, type, and origin of refuse. Topographic surveys need to be made to determine the rate of space utilization, amount of compaction, and degree of decomposition and settlement. Surveillance stations for sampling water in adjacent streams, and underlying groundwater need to be established. Regular visual inspection of the site is needed. Wastes should be spread in thin layers, compacted with bulldozers, and covered daily with earth to reduce odor, blowing debris, and infestation by rodents, flies, birds, and other pests. An adequate drainage system from the sanitary landfill surface must be provided to prevent ponding, excessive seepage into the landfill, and erosion of the cover.

Wherever solid wastes are disposed of by spreading a potential for water-quality impairment exists. Surface-water pollution by solid wastes may result from rain, tidal, or stream-water seepage into and out of the landfills. This seepage leaches undesirable constituents from disposed wastes forming a liquid called leachate. Leachate is usually bacteriologically and chemically contaminated. In the bay region, disposal sites located on the margins of the bay have displayed the greatest surface-water quality-impairment problems. The California Department of Public Health sampled leachate from several of these disposal sites and also the adjacent bay water. Significant concentrations of coliform bacteria, odor-causing sulfides, and dissolved solids were found. However, these conditions have been greatly abated by recent actions of the San Francisco Bay Regional Water Quality Control Board.

Solid wastes may degrade groundwater quality by leachate infiltration and gas migration. Methane (CH_4) and carbon dioxide (CO_2) gases are produced by anaerobic (without oxygen) fermentation in a landfill, but only the carbon dioxide is appreciably soluble in water. The resulting acidic solution can dissolve common soil salts and possibly pollute the surrounding groundwater. Groundwater quality on the margins of San Francisco Bay should not be adversely affected by carbon dioxide production in landfills. These areas lie over bay muds which contain enough moisture to block gas movement. Methane has been found to migrate hundreds of feet underground from landfills. This should be considered in selecting and monitoring disposal sites because of methane's high flammability.

Gas migration can be blocked artificially by covering the bottom of a landfill site with soil compacted at optimum moisture. Gas migration has not been observed as a problem in the bay region, but may become a problem in some of the old borrow pits that have been used for waste disposal in Santa Clara County. Most groundwater quality-impairment problems in the bay region have been found in areas of shallow groundwater such as eastern Solano County.

Kenilworth Demonstration Sanitary Landfill

The material contained within this chapter has been obtained from PB 217,835 published in 1969 by the U.S. Department of Health, Education, and Welfare. In 1942 the District of Columbia began using a low area on the east side of the Anacostia River in a section of the District known as Kenilworth for the disposal of solid wastes. Refuse production had exceeded the capacity of the two existing incinerators and wartime restrictions prevented new construction. The wastes were burned in the open to conserve the available volume and thus began 26 years of open dumping and burning three and a half miles from the Nation's Capitol.

Early in 1966 the Department of Sanitary Engineering began investigating the sanitary landfill as an interim disposal method in order to cease the open burning at Kenilworth. The Department had been negotiating with the National Park Service, Department of Interior, owner of the Kenilworth site, to increase and broaden the previously established final grades to permit Kenilworth to be used for a sanitary landfill for a period of 12 to 15 months.

The residents of the metropolitan area had the usual misunderstandings relative to sanitary landfills and as a result there was some opposition. Since the District was of the opinion that sanitary landfilling was the best solution to its immediate solid waste disposal problem, the decision was made to operate a model facility with maximum publicity. It was believed that such a demonstration would soften public objection to other sanitary landfills in the metropolitan area.

The District had no personnel trained in sanitary landfill operations, and the scarcity of properly operated sanitary landfills in the eastern part of the United States made it improbable that they could obtain such personnel. For these reasons the District decided to operate the landfill by contract.

On March 5, 1968, an award was made to Curtin and Johnson, Inc. – Landfill Inc., for the operation of the Kenilworth Model Sanitary Landfill.

EMERGENCY LANDFILL OPERATIONS

The requirement by the General Accounting Office that the Kenilworth landfill specifications be rewritten and readvertised made it impossible for the District to meet its original goal to cease open burning by January 1. As the project was again prepared for advertisement, a new target date of April 1 was established.

On the night of February 15, 1968, a seven-year-old child was tragically burned to death at Kenilworth while looking through refuse for bicycle parts. The next day Mayor Walter Washington ordered all open burning at the Kenilworth site to cease immediately and emergency sanitary landfill operations begun. Work continued Saturday, February 17, and Sunday, February 18, in an effort to quench the fires and prepare an area for sanitary landfill operations.

The District landfill operations began by using the ramp method. With this method less preliminary work was required in order to prepare an area for immediate use. However, after two weeks it was obvious that the site selected was not large enough and that further refuse deposits would violate the final grades established by the Park Service Development Plan. Adequate equipment and supervision was then available to operate the trench method in an area further north on the site. The area selected had once been used as part of the open burning dump, but had been filled in with earth by the National Park Service several years previously.

Trenches were staked out having a width of 40 feet and a length of approximately 600 feet. The trenches were then excavated to the old ash residue. The depth of the trenches varied from 8 to 13 feet. Earth removed from all trenches was stockpiled at one location and used, as required, for daily cover. The trench method of operation was found to have many advantages over the ramp method. The most important advantage, during these early days, was confining the operation. There was considerable wind during the month of March, and the trench operation allowed the operators to more easily control blowing paper.

The greatest difficulty encountered with the trench operation was drainage. The terrain was such that most of the trenches could be drained to an adjacent watercourse during excavation and prior to use. When this was not possible, the trench would become unusable following a rain.

The trenches were excavated in alternate sequence allowing for dumping and maneuvering space for incoming trucks. A wall of undisturbed earth 3 feet wide at the top was maintained between trenches. Although the excavation was fill material, there was no problem with the collapse of these walls.

The District's emergency operations ended on April 2, 1968. During the District's six weeks of emergency operations 38,600 tons of refuse and 23,100 tons of incinerator residue were disposed of at the Kenilworth site. The operation was in accordance with the National Park Service Development Plan and had been accomplished without serious incident, during severe winter weather, by personnel untrained and unfamiliar with sanitary landfill methods.

CONTRACT AWARD

On March 5, 1968, the contract for the operation of a model sanitary landfill at Kenilworth was awarded to Curtin and Johnson, Inc. – Landfill, Inc. The Kenilworth contract provided for these services or equipment:

(1)   Disposal of refuse and incinerator residue for a basic period of 18 months (540 days) either at Kenilworth or at Oxon Bay (an additional National Park Service site) with the District having the option to extend the period for an additional 6 months (180 days) at either site. The contractor was guaranteed payment for 3,600 tons of refuse each week.

(2)   Provide temporary facilities for field offices, scale office, sanitary facilities and equipment maintenance on a monthly rental basis. Except for equipment maintenance facilities, trailers were used for these installations. The life of the Kenilworth project was relatively short and trailers, which could be moved to a new location, appeared to be a satisfactory solution to the building problem.

(3)   Furnish various pieces of landfill equipment. Detailed specifications were provided for each item in the bid documents. The contractor was to use this equipment in the operation of the landfill. Upon completion of the contract, the equipment would become the property of the District of Columbia.

Required	Furnished
Motor grader	1 Galion motor grader, Model 118 Series B
Sanitary landfill compactor	2 Rex trashmasters, Model TRM-340
5 yd., rubber mounted, front-end loader	1 International Hough, Model H-120-C
Tractor dozer, track-mounted	1 International Harvester, Model TD-25-C
14 to 18 yd., self-propelled scraper	1 International Harvester, Model No. 270

(continued)

Required	Furnished
Water tank wagon	1 Roscoe flusher, Model MTA-3, 2,500 gallon mounted on a Ford chassis, Model C-850
Fuel servicing unit	1 Lubrication unit, Lincoln Mfg. Co. mounted on a Ford chassis, Model F-600
Scales	2 Toledo platform scales, 100,000 lbs. capacity

(4)   Prepare the site prior to landfill operation. This item included extinguishing of existing fires, covering exposed refuse and residue, vector extermination, entrance beautification, extension of the necessary utilities and the construction of access roads and berms as required.

(5)   Fine grading, fertilizing, seeding and maintenance of grass.

(6)   Moving operating facilities to Oxon Bay.

KENILWORTH DEVELOPMENT PLAN

The plan for operation of the sanitary landfill and the future development of the area by the National Park Service was completed early in February 1968. The plan outlines in detail how the daily landfill operations are to be carried out by the contractor, establishes a sequence of areas to be filled, outlines in general where more than one lift of refuse will be required, and establishes the final contours of the finished landfill.

One unique feature of the plan is the requirement that all areas proposed for park roadways and parking lots will be filled with incinerator residue. Thus, settlement under future pavement should be minimal, and satisfactory results can be obtained with a flexible pavement type construction.

In developing the grass turf on the completed landfill, the contractor would use air dried sludge from the District's Water Pollution Control Plant. This requirement in the plan will aid in building topsoil and will provide a means of disposal for another solid waste which has been a problem for the District.

The proposed Park Development Plan would provide picnic and playfield areas on the land south of Watts Branch Creek, a canoe center at the mouth of Watts Branch and the Anacostia River, demonstration gardens north of Watts Branch, and a developed recreational area at the northeast corner of the tract. Both the northeast corner and the southeast corner of the property are adjacent to elementary schools, which increases the value of this land for playfields or more formal recreational use. Swimming pools have been planned for both locations, these to be located just beyond the limits of the sanitary landfill.

At the extreme south end of the Kenilworth property, adjacent to a large Potomac Electric Power Company power plant, land has been reserved for the District to construct their new 1,500-ton-per-day incinerator. This plant, although large for a municipal incinerator, will be dwarfed by the huge power installation. The incinerator will be attractively designed and will provide a transition from the park to the power plant. Traffic to and from the future incinerator will travel over a new road from the south and will not enter the park area.

The Kenilworth Development Plan was produced as a combined effort between the District's Department of Sanitary Engineering, the District's consultant, Whitman, Requardt and Associates of Baltimore, Maryland, the planning staff of the National Park Service and the District Department of Recreation. Close cooperation during all phases of the planning reduced disagreements and helped to develop an understanding and appreciation of the problems that each organization had.

CONTRACT OPERATIONS

Curtin and Johnson, Inc. — Landfill, Inc. began sanitary landfill operations in the area south of Watts Branch on April 2, 1968. They had begun a preliminary cleanup of this area a few days after the contract was awarded on March 5. The cleanup included a complete rat abatement program over the entire Kenilworth site by a professional exterminator. Piles of burned or partially burned material were compacted and covered with 6 to 8 inches of earth. Although the District had spent some time in this area in mid-February extinguishing fires, more burning or smoldering spots were found as the contractor moved piles of metal and debris.

The contractor has used the area method of filling during his entire sanitary landfill operations thus far. Refuse is dumped from the incoming trucks at the bottom of the sloping face and compacted with the compactor dozers as they push the material up the slope. It was originally expected that the area south of Watts Branch would be completed in October or November. Test pits made earlier proved to be misleading and a considerable volume was made available for refuse disposal when earth from previously filled areas and some virgin areas was excavated to the limit.

The limit of excavation was either burned residue or groundwater. Where groundwater was encountered, a layer of several feet of earth was placed and compacted prior to the placement of any refuse. This additional fill volume has allowed the landfill operation to continue south of Watts Branch and the area was not expected to reach final contours until February or March 1969.

During the period of negotiations with the National Park Service and the development of the Kenilworth Plan, residue from the District's four incinerators was stockpiled north of Watts Branch. Adjustments were made in the plan to reduce the amount of this material which would have to be moved, but even after these changes it was necessary to move 86,000 cubic yards of residue. A change order to the existing contract was negotiated, which provided for the removal of this material to the south side of Watts Branch, where it was compacted in the areas set aside for incinerator residue.

It became apparent as the Kenilworth project developed that the volume under future roadways and parking lots which was filled with residue would take longer to complete than the areas available for refuse. It was, therefore, to the District's advantage in extending the life of the landfill not to place any of the stockpiled residue in refuse disposal areas.

From April 2, 1968, to November 30, 1968, the District disposed of 182,000 tons of refuse and 255,000 cubic yards of incinerator residue or an average of 5,200 tons of refuse per week and 7,300 cubic yards of incinerator residue per week at Kenilworth. The amount of refuse was 15.3% in excess of the amount estimated when the project was developed.

This excess was partially caused by the volume of debris which required disposal following the civil disturbances in Washington during April and the Poor People's March and encampment during the early summer. Noncombustible demolition material was not accepted at Kenilworth but was directed to another fill site. However, combustible material had to be disposed of at Kenilworth. Despite this additional volume, the Kenilworth site was expected to last until September 1969 because of the additional space available south of Watts Branch. A contract for the construction of the Watts Branch culvert was awarded to Hercules Construction Company on October 18, 1968, for $69,923.

An interesting program has been developed by the contractor and the District for calculating and checking the daily weights of refuse. The scale heads in use at the landfill print the weight of the truck on a ticket. After being weighed in, the driver was given the weight ticket which he returned to the scale operator on his way out. The ticket was printed with his out weight and deposited in a holding box for the day. At the end of each two week period, the contractor submitted to the District the weight tickets, packaged by days, the total weight deposited, and the total number of vehicles for each day of the two week period.

The District was then faced with the difficult task of checking the contractor's calculations from an average of 7,200 weight tickets every two weeks. It was soon apparent that this required the services of a clerk almost full time. It was decided to have the information on the tickets (weight in, weight out and date) punched on cards, verified, and processed with a simple program on a computer. The cards were punched and verified by a private contractor at a cost of $8.69 per 1,000 tickets or about $5.20 per day (600 vehicles per day). The computer program was written to provide the daily weights, the daily vehicle count, a weekly and monthly total weight, and amount due the contractor.

PUBLIC RELATIONS

An important aspect of the Kenilworth Model Sanitary Landfill Project was the need to demonstrate this method of refuse disposal to citizens in the Metropolitan Washington area. Not only did the general public need to be convinced that sanitary landfill was a satisfactory method of disposal for solid wastes, but it was also important that the National Park Service and other federal agencies controlling open lands be convinced.

From the beginning, Kenilworth had an open door policy for citizens, either in groups or as individuals, and for the news media. There has been an active effort to encourage officials and others to visit the project. By December 1, 1968, 233 persons had visited the site and signed the guest book.

On Monday, October 14, Mayor Walter E. Washington was host for a special program, dramatized with a picnic lunch, attended by approximately 75 area residents, federal officials, and representatives of the Metropolitan Council of Governments. A tent was erected on top of the completed landfill near the working face and sawdust was spread over the ground.

The theme of the program was "Kenilworth – Yesterday, Today and Tomorrow". Displays of photographs were set up around the tent showing Kenilworth as a burning dump, the landfill operation and Park Service plans and renderings of the future park. The program had excellent newspaper and television coverage and was well received by those in attendance.

An important item in public relations was the entrance beautification. When the area was operated as an open dump, the entrance roadway was usually lined with private trucks broken down and waiting repairs or crews parked for a lunch break. A rail fence has now been constructed on either side of the paved entrance which confines the trucks to the main roadway and parking is not permitted. The berms have been seeded and brick entrance gates constructed about midway along the road with lettering identifying the site as the Kenilworth Sanitary Landfill. Low plantings and flowers were an added improvement this fall to the entrance gate.

The project to demonstrate the sanitary landfill as a satisfactory method of disposal had positive results for the District of Columbia. The National Park Service, which entered the original Kenilworth agreement as a skeptic, appeared satisfied that such an operation could be carried out in proper locations to benefit both the Park Service and the District.

Negotiations developed between the District and the Park Service to reach agreement for the utilization of a sanitary landfill at the Oxon Bay site to develop an 18-hole championship golf course. The District proposed to design the golf course and build the contours with a sanitary landfill operation scheduled to begin when Kenilworth is completed.

SUMMARY AND CONCLUSIONS

The conversion of the Kenilworth burning dump to a model sanitary landfill is a major success in the opinion of District officials and residents. The pall of smoke is gone and the fallout of charred bits of paper, which at times extended far into Maryland, has ended. There have been problems but solutions have been found as the project progressed.

The delay in not getting the landfill underway by the original target date of January 1, 1968, and the subsequent tragic death of the young child in the Kenilworth fires during February resulted in the project beginning under most unfavorable circumstances. However, the emergency operations during February and March were carried out without further serious incidents and the model operations were begun on April 2, 1968. Greater depths of previously filled earth than had been expected in the area south of Watts Branch have extended the life of the landfill by several months even though the daily incoming refuse has been 15.3% higher than originally estimated. The sanitary landfill at this site was completed by September 1, 1969.

Costs were about $3.30 per ton, which was higher than expected. This price per ton is based on the total project costs including the purchase of the equipment, and the estimated tonnage of refuse and incinerator residue which was disposed of during the project period. Because of the classification as a "model" a considerable amount of money was spent to prepare the area for National Park Service development and the relatively short life of the fill caused these expenditures to have a greater impact on the price per ton.

When compared to District incinerator operation costs of $6.10 per ton, the landfill was still a bargain. A landfill located within a metropolitan area is expected to be more expensive than one operated at some remote location, but the reduced hauling costs can justify these additional expenditures.

Sanitary Landfill Disposal
in Northern States

Material presented in this chapter is derived from PB 215,883, prepared for the Federal Security Agency. The North Dakota Water and Sewage Works Conference, at one of its meetings appointed a committee to study the State's refuse collection and disposal problem. The results, disclosed that of 135 municipalities reporting on disposal methods, 129 used the open dump; three used incinerators (which because of age and resulting high operating costs, have since been abandoned); and three relied on the open-face-dump form of landfill.

Seeking a solution to the problem, the State Health Department faced a number of handicaps: (1) The state is sparsely populated. (2) The extreme winter weather made the utility of the sanitary landfill questionable. (3) Since communities in the state must observe state laws limiting taxation, few, if any, were able to obtain funds for incinerator construction and operation.

Most sanitary engineers who have reported on the subject agree that, where suitable land is available, the sanitary landfill is probably the most economical sanitary method of refuse disposal. The Public Health Service, Federal Security Agency, accepted the State Health Department's invitation to cooperate in a study of landfill techniques in winter conditions in North Dakota, since they are typical of those in other northern states. Mandan was selected, in March 1949, as the site of an experimental project.

THE SITE

Two sites were favored for the landfill out of several possible: (1) a 20-acre tract, held under option, 1.3 miles south of the main street, and (2) the city's open-face-dump area, located close to the center of town on low, submarginal land, which filling would make usable. The 20-acre tract was selected by the city commissioners because of the experimental nature of the project.

The site had a 2½% slope at the southern end, increasing gradually to 6% at the north. The smooth slope of the tract was broken by a shallow ravine in the central-east portion and a deep coulee on the northeastern end. Excellent drainage existed. Before operations were begun on the landfill site out of town, the rat population in the dump had to be eliminated; otherwise, their migration to new food sources could have had tragic consequences to the city. Therefore, under supervision of Mr. Mark Worchester, of the U.S. Fish and Wildlife Service, poisoning operations were carried out by employees of the city street department, with literally thousands of rats killed.

Plan of Operation

The first trench was excavated in June 1949. An over-all plan was designed which permitted daily changes of dumping practices, whereby refuse could be dumped with, instead of into, the wind. This is why the fill was constructed in the form of a wide "U," with trenches numbered 1 through 5 comprising the southern leg.

The topographical map was prepared to facilitate accurate planning with respect to grades, size of fill site, and other pertinent factors. It was decided to follow the natural north-south rise of 6 to 8% and the east-west slope of 2 to 4%. A 6-ft. high, dirt ramp on the west side provided a starting line, established the final grade, and provided an excellent windbreak which greatly reduced the amount of blowing paper when a truck backed into the trench to dump. Excess excavated dirt from high areas, then, could be used for cover when the fill reached the east side of the field, where the natural slope increased to 10%. The result would be a uniformly-sloping field with excellent drainage, which could be used again for farming.

Width and Depth of Trenches

Originally, the trenches were made no wider than 1½ times the width of the tractor, but they were widened later to approximately 17 ft. (or about 2½ times the tractor width). This permitted more maneuverability when backing the municipal collection truck into the trench to protect the refuse from high winds. Trenches that are wider than this tend to reduce efficiency, because they expose too much of the face and require more cover material each evening.

Under ideal conditions, recommendations for trench depth in a sanitary landfill call for an amount of excavated dirt equal to that required for cover material, normally about 3 ft. for a one-level fill. The reasons for an average trench depth of 6 ft. at Mandan were: (1) extra protection from the wind for vehicles dumping trash in the trench; and (2) additional dirt for the two-level fill. The trench also reduced indiscriminate dumping (since unsupervised citizens tended, by preference, to throw their refuse into an excavation rather than on the surface).

Two Level Fill

The two-level fill was decided on because it was desired to raise the western extremity about 6 ft. which, with the depth of the trench, meant a total depth of 12 ft. Handling this amount of refuse in a single level presents numerous problems in small operations: It is difficult for the tractor to maintain satisfactory compaction unless the material is deposited in thin layers; building up layers to the required height produces an incline of considerable length and increases the surface area of exposed material; and fire control is handicapped, since the smothering of fires by compaction is difficult with a 12-ft. high face.

The fill was constructed in two stages. First, the refuse was placed in the trench and compacted in layers to a depth of 5 or 6 ft. Then it was covered with 9 to 12 in. of dirt. When enough area on the first level was built up to permit free operation of the tractor and dumping vehicles, the second level was started. This made it possible to use the lower level when strong winds were blowing and the upper level during periods of calm. As the material in the upper level was compacted and made ready for cover, a second trench was excavated. This method was followed during the summer and fall of 1949.

Depth of Cover

For experimental purposes, the cover applied to the compacted fill varied from 1 to a little over 2 ft. One foot of the type of soil found at Mandan seemed sufficient for public-health purposes, but varying amounts of cover actually applied, and some uneven settling, indicated a need for the 2 ft. commonly recommended. Experience indicates that, with 2 ft. of cover under average conditions, there will be at least 1 ft. at all points.

Regulations at Site

The absence of regulations establishing daily dumping hours during the first year impaired the operation from both the public-health and public-nuisance viewpoints. Each evening, all refuse was covered, the fill was neat and orderly in appearance; and no fires ever occurred in completed cells. Fires did start, however, in materials dumped haphazardly during the evening or weekend. It is apparent, therefore, that control of all dumping, and rigid enforcement of dumping hours, are necessary.

Fire Hazards

Fire is not a problem when refuse is properly compacted and covered, but can occur in material deposited during the day or when the operator is off duty. In winter, especially, hot ashes may smoulder unnoticed until they burst into flame. Refuse which is compacted in the truck sufficiently to prevent fire may blaze suddenly when dumped and exposed to air. During the winter operations, trucks carrying smouldering material were unloaded at the far end of the trench in use, or in another trench. Fires which occur during the day can be extinguished by covering them quickly with refuse and compacting.

Settlement

Data on percentage and time of settlement were compiled by running a line of levels on the original site, at the time final cover was placed on the second level, and at some designated elapsed time the resultant data showed settlement varied from 0 to 18%

The data also showed that there was a marked increase in the settlement of frozen refuse which is placed, compacted, and covered during sub-zero weather. This may be due to (1) reduced compaction of frozen refuse, and (2) the probability that the operator will do a less-thorough job at $-20°F$. than at $60°F$.

Insects and Rodents

No breeding of flies or rats was observed during summer operations at the fill. Rats emerging from trucks were quickly buried under the compacted refuse. The tractor was sprayed with DDT to protect the operator from the swarms of flies which accompanied each truck and which were drawn to bits of garbage adhering to the tractor. Compaction and covering each day seemed to eliminate the fly-breeding problem.

SMALL COMMUNITY OPERATION

With proper planning and efficient operation a 5,000 population community should be able to operate a sanitary landfill. On a project of this size, the tractor is required only two or three hours daily. This arrangement would necessitate regulated dumping hours at the landfill site, to prevent refuse being scattered about during evenings and weekends, and making the area resemble an open dump.

Smaller communities might modify the landfill method by a form of sanitary trenching. It would usually be necessary to clean up the site before excavating a trench. The trench may have to be dug by county or rented contractor equipment. The refuse should be compacted and covered at least twice a week in warm weather, and as often as practicable in the winter.

If heavy equipment cannot be obtained, an ordinary farm tractor equipped with a small front-end-loading bucket or bulldozer blade can be used, provided such large items as tree limbs, car fenders, barrels, etc., are removed first. This can be accomplished by placing signs designating a separate dumping trench or area for such large objects. A simple outline of a program for a small community is:

(1) Tell the public how, why and what you are going to do.
(2) Clean up the old dump and build an all-weather road to the
       site, using rented heavy equipment, if necessary.

(3) Dig a trench, store dirt at ends or on sides, and designate a specific area for large objects.
(4) Work over refuse in the trench; cover the top and face with at least 2 ft. of dirt on the schedule mentioned above.
(5) Each spring, incorporate the large objects into the fill, burn the accumulated brush, and dig a new trench.

Sanitary trenching, while less desirable than a sanitary landfill, is a vast improvement over the usual small open dump.

SUMMARY

Choosing a Site

One of the primary reasons for the success of the first winter's operation was the sandy soil available at the first site. By excavating sufficient trenches in advance and stockpiling cover material it was possible to operate the sanitary landfill in temperatures as low as $-44°F$. Enough experimental winter-operating data were gathered to enable recommendation of the following soil-preparation procedures for possible operation in other areas:

(1) Scarify area prior to frost, and insulate with material such as leaves.
(2) Excavate trenches in advance; stockpile cover, insulating with material such as leaves, if necessary.
(3) Possibly, excavate undisturbed area.

Operation

The two most difficult problems encountered at the first site were promiscuous dumping and blowing paper. The former can be remedied by dumping regulations and public education; the latter by erection of fences as "paper catchers," proper planning of fill, and, most important of all, proper selection of site. There was no paper-blowing problem at the second site because it was protected by high hills. Special tractor needs in extreme winter operation are ice grousers, a heated cab, and a garage. These accessories will redeem themselves in added efficiency of operation.

Experimental Data

At Mandan, complete refuse decomposition was not experienced after a 2-year period of burial. Although considerable decomposition had taken place a great deal more remained to be accomplished. Settlement varied from 0 to 18%, depending on prevailing climatic and operating conditions during burial.

CONCLUSIONS

Since the ultimate use or re-use of any area reclaimed by the sanitary-landfill method of refuse disposal is governed primarily by the decomposition of the refuse, the possibility of seeding or providing a catalyst (such as control of moisture with water) when building the refuse cells warrants more detailed study.

The primary objective of the Mandan experimental sanitary-landfill project was to determine the feasibility of operating a sanitary landfill in extreme winter conditions. Although the techniques found successful at Mandan may need to be varied somewhat to meet local conditions, two years of highly successful, year-round operation have answered this question in the affirmative.

German Landfill Practice

The material in this chapter was derived from PB 206,585 and issued by the U.S. Department of Health, Education and Welfare in 1968.

CHARACTERISTICS AND CHANGES IN EUROPEAN SOLID WASTES

The first statement one usually hears regarding solid wastes management in Europe and the United States is that there is a great difference in the quantity, composition, and characteristics of the domestic refuse in the two lands. German waste disposal authorities figure that 1.3 to 1.5 lbs. of domestic refuse is collected per capita per day.

Domestic refuse is defined herein as that which the homeowner or apartment house dweller customarily puts into his garbage can or into a box alongside it and which is collected regularly by the collection truck. This refuse is the food scraps, cans, bottles, ashes, cartons, old paper, and similar discards of living. Yard and garden trimmings (but not fall-of-the-year tree prunings) as collected from individual homes are also included although the percentage of German families living in individual homes is small. Old furniture and bulky objects only occasionally discarded and requiring special pickup are not included as domestic refuse.

The refuse typically has a unit weight of 450 lbs./yd.^{3}, measured in the collection vehicle. The equivalent figure for American domestic refuse collection is 2.3 lbs. per capita per day, with a unit weight of about 350 lbs./yd.^{3}. German officials indicated that up to about 5 years ago the winter refuse contained a very large quantity of ash from home heating with lignite, coal, and wood. Gas and oil for individual heating and municipally produced central steam heating are replacing the old systems, and present-day refuse contains less ash than formerly.

The refuse observed by a study team at disposal facilities definitely appeared denser and heavier, and smelled "ashier" than American refuse. Waste paper and paper products appeared to be the major volume contributor to the German refuse, the same as in the United States. However, brown-paper grocery bags as garbage sacks were conspicuously absent. There were fewer empty tin cans (beer and soft drink cans have not yet become common in Germany), somewhat fewer bottles, about the same amount of plastic film and plastic bottles, and the typical array of shoes, rags, broken toys, metal, and similar materials. Garbage grinders (kitchen sink disposal units for food wastes) have been prohibited in Germany, so the German refuse contains this waste component, although it is usually wrapped in paper and is not particulary obvious. The German waste management authorities stated that the moisture content of domestic refuse averages 40 to 45% (wet weight basis) in summer, and about 30% in winter.

The calorific value of German domestic refuse ranges from 800 to 2,200 kilocalories per kilogram. This is the "lower heating value," which compensates for water as a product of combustion. This corresponds to 1,450 to 4,000 Btu per pound on the lower heat value basis, or 1,600 to 4,500 Btu on a higher heat value basis. Typical American domestic refuse has a higher heat value, between 3,000 and 5,500 Btu per pound.

It is notable that German authorities are observing that not only is the quantity of refuse per capita increasing, but its characteristics are trending toward that of American domestic refuse. In both the United States and Germany, domestic refuse has been estimated to comprise only about $1/3$ of the total quantity of solid waste that must be disposed of.

DOMESTIC REFUSE STORAGE AND COLLECTION

The standard, almost universal, container for domestic refuse is the 110 liter (about 29-gal.) refuse can designed for dustless collection. Collection of domestic refuse is almost invariably done by the city rather than by private scavenger companies. The typical collection vehicle has a capacity 14 to 18 m.^{3} (19 to 24 yd.^{3}). It is usually operated by a crew of one driver and three, four, or five loaders. The loaders roll the containers on the bottom rim over the back of the truck, actuate the lifting-dumping device, and roll the container back to the curb; containers are not lifted.

The Düsseldorf collection system was of particular interest. Its management includes use of computers to analyze data for equipment purchase, route allocation, cost control, personnel assignments, and labor negotiations (determination of incentives, shift setup, etc.). The German loading crews do a different work than their American counterparts. Refuse is not manually lifted; the machine does this work. The accident rate, especially relative to back injuries, should therefore be much reduced.

LANDFILLING

Landfilling problems in Germany are similar to those in the United States. Many small, uncontrolled, open dumps, are used by villages and towns. These are the same blight on the German landscape as they are in America. A concerted effort is being made in Germany to eliminate these small dumps, basically by getting several communities to go together and run a larger, cleaner, and better organized burying facility.

Large, controlled landfills are operated in Berlin and in Frankfurt. The solid waste disposal problem in West Berlin is extremely interesting. Although an appraisal of the Berlin situation is not yet directly applicable to anything facing American metropolises, it may be suggestive of the future when communities cannot export wastes to the surrounding countryside, because there will be no countryside. West Berlin is an island of 185 square miles (roughly triangular with base and altitude of 20 miles) within the heart of politically opposite East Germany. There is essentially no trade between West Berlin and either East Berlin or East Germany.

Almost all food and goods of the viable, modern, western-oriented city of 2.2 million inhabitants must be shipped in from West Germany. The cost of shipping out the wastes is obviously prohibitive, so the domestic, commercial, and industrial refuse, and the construction-demolition debris must be sequestered within the 185 square miles. There are presently five burial sites for refuse. Several of them began as "Trummerberge" or rubble mountains during the early postwar days when the residents were clearing their city of the bombing damage. The largest such Trummerberg is about 250 acres in size, and the back side of it is still being used for some commercial and industrial refuse, plus construction debris. A.U.S. radar installation is housed on the top, about 150 ft. above the surrounding plain. Most of the mountain is planted with trees and grass and is a recreation site; there is even a bobsled run designed into it.

Berlin's major landfill site, is located in the southwest corner of the city, adjacent to the iron curtain separating the city from East Germany. This site receives all kinds of solid wastes, domestic, commercial, industrial, and construction. Approximately 25% of the total volume of West Berlin's solid waste is being buried there. The original site was an abandoned gravel quarry, but it appeared that the landfilling operation had overrun the old quarry. The landfill is surrounded on the West Berlin side by a forested greenbelt. The site has been used for 10 years, and the authorities figure it may suffice for years more without encroaching on the forested recreational area around it.

Except for the height of the refuse above the normal land elevation (about 30 ft.), the landfilling operation appeared typical of many American operations. That is, it could not be called a "sanitary landfill" because the refuse was not covered every day, but it was not an open burning dump. Perhaps it can best be described by a rather literal translation of the German term for it — "geordnete Deponie" or "orderly depositing."

One of the research divisions of the Institute for Water, Soil, and Air Hygiene is conducting research at the Berlin landfill on the effect of compaction of the refuse upon the water regime within the fill. The fill is instrumented to measure temperature, moisture, and specific weight, as well as quantity and quality of leachate. Two-meter layers of domestic refuse are deposited with varying amounts of compaction, covered with earth, additional layers of refuse, and cover. Surface runoff is small, 90+% of the normal 26-in. rainfall infiltrates into the fill or evaporates. The study has been running 3 years. Results to the date indicate that maximum leachate occurs with maximum compaction. Temperatures to 180°F. have been recorded in more loosely compacted cells. This research is similar to some of the American research on landfills and groundwater pollution and will be a useful addition to the scientific literature.

A second controlled landfill is at Frankfurt. This landfill started 42 years ago as an open burning dump. Later this was brought under control and now it is in the final stages of accepting refuse. It is 55 acres in size and the top is 140 ft. above the surrounding 11,000-acre nature preserve (mostly fir forest). The landfill is 4 miles south of the heart of the city, on the south side of the Main River.

The Frankfurt landfill is in the process of being abandoned as a disposal site for raw domestic waste. The citizens complained about smoke when the fill caught fire, about odors, and about blowing paper. In the future, Frankfurt's domestic solid wastes will be incinerated, and only a small part of the landfill will be used for the incinerator ash and nonburnable raw wastes.

The completed landfill will actually be an asset to Frankfurt. The slopes are presently being tapered, covered with topsoil, and reforested to match the adjacent land. A luxury restaurant will be built on the summit, where the view overlooking the forest and nearby Frankfurt will be a fine attraction.

Officials of cities with compost plants or refuse incinerators were asked why they did not landfill raw wastes. The usual answer was that there was no land available, or that it was too expensive or reserved for a higher use, and that groundwater pollution was a matter of concern. However, basically the reason often appeared to be political, the residents just did not want a landfill in the neighborhood. The situation at Frankfurt was typical: the whole 11,000-acre forest in which the 55-acre landfill is located is owned by the local, regional, and federal governments. Yet the Frankfurt Public Works Department, itself a local governmental agency, could not get any other branch of the government to release additional land for a landfill.

On the other hand, it was noteworthy that at Berlin, with minimal land availability, landfilling is still considered to be a key part of the solid waste management program. A new incinerator has been built; it will burn one half of the city's domestic and commercial refuse. There is preliminary planning for an additional incinerator to take most of the remaining burnable wastes. However, it is recognized that a certain amount of landfill will always be required, and it is intended to keep landfilling technology and practice current. The German practice of going "above grade," higher than the surrounding land level, is a practice that might have application in certain communities in the United States.

ENERGY
FROM SOLID WASTE 1974

by Frederick R. Jackson

Pollution Technology Review No. 8

Energy Technology Review No. 1

The solid waste disposal problem is reaching alarming proportions everywhere. The United States alone produces close to 300 million tons of solid waste per year, which is equivalent to about one ton per person.

At the present time the prevalent methods of disposal are dumping and sanitary landfill. Municipal incineration disposes of a small portion only, with attendant high capital and operating costs.

Many methods have been proposed for coping with the problem, such as source separation, source reduction, or material recovery. However, with the energy crisis descending upon us, producing energy from waste is becoming more and more attractive. An estimate currently making the rounds in financial circles is that when the price of crude oil reaches $7.00 a barrel, alternate sources of energy become practicable.

This book is based primarily upon information from studies conducted under the auspices of the EPA. Its foremost topic is burning of solid wastes to create steam directly. The air pollution problem created by burning can be solved quite easily with known technology. Solid wastes are low in sulfur, consequently there is no SO_2 removal problem.

Another technique that may assume more importance in the future is the controlled pyrolysis of wastes, yielding so-called pyrolysis gas or oil. Chapter seven is devoted to this. The final chapter discusses European practice, which is historically far more extensive than that of the U.S. A condensed table of contents follows here:

ISBN 0-8155-0528-0

163 pages

POLLUTANT REMOVAL HANDBOOK
1973

by Marshall Sittig

The purpose of this handbook is to provide a one volume practical reference book showing specifically how to remove pollutants, particularly those emanating from industrial processes. This book contains substantial technical information.

This volume is designed to save the concerned reader time and money in the search for pertinent information relating to the control of specific pollutants. Through citations from numerous reports and other sources, hundreds of references to books and periodicals are given.

In this manner this book constitutes a ready reference manual to the entire spectrum of pollutant removal technology. While much of this material is presumably available and in the public domain, the locating thereof is a tedious, time-consuming, and expensive process.

The book is addressed to the industrialist, to local air and water pollution control officers, to legislators who are contemplating new and more stringent control measures, to naturalists and conservationists who are interested in exactly what can be done about the effluents of local factories, to concerned citizens, and also to those eager students who can foresee new and brilliant careers in the fields of antipollution engineering and pollution abatement.

During the past few years, the words "pollution", "environment" and "ecology" have come into more and more frequent usage and the cleanliness of the world we live in has become the concern of all people. Pollution, for example, is no longer just a local problem involving litter in the streets or the condition of a nearby beach. Areas of the oceans, far-reaching rivers and the largest lakes are now classified as polluted or subject to polluting conditions. In addition, very surprisingly, lakes and streams remote from industry and population centers have been found to be contaminated.

This handbook therefore gives pertinent and concise information on such widely divergent topics as the removal of oil slicks in oceans to the containing of odors and particulates from paper mills.

Aside from the practical considerations, including teaching you where to look further and what books and journals to consult for additional information, this book is also helpful in explaining the new lingo of pollution abatement, which is developing new concepts and a new terminology all of its own, for instance: "particulates, microns, polyelectrolytes, flocculation, recycling, activated sludge, gas incineration, catalytic conversion, industrial ecology, etc."

In order to have a safe and healthful environment we must all continue to learn and discover more about the new technology of pollution abatement. Every effort has been made in this manual to give specific instructions and to provide helpful information pointing in the right direction on the arduous and costly antipollution road that industry is now forced to take under ecologic and sociologic pressures. The world over, technological and manpower resources are being directed on an increasing scale toward the control and solution of contamination and pollution problems.

In the United States of America we are fortunate in receiving direct help from the numerous surveys together with active research and development programs that are being supported by the Federal Government to help industry and municipalities control their wastes and harmful emissions.

A partial and condensed table of contents is given here. The book contains a total of 128 subject entries arranged in an alphabetical and encyclopedic fashion. The subject name refers to the polluting substance and the text underneath each entry tells how to combat pollution by said substance:

CARBON MONOXIDE
CARBONYL SULFIDE
CEMENT KILN DUSTS
CHLORIDES
CHLORINATED HYDROCARBONS
CHLORINE
CHROMIUM
CLAY
COKE OVEN EFFLUENTS
COLOR PHOTOGRAPHY EFFLUENTS
COPPER
CRACKING CATALYSTS
CYANIDES
CYCLOHEXANE OXIDATION WASTES
DETERGENTS
DYESTUFFS
FATS
FERTILIZER PLANT EFFLUENTS
FLOUR
FLUORINE COMPOUNDS
FLY ASH
FORMALDEHYDE
FOUNDRY EFFLUENTS
FRUIT PROCESSING INDUSTRY
  EFFLUENTS
GLYCOLS
GREASE
HYDRAZINE
HYDROCARBONS
HYDROGEN CHLORIDE
HYDROGEN CYANIDE
HYDROGEN FLUORIDE
HYDROGEN SULFIDE
IODINE
IRON
IRON OXIDES
LAUNDRY WASTES
LEAD
LEAD TETRAALKYLS
MAGNESIUM CHLORIDE
MANGANESE
MEAT PACKING FUMES
MERCAPTANS
MERCURY
METAL CARBONYLS
MINE DRAINAGE WATERS
NAPHTHOQUINONES
NICKEL
NITRATES
NITRITES
NITROANILINES
NITROGEN OXIDES
OIL
OIL (INDUSTRIAL WASTE)

OIL (PETROCHEMICAL WASTE)
OIL (PRODUCTION WASTE)
OIL (REFINERY WASTE)
OIL (TRANSPORT SPILLS)
OIL (VEGETABLE)
ORGANIC VAPORS
OXYDEHYDROGENATION PROCESS
  EFFLUENTS
PAINT AND PAINTING EFFLUENTS
PAPER MILL EFFLUENTS
PARTICULATES
PESTICIDES
PHENOLS
PHOSGENE
PHOSPHATES
PHOSPHORIC ACID
PHOSPHORUS
PICKLING CHEMICALS
PLASTIC WASTES
PLATING CHEMICALS
PLATINUM
PROTEINS
RADIOACTIVE MATERIAL
RARE EARTH
ROLLING MILL DUST & FUMES
ROOFING FACTORY WASTES
RUBBER
SELENIUM
SILVER
SODA ASH
SODIUM MONOXIDE
SOLVENTS
STARCH
STEEL MILL CONVERTER EMISSIONS
STRONTIUM
SULFIDES
SULFUR
SULFUR DIOXIDE
SULFURIC ACID
TANTALUM
TELLURIUM HEXAFLUORIDE
TETRABROMOETHANE
TEXTILE INDUSTRY EFFLUENTS
THIOSULFATES
TIN
TITANIUM
TRIARYLPHOSPHATES
URANIUM
VANADIUM
VEGETABLE PROCESSING INDUSTRY
  EFFLUENTS
VIRUSES
ZINC

ISBN 0-8155-0489-6

528 pages

WASTEWATER CLEANUP
EQUIPMENT 1973

Second Edition

Water pollution is becoming more of a problem with every passing year. Plants engaged in all types of manufacture are being more and more carefully watched by federal, state, and municipal governments to prevent them from pouring their untreated effluents into the nation's waterways, as they used to do. The sewage treatment plants of many municipalities are becoming too small for the burgeoning population, and many communities once served by individual septic tanks are having to build sewers and treatment plants.

Water pollution will be solved primarily by application of techniques, processes, and devices already known or in existence today, supplemented by modifications of these known methods based on advanced technology. This book gives you basic technical information and specifications pertaining to commercial equipment currently available from equipment manufacturers. Altogether the products of 94 companies are represented.

This second edition of "Wastewater Cleanup Equipment" supplies technical data, diagrams, pictures, specifications and other information on commercial equipment useful in water pollution control and sewage treatment. The data appearing in this book were selected by the publisher from each manufacturer's literature at no cost to, nor influence from, the manufacturers of the equipment.

It is expected that vast sums will be spent in the United States during the remaining portion of this decade for control and abatement of water pollution. Much of the expenditure will be for the type of equipment described in this book.

Today's environmental control is taken to mean a specialized technology employing specialized equipment designed to process the discarded and excreted wastes of human metabolism and human activity of any sort.

Next to air, water is the most abundant and utilized commodity necessary for the maintenance of human life. The average consumption of water per person in residential communities in the United States is between 40 and 100 gallons in one day. In highly industrialized communities the average consumption pro head can be as high as 250 gallons per day.

The reuse of wastewater after cleanup is not only becoming a cogent necessity, but it is also becoming more attractive economically. The degree of purity required for industrial water use is in many cases greater or vastly different from that acceptable for potable water.

Special equipment for cleanup of wastewater is therefore an absolute must, and this book is offered with the intention of providing real help in the selection of the proper equipment.

The descriptions and illustrations given by the original equipment manufacturer include one or more of the following:

1. Diagrams of commercial equipment with descriptions of components.

2. A technical description of the apparatus and the processes involved in its use.

3. Specifications of the apparatus, including dimensions, capacities, etc.

4. Examples of practical applications.

5. Graphs relating to the various parameters involved.

Arrangement is alphabetically by manufacturer. A detailed subject index by type of equipment is included, as well as a company name cross reference index.

ISBN 0-8155-0487-X

372 pages

AIR AND GAS CLEANUP EQUIPMENT
Second Edition 1972

In the past few years there has appeared a vast amount of literature telling us what the pollution problems are. Yet there is very little practical material gathered together on the type of equipment presently available to solve these problems. This book closes the gap by supplying detailed technical data, diagrams, specifications and other information on commercial equipment useful in air pollution control.

The data appearing in this book were selected by the publisher from each manufacturer's literature at no cost to, nor influence from, the manufacturers of the equipment and material. The products of 115 companies are represented.

The descriptions and illustrations as given by the OEM (original equipment manufacturer) include one or more of the following:

1. **Diagrams of commercial equipment with descriptions of components. Nearly every page contains a diagram.**
2. **Technical description of the apparatus and of the chemical reactions or processes applied, if pertinent.**
3. **Detailed specifications of the apparatus, including dimensions, capacities, etc.**
4. **Examples of practical applications, including information on how to determine capacity requirements.**
5. **Graphs relating to the various parameters involved.**

The comprehensive materials index classifies all equipment under the following categories:

I. **DRY DUST COLLECTORS**
   1. **Electrostatic Precipitators**
   2. **Inertial Separators**
       Small Diameter Multiple Tubes
       Small Cyclones
       Cones
       Cyclones—Medium and Large Sizes
       Centrifugal Collectors
   3. **Fabric Filters**
       Baghouses
       Cabinets
       Custom Units
       Oil Mist Separators
       High Temperature Applications
       Portable Equipment

4. **Components and Auxiliary Equipment**
    Filter Media
    Flexible Hoses
    Flexible Ducts

II. **WET SCRUBBERS**
   5. **Packed Towers and Beds**
       Fluidized Beds
   6. **Cyclones**
   7. **Venturi Scrubbers**
   8. **Impingement Apparatus**
       Impingement Scrubbers
       Fume Scrubbers
       Inertial Impingement
       Capillary Impingement
   9. **Gas Coolers and Separators**
       Combined Coolers and Separators

III. **COMBUSTION—INCINERATION AND GAS PROCESSING**
   10. **Thermal Incineration of Gases**
   12. **Oxidation**
       Ozone
       Potassium Permanganate
       Engine Exhausts
       Flue Gas Desulfurization
   13. **Adsorption of Gases**
       By Activated Charcoal and Similar Carbons

It appears that our air pollution problems can be solved to a large extent through the application of techniques, processes, and devices already known or in existence today, supplemented by modifications of these known methods, based on advanced technology.

This book gives you basic technical information and specifications pertaining to commercial equipment currently available from North American equipment manufacturers with standard product lines.

In addition to the extensive equipment and materials index cited above, there is a company index with complete addresses of all the 115 companies represented in this volume.

577 pages

SEWAGE SLUDGE TREATMENT 1972

by R. W. James

Pollution Control Review No. 12

Raw sewage sludge is about 95% water, and removal of the water, along with odor control, has been the subject of much research effort over the years.

The activated sludge process involves aeration of the sewage in a tank which produces a floc by aerobic growth of unicellular and filamentous bacteria. Protozoa and other organisms, present in the floc matrix, gain food and energy by feeding on the sewage.

During digestion, methane is generated in sufficient quantities to serve as a fuel source to maintain the digesting sludge at the required temperature.

The digested sludge is relatively inert, but still contains substantial quantities of water. Dewatering techniques include drying beds, filtration, wet oxidation, incineration, and centrifugal methods. Special, compact units or plants have been developed to meet the needs of ships and small communities.

This book describes 119 processes relating to the treatment of sewage sludge. Such treatment is coming under strict governmental legislation everywhere as part of the total systems approach to pollution abatement. Numbers in ( ) indicate a plurality of processes per topic. Chapter headings are given, followed by examples of important subtitles.

276 pages

ENERGY IN THE CITY
ENVIRONMENT 1973
Edited by Robert N. Rickles

This book is based upon material supplied by
Robert Rickles, the Institute for Public Transportation, and the New York Board of Trade.

The important **charts** in the **appendix** present a list of energy conservation measures for the short-term (1972-1975), mid-term (1976-1980) and the long-term (beyond 1980) for the Transportation, Residential/Commercial, Industrial and Electric Utility sectors. The charts also indicate estimated maximum attainable energy savings, possible means for implementing each conservation measure, and pros and cons.

ISBN 0-8155-5019-7

173 pages